Albany Medical College and Albany Hospital A History: 1839-1982

Published in the United States of America

Printing: New Art Printing, Albany, N.Y.
        Hamilton Printing Co., East Greenbush, N.Y.

Typography: Unicomp, Albany, N.Y.

Cover Design: The Type & Design Center, Inc., Latham, N.Y.

Library of Congress Catalog Card Number: 83-70705

ISBN 0-912809-00-0

ALBANY MEDICAL COLLEGE
AND
ALBANY HOSPITAL
A HISTORY: 1839-1982

RICHARD T. BEEBE, M.D., Sc.D.

Printed through the support of the
MISS MARION VAN BENTHUYSEN FUND
of Albany Medical Center

About the Author

The eminent physician-author of this superbly narrated treatise, which reveals the progressive phases through which the academic Albany Medical Center came into being, is to be highly commended. There is no more fitting person than Dr. Richard T. Beebe, Distinguished Professor of Medicine, former Chairman of the Department of Medicine at Albany Medical College of Union University, and former Physician-in-Chief in the Albany Medical Center Hospital, who has contributed so much to these venerable institutions during the last half-century, to undertake this formidable historic task. He has meticulously traced the simultaneous growth and development of the Medical College and Albany Hospital, from small institutions of provincial outlook and stature, into the current, large, highly integrated Albany Medical Center, with perspectives and performances of regional, state and national esteem.

Dr. Beebe has played a vital role in these years of remarkable development. After graduating from Johns Hopkins Medical School in 1928 and after four years of graduate training in internal medicine at Hopkins and Harvard Medical School's Thorndike Laboratory, he began his professional career here as an Associate in Medicine in the Medical College and as an Assistant Physician in the Hospital. His display of unusual diagnostic skills and medical knowledge soon gained him the admiring respect of faculty colleagues, medical students and house staff. Although Dr. Beebe has always savored the challenges of practicing good medicine, one suspects that his primary satisfaction has derived from his teaching experiences. He has set an outstanding example as a teacher because he has portrayed himself as a continuing student of medicine, always engaging in a disciplined course of self-instruction throughout his professional career.

Shortly after his arrival in Albany, he planned and established the first well-organized Out-Patient Clinic, in order to improve the care of ambulatory patients as well as to provide a better setting in which students could hone their diagnostic skills and gain over-all experience in the art of patient management. By actions rather than words, he demonstrated the importance of professional ethics and integrity. The

IV

positive, beneficial impact which he has exerted upon the professional careers of generations of medical students, house staff and clinical fellows cannot begin to be approached by any other individual. All who have worked or studied in his presence can hardly have avoided having some of his good traits rub off on them, his keen and orderly approach to diagnostic problems, his wisdom, inspiration, his calm and collective poise and his dedication to every task he undertook. His propensity for keeping physically fit through walking, tennis, golf, and paddle ball throughout the year sets a fine example for all to follow. As chief executive officer of the Medical College, I was frequently comforted by having him available to provide preliminary judgment and criticism of new policies or projects I hoped to initiate. His insight, sagacity and judgment often led to important modifications in these plans which were largely responsible for their ultimate general acceptance. His requests for assistance in strengthening or expanding the Department of Medicine were always reasonable, unselfish and attuned to and considerate of the needs of other departments and of the school as a whole.

His accomplishments as Chairman of the Department of Medicine for 19 years are legion, and led, upon his retirement as Chairman in 1967, to his appointment as Distinguished Professor of Medicine: the ultimate honor which the Medical College can bestow. In truth, it can be said that Dr. Beebe has become an institution within an institution. The Albany Medical Center and the extended community which is the beneficiary of its services are deeply indebted to Dr. Beebe for piecing together this excellent historical treatise.

Dr. Harold C. Wiggers
President and Dean Emeritus
Albany Medical College of Union University

Acknowledgements

Special recognition is given to the Trustees of Albany Medical College, the Board of Governors of Albany Medical Center Hospital, Deans past and present, and the Alumni of this institution for making the unique story related in this book.

Mr. and Mrs. William N. Young were a continuing source of encouragement to the author throughout the accumulation of this history. They willingly searched through the archives for dates and many of the little "stories" that comprise the total story. As lay persons, they recognized the humor of some situations which might have escaped the professionally involved. Mr. Young organized the volume of material generated by others, who through the years had prepared biographies of the luminaries of the College and Hospital. This substantially simplified the final editing of the book. Mr. and Mrs. Young with others shared the chore of proofreading the seemingly endless galleys.

Mrs. Frances Dwight Buell, Dr. March's great-granddaughter, wrote an excellent biography of Dr. March which was published a year prior to this book. It provided a valued source of information on Dr. March and was "borrowed" from for the biography of Dr. March in this book.

Thanks are extended to Ms. Pamela A. Johnson who deciphered the undecipherable and produced beautifully typewritten copy; to Mrs. Carol Kingston for many hours operating the duplicating machines so that all concerned could have draft copies for criticism and contribution; to the personnel in the Public Relations Office of Albany Hospital who always willingly provided material from their files; to the Department of Medical Illustrations who worked wonders with their cameras to furnish the many copy prints requested; to the Dean's Office who made available the log books of long past Faculty and Board of Trustees meetings; and to the Directors of the Hospital (Drs. Hawkins and Vanko) for providing access to historical files maintained by their office.

Appreciation is given to the late Miss Helen Fraser, formerly chief librarian, for the use of the many fine biographies which she had written.

Mrs. Ursula H. (Anker) Poland was an unfailing source for identification of dates, names and detailed information which no one else could find. Mrs. Poland made another major contribution by providing the history of Albany Medical College's Schaffer Library of Health Sciences. When everyone else finished their contribution, Mrs. Anita Flores had the unenviable task of preparing the index in time to meet the publication schedule.

The Archives so carefully compiled by the late Dr. Emerson C. Kelly and on display in the room of the Schaffer Library dedicated in his name, made the continuity of this history much easier to achieve.

Thanks to Commissioner John McEneny, Chairman of the Historic Sites Commission of the City of Albany, and Mrs. Cynthia Bounds Galivan for editing this volume. Mr. Dennis Holzman was the illustration editor and searched through files in many locations to provide photographs used throughout.

Miss Mary E. Carroll, Secretary of the Alumni Association, was, as always, most helpful in researching the answers to innumerable questions about the graduates of the past 144 years.

We wish also to thank Mrs. John Ghormley for all the help she gave us.

Special thanks to my wife, Jean, who was supportive and encouraging during the preparation of this book as she has been throughout our fifty years of marriage.

*   *   *   *

The proceeds of this work will replenish the Van Benthuysen Fund which has made publication of this book possible; a part of the Van Benthuysen Fund provides books for the College Library.

Dedication

One of the more difficult problems in the completion of this history was to whom it should be dedicated. Perhaps, the obvious solution would be to just omit the convention. But dedication it was decided there must be.

Anyone knowing the history of Albany Medical Center appreciates the problem of selecting one person or group that can be singled out above all others. If a list were to be made, Dr. Alden March's name would be among the top, if not the top name. If the decision were to be made in open forum, hands would be raised for Dr. Albert Vander Veer, Dr. Thomas Hun, and Dr. Thomas Ordway. Then one must remember that Dr. Harold C. Wiggers was a prime mover of Albany Medical Center. Chairmen and Presidents of the Boards of Trustees and Governors have rendered distinguished service to the institution.

Dedication could have been made to the group of Founding Fathers of the College and Hospital. Dr. Theobald Smith, perhaps the College's most distinguished graduate, was certainly a candidate. Had any of those mentioned been selected the decision would have been valid. But to single out one would have necessitated the exclusion of all others.

All of these men have been honored in one form or another. They have all received recognition for their service. In all instances, perhaps, not enough recognition or honor has been given but none has gone unrecognized.

The dilemma was resolved by dedicating this work, to all of those who have served in the College and Hospital without receiving deserved recognition. Such persons arc: the nurse who willingly stays beyond the hours of her shift because she is needed; the resident who leaves a warm bed because he senses that a patient is in difficulty; the technician who repeats a test because the first result was suspiciously out-of-line; the research scientist who continues to pursue the answer which he has no assurance will come in his time; the doctor who foregoes a lucrative private practice to devote his life to the education of others. There are those who perform the menial tasks of the Hospital and College deriving satisfaction from having served as much and as well as they could.

It is to those heretofore unrecognized individuals that this dedication is made. They know who they are and that is what is most important.

Table of Contents

List of Illustrations

*　　*　　*　　*　　*

All photographs are from the archives of the Schaffer Library of Health
Sciences, Albany Medical Center Public Relations Department, or
taken by Albany Medical Center Medical Illustrations specifically for
this text, unless otherwise noted.

Introduction

The intent of this history is to describe the remarkable beginnings and subsequent development of one of the oldest medical colleges in the nation. We have attempted to describe the difficulties it so frequently encountered, many of which were due to its precarious financial support, others due to what might have been diagnosed as growing pains.

A second, but not secondary, intent is to describe the equally remarkable growth of what was earlier known as Albany Hospital. It also grew from humble origins and at one time even suffered the indignity of the sheriff's padlock for failure to pay its bills.

To dwell overlong on these aspects of the history of the Albany Medical Center, however, would be as tiresome as the boring guest who overstays his visit. Some of the history has homely humor, other incidents are portrayals of pathos, and we hope that most will be inspiring to those who now staff the College and Hospital, and lastly, will provide a graphic demonstration of how much is needed from those who support the Albany Medical Center.

We regret that this is not a more scholarly work complete with copious footnoting of all the facts related herein. We regret that it is not more complete in detail and fully encompassing the growth of the Center from its origin in 1839 to 1982. But the hourglass never stops and if the history was to be published, certain limitations were imposed. It is hoped these condensations will not impair the effectiveness of the effort, but will inspire others to continue this historical endeavor.

The single nightmare of such an attempt as this is the inevitable omission of one or many who so richly deserve recognition. So many times this work was thought to be finished and then another name or achievement would be recalled and an appropriate addition made. If time were not a factor many more such additions would be made. I offer sincere apology for those omissions and hope that later professional historians will be more inclusive. While focusing on the lives of a few individuals we have tried to illustrate the spirit and brilliance of their generations.

This history of Albany Medical Center begins in the early days of Albany so that one might see the early tracings of the growth of the Medical Center. Choosing the year 1975 as a "cut-off" date was an arbitrary decision by the author. Much has been accomplished in the intervening years and the last brief segment of this history was the result of an irresistible urge to tell more. The activities of Albany Medical Center will continue and the present will soon resemble the past.

Richart T. Beebe, M.D.

XXV

Albany Medical College
and Albany Hospital
A History: 1839-1982

(Frontispiece)
An engraving of the 1858 Albany Medical College faculty
with facsimile signatures. Clockwise from top are: Alden March,
J.H. Armsby, Amos Dean, J.V.P. Quackenbush, Chas. H. Porter,
Howard Townsend, Thomas Hun, James McNaughton.

The
Beginning

To understand the history of Albany Medical Center it is first necessary to know a bit about the background and forces which shaped the worlds of its founders and created the human environment in which the fledgeling institution would first come to life.

In the interest of recreating that framework, we must cast our mind's eye back to an age when Hudson and Mohawk valleys were virtually unknown to Europeans.

COLONIAL BACKGROUND

In 1609, Henry Hudson ordered his vessel, the *Half-Moon,* be sailed up the Hudson River to determine if this impressive waterway would provide the sought after Northwest Passage through America to the Orient. Hudson was not the first European to enter the river, for Giovanni da Verrazano had entered it in 1524 and sailed as far north as the Palisades. In 1540, the French also entered the river and sailed up to what is now Westerlo Island where tradition relates that they built a rude fort. The French were interested in the possibilities of fur trapping, not settlement, and they stayed but a short time. Perhaps their fort met the same fate as Fort Nassau, built by the Netherlands Company on Castle Island seventy-four years later—devastation by the spring flood.

Although the river failed to provide Hudson with the long sought avenue to the West, his description of the land bordering on the river may have been of eventual greater significance to the Dutch East India Company which was sponsoring Hudson's exploration. Hudson's impressions of the land lying between the present sites of Kingston and Albany is recorded in his log as follows:

> The land is the finest for cultivation I have ever set foot upon and it abounds in trees of every kind and description. Were our industrious farmers to settle here they would soon transfer this wilderness into a paradise where no man need ever go hungry, and there is in the forest deer, wild boar and other game in such numbers that no table need ever lack meat. For variety, there are fish in hoardes to be taken from the river and multitudes of plump birds overhead all good for the eating thereof. Never have I beheld such a rich land.

3

While the elusive Northwest Passage was never discovered because no such navigable route existed, the information brought back by Hudson's and other such explorations of the vast rich territories of North America eventually persuaded Europeans of diverse backgrounds, seeking freedom and a better life, to risk their lives and whatever fortunes they possessed, to come to the New World. As would be expected, the first settlements were established on the perimeter of the continent. New Amsterdam, now New York City, was among the first of these new outposts of civilization. One of the most fortuitous qualities of man is that he is never satisfied with letting the unknown remain unexplored whether it be in science, dark forest, deep rivers or space itself. In a short time, the newcomers had thrust inland and up the rivers of the coast and, in 1614, Fort Nassau was established on Castle Island in the Hudson River a few miles south of Henry Hudson's furthest penetration five years earlier.

The purpose of Fort Nassau was to provide a trading post through which the Dutch trading company could trade European goods for the furs in which the New World was rich. Within a year, the business of the Fort was moved from Castle Island because the island was subject to flooding and a second fort was constructed on the west side of the Hudson River at a site of the future City of Albany. In 1624 a new company, the Dutch West India Company, constructed a fort in today's downtown Albany naming it Fort Orange, after the Duke of Orange. The Dutch influence present at the founding of Fort Orange was to prevail. Many of the Founding Families of Albany are of Dutch extraction. The architecture of the settlement was Dutch; and many of the customs of the Dutch were transported to the outposts of the New World.

THE PATROONS

Nineteen directors comprised the executive body of the Dutch West India Company including Killian Van Rensselaer, a fabulously wealthy pearl and diamond merchant. These men had accumulated fortunes by trading and importing goods from around the world. In 1629 a scheme of Van Rensselaer's allowed investors to achieve feudal status by sponsoring settlers to develop the land in the Hudson Valley. Huge hereditary estates, each of which encompassed hundreds of square miles, were managed by agents and judges appointed by the lord of the manor, who was known as the Patroon. The most successful of these estates, not surprisingly, was Rensselaerswyck which lasted over 200 years and at its greatest expansion included most of today's Albany and Rensselaer counties.

It was soon recognized that the fur trade was but one facet of riches to be derived from the area. The possibility of financial reward to be gained by harvesting the forest, and raising crops in the rich soil of the valley resulted in the transporting of colonists to develop the land. Each Patroon was responsible for procuring, transporting and establishing a specific number of colonists on his estate. The colonists who accepted the opportunity were usually poor Dutch citizens or refugees from states bordering the Netherlands who accepted the perils of the New World in exchange for the hope of improved fortunes. Each colonist was allotted a portion of the estate on which he was settled and, in return for the use of the land, he was required to pay the Patroon a tithe of produce or personal service. What was initially accepted as an equitable arrangement between Patroon and settler was later resisted by the settler or his descendents and resistance grew to the proportion that it is identified as the period of the Anti-Rent Wars that wreaked havoc in the Hudson Valley.

With the establishment of the Patroon System of settlement, Fort Orange began to rival New Amsterdam in size and importance.

The Dutch claimed the area from Cape Cod to Cheasepeake Bay on the discoveries of Henry Hudson, whose exploration had been sponsored by the Dutch East India Company. However, England had claimed the entire continent in 1497 as a result of the Cabot explorations. In 1664 England seized control of New Amsterdam and the entire Dutch holdings. The area changed hands twice more; in 1672 the Dutch regained control only to relinquish it forever a year later by treaty. Britain's domination was to last another 102 years until 1776 when the colonists were to declare themselves independent of the crown.

To solidify their position, the British further encouraged migration to America. The growing migration of English speaking colonists brought persons who looked beyond exploitation of the natural treasures available for the taking to the greater promise which lay in developing the land. Soon, artisans of all skills came to work on the estates of the Patroon; and farms were mapped out, gardens cultivated, fruit orchards planted, and craftsmen plied their skills as itinerant workmen journeying among the estates. Even with these improvements life was difficult; and work to achieve survival, for most, was continuous. Winters were long and cold, housing only sufficient to provide protection from the elements, and the Indians of the Iroquois nation were uncertain neighbors.

ALBANY AND THE DRIVE FOR INDEPENDENCE

Throughout this period of British colonization, Albany was growing from a small cluster of buildings on the shore of the Hudson River to a city sizeable for its time. Because of its location on the Hudson River, which flowed from north of Albany south to New York City, and proximity to the Mohawk river which flowed from the western part of the state, Albany was strategically placed at the hub of the avenues of commerce throughout New England. Albany's geographical location brought to the city, from its earliest days, explorers, hunters, merchants, scientists, and politicians. In 1754, Benjamin Franklin had headed a group of statesmen who gathered in Albany to propose a union of the colonies. On the two hundredth anniversary of this meeting in 1954, the national government recognized Albany as "the birthplace of the national union."

Although opposition to British rule was not as openly virulent in Albany as in other New England cities, the revolutionary effort had been encouraged and supported by the residents, many of whom were of Dutch ancestry and still resented the seizure of the colonies and the City by the British.

However, as throughout the colonies, Albany did have those who favored the continuation of status quo and supported the King. Abraham C. Cuyler who became Mayor of Albany in 1770 was expelled from the City in 1776 because of his very apparent Loyalist sympathies. Others of a similar bent were jailed and later exiled to New England towns or made to work their farms under the surveillance of their neighbors.

Albany's last occupation by British troops occured during the period of the French and Indian War when, in 1758, 6,000 British troops were quartered at Fort Crailo. During the Revolution, Albany was one of the targets of British efforts to divide and subdue the colonies but it was never captured. It did serve as a northern headquarters for the revolutionaries through which information and supplies were disseminated.

In 1776, a military hospital was built at Pine and Lodge Streets, the present site of St. Mary's Church, and Dr. Samuel Stringer, physician to General Philip Schuyler, was stationed there when, by Congressional appointment, he became Surgeon-in-Chief of the Northern Continental Army. The hospital, which contained 40 wards, was a large building for its time, being two stories high and having wings at each end. To that hospital General Benedict Arnold was brought, wounded from the Battle of Saratoga as were thousands of other men, to overflow the 800 bed capacity of the building. British casualties from the battle were cared for in St. Peter's Church, the Dutch Reformed Church, and the home of Mayor Cuyler who had fled to England. It can be reasoned that Albany's emergence as a prominent medical center was ordained at this early date.

HEALTH CARE OF THE EARLY SETTLERS

It can be assumed that those who came to settle in the New World were initially youthful, healthy and vigorous persons because it is unlikely that the business-wise Patroons would underwrite the expense of transporting and settling those who did not give visual promise, at least, of being physically able to cope with a very rigorous life. So the settlers, as a group. were in little need of a physician's care. The waters were clean and plentiful, the air free of pollutants, and food for most was plentiful and varied.

Indeed the American Indian had lived on the continent for centuries without benefit of medical care other than that furnished by the Shamans who had learned the properties of medicinal plants. They prescribed hot pennyroyal tea to induce labor; they applied puff balls to stop bleeding; they taught mothers to use moss for diapering infants. The Shamans also knew the value of mineral springs such as those which flowed from the earth at Saratoga and Ballston for alleviating rheumatic and arthritic conditions. They developed concoctions to cope with scurvy, and they recognized some ailments that today we ascribe to psychosomatic origin.

The Patroons of the Dutch West India Company prudently, however, recruited "Comforters of the Sick" *(krank-besoeckers)* to accompany the colonists. The Comforters not only provided spiritual direction but also emergency medicine such as setting bones and arresting bleeding. They were often clergymen who had studied medicine as apprentices in Europe without having attended medical school. They did occasionally assist at births but normally women were delivered by midwives. In addition to the "Comforters of the Sick," Fort Orange had the spiritual ministrations, in its early days, of Domine Megapolensis and the Reverend George Mancius.

The Company demonstrated more foresight by including with the other migrants trained midwives who were paid 100 guilders and were provided with a private house for services rendered to their colonists. The Dutch West India Company intended that in addition to maintaining their health, the colonists should multiply. That this primitive medical care was not unregulated is evidenced by an ordinance of New York which provided that:

> no woman within the corporation shall exercise the employment of midwife until she has taken oath before the mayor, recorder or an alderman to the following effect: that she will be diligent and ready to help any woman in labor whether poor or rich; that in time of necessity she will not forsake the poorer woman and go to the rich; that she will not suffer any woman to name or put any other father to the child but only him who is the true father thereof, indeed unto the utmost of her power; that she will not suffer any woman to pretend to be delivered, or a child who is not indeed; neither to claim any other woman's child for her own; that she will not suffer any woman's child to be murdered or hurt; and as often as she shall see any peril or jeopardy either in the mother or the child, she will call in other midwives for counsel; that she will not administer any medicine to

produce miscarriage; that she will not overcharge for her services; that she will not collude to keep secret the birth of a child, will not conceal the birth of bastards.

The use of feminine pronouns in the ordinance seems to preclude the professional attendance at birth by men. During the 17th and 18th centuries, practically all obstetrical work in New Amsterdam was done by midwives. Only in the middle of the 18th century did the practice of obstetrics by men come into popular favor.

FIRST PHYSICIANS

The first regularly trained physician in Fort Orange was Jean de la Montague, who arrived in 1629. Other accounts record Juse De Forest as also being a qualified doctor who arrived that same year. Of Jean de la Montague it is known that his family were Huguenots who had fled from France to Holland. In 1619, he began the study of medicine at Leyden. Arriving in Fort Orange, he stayed but a short time before returning to Holland. He returned to Fort Orange in 1636 and built the first stone house in the settlement. Apparently a man of recognized ability, he was appointed Vice Director of the community. The Council of New Amsterdam gave him the right to issue permits to qualified physicians for the practice of medicine. This legislation was the first legal enactment regarding medical practice in New York. Sometime later, de la Montague again returned to Europe, where he died in 1670.

Many ships sailing to the New World had ship's surgeons aboard who chose to remain in the colonies. Such was Herman Mynderts Van den Boogaerdt, who served on the *Eendracht* which reached New Amsterdam in 1631. At that time de la Montague was again in Holland, leaving Fort Orange without formal medical care. Perhaps, as a result of this, Van den Boogaerdt was appointed surgeon to Fort Orange in 1633. His practice must not have been large or confining, as his recently discovered log tells that he spent two months exploring the Mohawk Valley, during which time he attempted to develop an amicable relationship with the Iroquois Indians. Van den Boogaerdt met his death in a flaming longhouse in 1648. It is not known if this was a reprisal by the Indians for his having ministered to Father Isaac Jogues who had escaped after severe torture by the Mohawks and was later martyred by them.

The first doctor to permanently establish practice in Fort Orange was Dr. Abraham Staats who arrived in 1642. He had been recruited by the Patroon for this purpose. Fort Orange in that year was a struggling community of approximately 100 inhabitants who lived in 30 houses. As a result of the small demand for medical care and the apparent varied talent of Dr. Staats, he had the time and abilities to drill soldiers during the week and preach sermons on the Sabbath. Dr. Staats' home was on the site of what is now the old Federal Building, now a part of University Plaza on Broadway. The location was named Staats Alley and later anglicized to its present name, State Street.

When the British recaptured control of the New York State area from the Dutch in 1664, the name Fort Orange was changed to Albany and New Amsterdam was renamed New York in honor of the colony's new royal patron who numbered among his titles those of Duke of York and Albany. Albany continued to grow both in population and prosperity during the next 100 years. It was no longer an outpost but rather the hub for the communities which gradually extended to the West and North. As Albany grew, additional physicians established their practices in the area. Dr. Samuel Stringer came north from Maryland and subsequently served as Physician to General Phillip Schuyler. His position in the community may have been enhanced by his marriage to an Albany Dutch heiress. He was a member of the Committee of Correspondence at the outset of the Revolutionary War. Present "on the other side of the fence" was Dr. Richard Shuckberg who was a young surgeon serving on General Abercrombie's staff. Perhaps Shuckberg's most notable achievement occurred in 1758 at Fort Crailo when, according to tradition, he composed the intended derisive lyrics of "Yankee Doodle Dandy." Dr. Ellis Willand and Dr. Walter Colder, the latter an intimate friend of Benjamin Franklin, were others who practiced in Albany during this period.

COLONIAL REGULATION OF MEDICAL PRACTICE

While medical practice in the 18th century was primitive and the principle of *caveat emptor* prevailed to a certain degree, the practice of medicine was not entirely without regulation as witnessed by the ordinance pertaining to the practice of midwives stated earlier. Further control was evidenced by an ordinance issued in 1753 in New York City which declared:

> All the physicians, surgeons and apothecaries in the Province are to be licensed by a board consisting of four elected members of His Majesty's Council, the Judges of the Supreme Court, the Representatives of New York City and Assembly, the Mayor and Recorder, or any seven of them with the assistance of two physicians and two surgeons, or the majority of them elected.

The first act regulating medical practice in New York City was passed in 1760, but similar legislation was not enacted relating to the entire province until 1797. Thus the door was open for quackery to flourish in the province, except for New York City, for another 37 years.

Before the end of the Revolution, many proprietary remedies were hawked, along with cures learned from the Indians *(Figure 1)*. Popular nostrums included British Oil, anodyne necklaces for chilren, Velmor's Vegetable Syrup to alleviate venereal diseases and scorbutic disorders.

Botanic practitioners who were unlicensed physicians, at a later date were free to cure by using "roots or herbs, the growth or produce of the United States." A New York Legislature granted one thousand dollars to John M. Crous for a cure of rabies that he claimed to possess. He had to post a $2,000 bond to protect the lawmakers, should the remedy prove ineffective. It would be interesting to know if Mr. Crous recovered his bond and, if so, the nature of the cure.

POST REVOLUTIONARY EDUCATION IN ALBANY

After successful completion of the revolution, Albany resumed its position in the growing commerce of the nation. In 1784, Nicholas Barrington opened a school in Albany and tuition was set "at the low price of 10, 12 and 14 shillings a quarter for spellers, writers and cypherers and three pounds for bookkeeping and navigation." In 1813, the Albany Academy was organized with an appropriation from the Common Council. The Albany Institute of History and Art had its beginning when the Soci-

Mansion House
FOR FIVE DAYS ONLY!
Commencing Tuesday, July 26

DR. G. LOVATT,

INDIAN PHYSICIAN

In order to introduce his new system of treatment, and convince the public that most of those diseases hitherto considered incurable, can readily and speedily be cured, will on his present visit to this place, examine all those who may call on him at the above place during the time specified

Free of Charge.

The Dr. will treat all chronic or long-standing diseases, such as

Catarrh, Dyspepsia, Epileptic Fits,
SCROFULA, CONSUMPTION,

Seminal Weakness, Female Weakness, all diseases of the Eye and Ear, Heart, Lungs, Liver, Stomach, Bowels, Blood, Kidneys and Spine.

All Diseases of Females.

Tape Worms Removed in Twelve Hours.

(Call and see some mammoth specimens recently removed.)
All Chronic Diseases located, and Symptoms Described without asking a question.

MEDICINE PURELY VEGETABLE.

NO CURE, NO PAY!

He treats all diseases, of whatever name and nature. In each case, a cure is warranted. If the patient is not cured within three months from the time the prescription is given, no charge will be made.
Price of Prescription $5, to be paid after the cure is effected.
Call at once, you may never have an other opportunity like it.

Office Hours, from 9 A. M. to 8 P. M.

(Fig. 1) Some of the questionable "medical" practices that medical science had to confront late into the 19th century can be seen in this 1870's broadside.

ety for the Promotion of Agriculture, Arts and Manufacture, founded in New York City in 1791, moved to Albany in 1804. In 1829, it joined with the Albany Lyceum, established in 1823, to form the present Institute. Such institutions certainly raised the cultural level of the area but the problem of the development of professional medical skills had still not been solved.

SHORTAGE OF TRAINED PHYSICIANS

Early knowledge of medical practice in New York State is quite incomplete because documents belonging to the Dutch West India Company which recorded the internal administration of the colony were disposed of in Holland in 1831. Other records and conclusions reached through deduction, however, enable some insight. It is probable that at the time of the Revolution there were not in all of the colonies 400 physicians who had received medical degrees, yet there were presumed to be more than 3,500 practitioners. The first census taken in the United States was in 1790 and it placed the population at 3,872,000 persons not including native Indians. If the total population is estimated at 4,000,000 persons this would indicate that there was one licensed physician for each 10,000 inhabitants. As the dispersion of population extended from Florida to the Canadian border and west to Ohio, this meant that the attendance by a licensed physician was limited to the more populated locations. Here perhaps, in these more remote areas, is where the 3,500 unlicensed practitioners were of service fulfilling the adage that something is better than nothing.

EARLY MEDICAL SCHOOLS

By 1776, American medical colleges had conferred only 51 degrees including that of Bachelor of Medicine. Even at the close of the 18th century, those who had medical degrees from American colleges numbered less than 250. But probably five times that number had attended one course of lectures and were in practice.

The first medical school in the American colonies was established at the College of Philadelphia in 1765. John Morgan and Thomas Bond taught there using the facilities of Philadelphia Hospital which had been built in 1752. Teaching was didactic and repetitive. In 1791, the medical school became the medical department of the University of Pennsylvania.

In 1768, a medical school that later became the medical department of King's College was begun in New York City. During the Revolution it was compelled to close, but was reopened sometime after the conclusion of the war. In 1814, the school became affiliated with the College of Physicians and Surgeons, which the Regents of New York State had licensed in 1807. The combined schools eventually became the College of Physicians and Surgeons of Columbia University.

Harvard Medical College began in Cambridge, Massachusetts in 1783 but removed to Boston in 1810 to take advantage of the hospitals there. Yale Medical College was established in 1810. To place the scope of medical practice in perspective, it is significant that Dartmouth Medical College had, for its first twelve years after its establishment in 1797, a faculty that consisted of one person, its founder, Dr Nathan Smith.

APPRENTICESHIPS AND TRAINING

Before the founding of these early medical colleges, prospective physicians studied with established practitioners. The students became apprentices much the same as others desiring to learn a trade. They accompanied the preceptors on daily rounds thereby learning to identify sicknesses and attend victims of injury. They studied their teachers' books, mixed prescriptions, swept the office, and may even have cared for the preceptor's horse and buggy if he owned one. Prior to the founding of American medical schools, if the student desired additional training he was compelled to go abroad. Formal documentation of medical knowledge was very meager being restricted to small collections of medical textbooks owned by physicians. Public libraries did not exist. David Hosack, founder of the New York Botanical Garden, had a large personal library from which he established a medical library in the New York Hospital.

The informality and somewhat precarious nature of medical education prior to the founding of these medical schools is illustrated by the existence of private courses in anatomy by dissection, taught by Dr. John Bard and Dr. Peter Middleton in New York City. The obtaining of human specimens for such demonstrations was difficult and even dangerous. One legal source for specimens was opened by a New York law dated January 6, 1789 stating:

> When any offender shall be convicted of murder, arson or burglary, for which he shall be sentenced to suffer death, the court may, at their discretion add to the judgement that the body of the offender shall be delivered to the surgeons for dissection.

Was dissection considered to be a further punishment to be inflicted after death? If not, upon what criteria did the court make its decision? More than 100 years were to pass before the New York State Legislature enacted a law in 1854 popularly called the "Bone Bill" that permitted dissection of human material.

STATE LICENSING OF PHYSICIANS

Applicants for admission to early medical colleges had to produce evidence that they were proficient in the natural sciences and in Latin.

In addition, they were also required to prove an apprenticeship of three years with a certified practitioner. Preceptors with whom medical students worked were required by law to file a certificate in each student's behalf. Some preceptors were remiss in fulfilling this reasonable obligation and the student suffered the loss of time served. The Albany County Medical Society encouraged the insertion of a clause in the bill of 1818 incorporating medical societies, to protect students from further such injustice. Candidates for the M.D. degree were required to obtain two years of practical and theoretical study in anatomy, Materia Medica, chemistry and theory and the practice of medicine with attendance at clinical lectures.

New York State placed the regulation of medical practice in the hands of county medical societies in 1806. Until 1809 the societies held exclusive control and maintained modified control until 1880. Between 1806 and 1907 three forces contended for dominance over licensing practitioners. They were: the organized medical profession through its state and county societies; the medical colleges; and the State of New York acting through the Regents of the State University.

A New York State law of 1827 provided that a license to practice medicine could be obtained by one of three procedures: study for four years under a licensed practitioner, or for three years in a medical college, or by completing a course of all lectures given by an incorporated medical society. It is assumed that whichever course of procedure was pursued by the candidate for licensing, an examination which certified successful completion of the procedure was required. In 1872, New York State established the principle that medical licenses should be granted by the State Department of Education, and not by practitioners or teachers of medicine. Obviously, this was intended to provide a uniformity of standards for the State and remove the potential for nepotism and indiscriminate bestowal of credentials.

ALBANY COUNTY MEDICAL SOCIETY

The Albany County Medical Society was organized on July 29, 1806 by Doctors Wilhelmus Mancus, Hunloke Woodruff, William McClelland, John S. Knauff, Charles D. Townsend, all of Albany; Caleb Gauff and Augustus Harris of Bethlehem; and Joseph W. Hegeman and Cornelius Vrooman, Jr. from Schenectady. As stated earlier, 1806 was the same year in which New York State placed the regulation of medical practice, including the control of licensing, in the hands of county medical societies. It is probable that the formation of the Albany County Medical Society in that same year was accomplished so that the county would have a body of physicians who would see that medical practitioners properly adhered to ethical and professional standards. Until that time there was no legal restriction worthy of the name governing the practice of medicine. The mere fact that a man had studied medicine with a doctor for two years was no evidence that he had acquired any medical knowledge whatever, nor were the judges capable of evaluating his medical attainment.

Examples of the early activities of the Society clearly demonstrate that it maintained wide ranging control. For example, on July 9, 1811, the Society expelled from membership Dr. Elias Willard for refusing to communicate to the Society the composition of his nostrum for the cure of cancer and scrofula. Apparently the efficacy of the cure was not questioned, the refusal to share his secret concoction was the cause of the anger. Much suffering could have been alleviated and how much research could have been directed to other diseases had the Society used whatever means necessary to force Dr. Willard to tell all is not yet known.

In 1813, the Society came to grips with their responsibility to license medical practitioners by requiring candidates seeking qualification as medical practitioners to produce a certificate testifying to their attendance of at least one course of lectures at some medical institution in the United States or in a foreign country. This was in addition to satisfactory evidence that the applicant had studied for three years with a physician. On the surface these regulations seem rather vague, it being possible to attend without learning and the sites of the lectures "in the United States or a foreign country" are exclusive only of unearthly medical institutions.

Evidence of the Society's vigilance in the suppression of quackery was the appointment of Doctors Eights, Treat and March in 1825 to determine whether Dr. Thompson had a legal right to dispense vegetable compounds as medicine.

So that medical education might be augmented, in 1835 the Society appointed Doctors Platt Williams, Sydney Sawyer, and Alden March to "inquire into the expediency of establishing a reading room" open to all practitioners. Ten years later the Society wondered where many of the books and journals had gone. A list of those missing was published in the local papers with the hope that it would stir the conscience of some people.

In 1853, the society published a schedule of fees: Day Visits, $1.00; Night Visits, $2.00-$3.00; Instrumental Labor, $10.00-$50.00; and one-third additional charge for attendance on malignant or contagious disease cases. While these fees are miniscule compared to those of later years, they were not a rare bargain for those whose hard labor was rewarded with 10 cents an hour. Doctors were busy and their rates ample but most did not become wealthy because many persons failed to pay bills rendered by physicians. Here again publication may have been used to stimulate the conscience of the defaulters.

The Albany Medical Society continued to press for better medical education and regulation of licensing. It held the position that certification of practitioners should remain within the domain of the Society, that professors and persons teaching medical students should be ineligible for the office of censor, and it recommended that students dissatisfied by the decision of individual medical societies not to admit a candidate to practice should have the recourse of appeal to a board composed of examiners from other societies.

The Call for a
Medical College and Hospital

The Gansevoort-Lansing Collection of historical documents contains a printed copy of a lecture delivered by Doctor Alden March on January 11, 1830 at the outset of a series of lectures on the subject of Anatomy and Operative Surgery. The lecture, contained in Appendix A in its entirety, is the first formal expression of a proposal for the establishment of what was to become Albany Medical College, Albany Hospital and eventually the Albany Medical Center. At the time he delivered the lecture, Dr. Alden March was the Professor of Anatomy and Physiology in the Vermont Academy of Medicine, which was located in Castleton, Vt. The lecture was sufficiently well received by those present to elicit a request by a committee of Messrs. L. Wellington, A.F. Lawyer and O. Crosby,Jr. on January 12, 1830 to Dr. March that they be given a copy of the address for publication. In the letter the committee expressed the opinion that the importance of the subject be given wider attention which would accrue to it by published distribution.

On the same day, Dr. March replied granting permission to the committee to publish the content of the lecture. However, in his letter he did demur to a point stating that it was not "designed for the public eye" and further "it affords but a hasty and imperfect sketch of my views." We must assume that Dr. March was sincere in taking this position, realizing that much more thought and consideration be given to his proposal. And we may further assume that he anticipated that acceptance of the proposal would not be unanimous or immediate. Nine more years would pass before the medical school became a reality.

DR. ALDEN MARCH

Alden March *(Figure 2)* was born in 1795 in Sutton, Massachusetts and, as were most youths of that era, was reared on a farm. Nothing specific is known of his adolescence beyond these few facts. When of an appropriate age he and his older brother, David, served a medical apprenticeship in Boston with a Dr. Ingalls. David March had been an

16

(Fig. 2) Dr. Alden March

Army surgeon and it is through his influence that Alden March became interested in medicine. In 1820, at the age of 25, Alden received a medical degree from Brown University in Providence, Rhode Island. Before receiving his degree, Dr. Alden March had taught for a short time in a public school from which experience he developed a propensity for teaching. Perhaps in search of an area with more opportunity for a young physician and spurrred by the spirit of adventure offered in the bustling captial of New York, he came to Albany in 1821.

Young March must have been energetic, enterprising, and confident because, in the same year as his arrival in Albany, he established a private class in anatomy which was comprised of 14 students and identified as "Dr. March's practical School of Anatomy and Surgery." A circular published in 1833 described yet a second medical school conducted by Dr. March which was identified as "Albany Medical School." The circular or catalog listed as instructors Edwin James, M.D., Chemistry and Natural History; Alden March, M.D., Anatomy, Physiology and Operative Surgery; Henry Greene, M.D., Obstetrics and Diseases of Women and Children; William Tully, M.D., Materia Medica, Pharmacy and Therapeutics; Theodore Woodward, M.D., Principles and Practice of Surgery; and John James, M.D., Theory and Practice of Medicine. Dr. March's Practical School began in January and lectures in the "Albany Medical School" commenced on the first Wednesday in March. The two schools were closely associated, but distinct, and it is not known if students from one school also attended the other. With the demands of conducting two schools, maintaining a practice, and fulfilling his obligations as an officer in the Albany County Medical Society, when Dr. March slept is a matter for conjecture.

The student body increased to fifty-one, of which twenty-eight were senior students and twenty-three junior students. It is difficult to understand how Dr. March accomplished the feat, for at the same time that he was conducting the schools in Albany he taught for ten years at the Castleton Medical College. Castleton, Vt., is several miles north of Rutland, Vt., and approximately 60 miles northeast of Albany. His means of commutation was horse and carriage over the dirt roads of that time. The "Bone Bill" not yet having been passed, Dr. March was hard pressed to obtain human material for dissection in his anatomy course in Albany. To obtain cadavers he had to travel to and from Boston where the necessary material could be obtained. The arduous trips were made in a two wheeled wagon and danger to life and limb was always present not only from the conveyance and condition of the roads but also from public resentment of the intended use of his cargo. Why the source of supply existed in Boston and not Albany or a nearer locality is not known.

Dr. March was active in the Albany Medical Society to which he was elected on July 14, 1823, two years after his arrival in Albany. That same year he read a paper to the group "on the morbid pelvic viscera of a female subject who died of an affliction of the organs of generation." At a later date he delivered another paper which dealt with "the history, treatment, and post mortum examination of a fractured cranium." He also served on a committee appointed by the Society to establish a medical reading room in the city. Recognition of his ability and activity in the Society is evidenced by his appointment as President of the Society in 1832 and 1833, and his selection as a Censor in 1838.

CHOLERA EPIDEMICS

However, Dr.March was not without detractors who resented his professional ability and his willingness to take a public position on matters affecting health in the city. An example of the latter characteristic concerned a proposal by the City's Board of Health to spread lime in the streets to ward off a cholera epidemic to which Dr. March commented, "Neither lime nor chloride of lime possesses any power to prevent the introduction or spread of cholera; the practice of spreading lime is not only useless, but indirectly injurious to the health and happiness of citizens, and highly destructive to the business interests of the city." In 1832, there was a cholera epidemic in Albany which affected 1,147 persons and resulted in 422 deaths. The medical profession conferred every evening at City Hall to record deaths and the devastating progress of the disease. Tar was burned in barrels as an anodyne, which succeeded only in casting a black pall over the stricken city. The dead were carried off during the night and buried without coffins. Cholera again struck the city in 1834, resulting in seventy-eight deaths from among the one hundred and twenty-four persons who were stricken.

ALBANY HOSPITAL AND MEDICAL SCHOOL
TO SERVE REGION

When, in 1830, Dr. March proposed the establishment of a hospital and medical school in Albany, he presented a sound basis for their establishment. He recognized that there were already numerous medical schools in the nation, and keen competition existed among them for student enrollment; but he also recognized the population growth whose requirement for doctors would outstrip the capacity of existing schools to train needed physicians. A typical example of Dr. March's foresight was to be seen in Albany County. The County at that time had only 65 qualified doctors to administer all categories of treatment to its 53,570 residents. Albany had sufficient population at the time to justify the establishment of a hospital and an abundance of persons in need of medical aid to provide opportunity for the observation and education of students. This was not the case in Castleton and Fairfield, where two medical schools were located in comparatively rural areas. As to the availabilty of students, Dr. March cited the statistics of students from New York State attending the Vermont Academy of Medicine and the Berkshire Medical Institution in Pittsfield, Mass. for the years 1823 through 1828. In the lecture, he presented, among other recommendations for the medical school and hospital, the cogent suggestion that a physician's education was unending and that to remain proficient the doctor must "keep up with the improvements of the day, and in instructing others, to instruct himself." In this, as in other respects, Albany Medical Center has remained faithful to the tenets of its founder. Vivid testimony to this canon is contained in a letter written by Doctor John A. Sampson to a Doctor Klinck on June 27, 1938. In the letter Doctor Sampson expressed thanks to the Executive Faculty of the College and gave his decision to retire from his executive duties in August of that year having reached age 65. Dr. Sampson stated that in preparation for his duties as a teacher in the College he found many things which he had not known before; and "Without Albany Medical College I would not have had the excellent laboratory facilities which I have enjoyed so much." At the time, Dr. Sampson was a national authority in the field of gynecology. In conclusion, Dr. Sampson stated, "I can safely say that in my case the teacher learned far more than the student." This, from a man eminent in his field, is but one testimony to Dr. March's farsightedness.

It would be assumed from the power of the facts presented in Dr. March's lecture that unanimous endorsement of the proposal would be immediate and enthusiastic. This, however, was not to be. Strenuous opposition arose from other medical schools which regarded this proposition as a portent to futher competition and also from some physicians in the city who may also have viewed the potential graduates as economic threats to their practices.

In 1831, Dr. March gained an able ally in his effort. Dr. James H. Armsby joined him in Albany.

DR. JAMES ARMSBY

Like Dr. March, Dr. Armsby *(Figure 3)* was born in Sutton, Massachusetts in 1810. Armsby graduated from the Vermont Academy of Medicine at the age of 20 and entered practice with Dr. March. Thus a lifelong association was begun. The bond of friendship was further strengthened when Dr. Armsby became Dr. March's brother-in-law, Dr. March having married Joanna, the sister of Dr. Armsby, in 1824. This fact explains the affection and cooperation of these two men. Dr.

(Fig. 3) Dr. James Armsby

Armsby succeeded Dr. March as Professor of Anatomy and Physiology in Castleton Medical College at Castleton, Vt., and commuted between Albany and Castleton, until 1833 when he resigned to join Dr. March in an intensive effort to establish a medical college and hospital in Albany. Dr. Armsby's efforts toward the incorporation of a medical school and the legalization of dissection included a popular course of lectures attended by leading citizens of Albany and members of the New York State Legislature. The lectures were illustrated by dissection and netted $10,000 in admissions. Why lay persons would attend lectures which included dissection is difficult to understand unless the situation is placed in the context of modern television programming which has portrayed open heart surgery with close up camera coverage and human birth with audio effects.

ALBANY MEDICAL COLLEGE IS ESTABLISHED

In 1838, Dr. March succeeded in a partial realization of his goal when the New York State Legislature approved the medical school at the insistence of influential residents of the city, included amongst whom was Erastus Corning I. The archives of Albany Medical College contain the original copy of a petition from the "Young Men's Association for Mutual Improvement of the City of Albany," respectfully submitted to the "Honorable State Legislature of the State of New York," requesting that a location be granted in Albany for a medical school. The petition was signed by 146 persons, many of whose family names are still prominent in civic affairs of Albany, and who either themselves or their antecedents had close connections with Albany Medical College or Albany Hospital. In turn, the city granted the school free use, for five years, of the unoccupied Lancaster School Academy on the corner of Lancaster and Eagle Streets *(Figures 4 and 5)*. The departments of Surgery, Anatomy and Physiology, Chemistry and Natural History, Obstetrics and the Diseases of Women and Children, Materia Medica and Pharmacy, and Theory and Practice of Medicine, and Medical Jurisprudence were established and constituted the curriculum for the 57 students who enrolled. However, in 1838 the school had no charter nor power to confer degrees until with further determined insistence by citizens of Albany, the Legislature was persuaded to pass an act of incorporation. Another factor which may have significantly influenced support for the medical school was that the city had been ravaged at intervals by small pox, yellow fever and typhoid. Dreaded cholera epidemics had struck the city in 1832 and again in 1834. The trustees then appointed physicians to serve as curators to attend the annual examination of candidates for the degree of Doctor of Medicine. Albany Medical College was established.

DR. THEODRIC ROMEYN BECK

Of the many unusual persons portrayed in this history, Dr. Theodric Romeyn Beck *(Figure 6)* must be included among the top few. He was a man of many talents all of which he demonstrated during his sixty-four years.

Theodric Beck was born in Schenectady, New York. After four years of study he graduated from Union College in 1807 at the age of 16. After graduation, he entered the office of Drs. Low and McClelland to study medicine. Four years later, at the age of 20, in 1811, he received the degree of Doctor of Medicine. His graduation thesis was on the subject of insanity, which, throughout his life remained of great interest to him. At this early date, Dr. Beck recommended humane treatment of those

(Fig. 4) The founding of Lancaster School House (1815) was commemorated by this Liverpool pitcher.

(Fig. 5) An 1843 lithographic view of the Lancaster School, the first site of Albany Medical College.

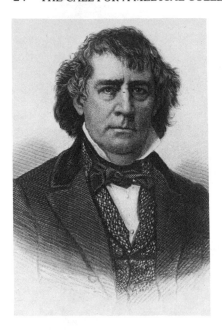

(Fig. 6)
Dr. Theodric Romeyn Beck

afflicted and a form of work therapy. It is amazing to realize that a twenty-year-old youth could have such knowledge and concern for the treatment of the insane, and until Dr. Mosher organized Pavilion F in Albany Hospital in 1902, the ideas advanced by Dr. Beck went unheeded. Pavilion F, which became a model for the treatment of mental illness, was established approximately a century later. Today, Dr. Beck would be regarded as a prodigy. In his graduate thesis, he reviewed the forms of treatment such as "bleeding from the head," emetics to induce vomiting, and other similarly useless efforts to restore sanity which were then the basis for treating the insane.

He began practice in Albany and became physician to the almshouse. At twenty-four, in 1815, he was appointed Professor of the Institute of Medicine and lecturer on Medical Jurisprudence in the College of Physicians and Surgeons for the Western District, established by the Regents, at Fairfield Medical College, Herkimer County, New York. In 1823, he published *Elements of Medical Jurisprudence.* The work was outstanding and was published in many languages. The book contained 12,000 pages and Dr. Beck continued for the remainder of his life to contribute to the subject.

In 1817, he was appointed principal of the Albany Academy. At that time Dr. Beck was wearing three hats: medical practitioner, Professor at Fairfield, and principal of Albany Academy. Perhaps because of the tremendous demands placed on his energy to fulfill all three responsibilities, his health was affected and he resigned from private practice after six years. He continued at Fairfield Medical College until it was closed in 1840. Albany Medical College had been founded a year earlier in 1839.

Figure 7 illustrates an admission card to a lecture series by Dr. Beck on chemistry. The card is issued to Dr. A. March. The location of the lectures is not stated on the card and may have been at Albany Academy, Fairfield Medical College or a suitable hall in Albany.

Immediately on the closing of Fairfield, Dr. Beck was elected Professor of the Institutes of Medicine at the new Albany Medical College. It would seem logical that being such an eminent authority and author on the subject of medical jurisprudence that he would have been appointed to that position. However, Amos Dean was then professor of Medical Jurisprudence.

Dr. Theodric Romeyn Beck remained as professor of the Institutes of Medicine until 1854, having been a teacher of medicine for 39 years. He became Professor Emeritus and died one year later.

Dr. Beck was of massive build and by temperament a strict disciplinarian. He was liberal to the poor, kind to all under his charge, and an advocate of kindness to dumb animals. His life linked the primitive ideas of the 18th century with the emerging enlightenment of the 19th.

A eulogy of Dr. Theodric Romeyn Beck said "He was a great man. He was a good man."

MEDICAL KNOWLEDGE IN THE 19TH CENTURY

At the time that Albany Medical College was founded, trained qualified physicians had the medical knowledge to diagnose common diseases. They could recognize fractures, infections and other fundamental problems. The lectures and demonstrations concentrated

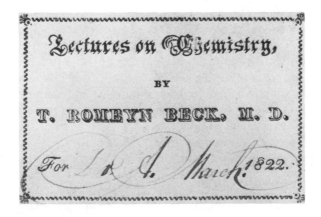

(Fig. 7) Alden March's admission card to T. Romeyn Beck's chemistry lectures.

on these areas of medical knowledge.

In 1832 and again in 1834 when a cholera epidemic struck Albany, the only recourse was to burn tar or spread lime in the streets. No cure or prevention of cholera was taught because none was known. No major surgical procedures were taught as it was not until 1846 that anesthesia became available, and without it, major surgery was unthinkable. The majority of demonstrations were concerned with treatment of fractures, lacerations, amputations, and obstetrical procedures. Even the latter, which is now considered routine and without great danger, was attended by great morbidity and mortality until 1846 when Ignaz P. Semmelweis demonstrated the role of bacteria as the cause of puerperal fever complicating delivery. Even after anesthesia became available, surgical procedures were generally attended by infections until 1860 when Joseph Lister demonstrated the value of carbolic acid. Not until 1891 was the wearing of rubber gloves, hair nets and the washing of hands required for attendance at the operating table. Surgery is indebted to Dr. William Halstead of Johns Hopkins for the recognition of the necessity for this basic approach to antiseptic conditions in the operating theater.

Lister's contribution, the value of carbolic acid, was summarized by Dr. Irving I. Edgar, *Journal of History and Allied Sciences,* Vol. 16, No. 2, 1961.

> *The treatment of our water supply, the preservation of foods and numerous other important procedures all draw upon the principles of antisepsis. Lister raised surgery from a lottery, a game of chance and craft, to a safe scientific art and science. He removed the obstacle limiting surgery to a small sphere of application and made only the skill and dexterity of the surgeon as real limits. The present hospital system exists because of Lister, for without antisepsis hospitals were houses of torture and death. Lord Lister's discoveries gave hospitals all over the world a new Lease on Life making them houses of healing and cure.*

Surgery kept pace with other medical advances whereby the control of infection by Lister using carbolic acid in 1860, and later the prevention of infection by Dr. Halstead in 1891, made surgery for compound fractures and other injuries a safe procedure. They also made it possible to deal with abdominal, brain, and thoracic and cardiac surgery. In 1839, all of the latter procedures were impossible to perform and that whole body of information was not included in the lectures, consequently training in surgery was comparatively elemental.

Medical lectures were limited to discussions of the value of venesection and catharsis for all manner of maladies and it is safe to assume that many of these theories were taught to the students at the incipient Albany Medical College as they were in other medical schools of that day. Other lectures concentrated on the voluminous pharmacopeia largely made up of herbs and other "hand me down" remedies from physicians and housewives, many completely harmless, but some less so. A doctor's ability to combine long complicated mixtures of chemicals and syrups was a measure of his skills. Because specimens for dissection were difficult to obtain, the students were restricted to observing the information revealed by dissection as best they could from their seats in the amphitheater.

Compared with medical knowledge of the 18th century, however, the knowledge of the early and mid-nineteenth centuy opened vast new territories for the instructor and student. The first alternate case study demonstrating the value of vitamin C in the prevention of scurvy had been performed by James Lind in 1753; the self experiment of John Hunter in 1770 demonstrated the ravages of syphilis; the anesthetic properties of nitrous oxide were discovered in 1799; and Morton demonstrated the use of ether as a general anesthetic in 1846. In 1816, René Laennec developed the stethoscope, and the use of quinine to control malaria was discovered in 1820 by Pelletier. So when Albany Medical School opened its doors in 1839, there was much to inspire the students because of the great strides of the recent past and the promise of a broadening understanding of bacteriology and the nature of infectious diseases.

FIRST ADMINISTRATION AND FACULTY

What a thrilling time to teach it must have been as the answers to problems evolved with the improvement of medical education and hospitals and laboratory facilities.

The Circular of the Trustees of the Albany Medical College, published in 1838, was actually the first Albany Medical College catalog. It consisted of 36 pages enclosed by a light weight paper cover, very different from the 144 page catalog for the academic year 1982-83. Though considered condensed when compared to the modern catalog, it does provide detailed records of the governing body, the faculty, curriculum, requirements for admission and fees, as well as other subtle insights into the College. The preservation of this and succeeding catalogs affords a valuable record and, in many instances, the only detailed record of early Albany Medical College history. The 1838 circular, to use the term chosen by its author, listed the first board of trustees of the College as follows:

Hon. Teunis Van Vechten, Mayor, Ex Officio, President
Hon. James M'Kown, Recorder, Ex Officio, Vice President
John Davis, Secretary
George Dexter, Treasurer

Daniel D. Barnard	John O. Cole
Samuel Stevens	William Seymour

John Taylor	Israel Williams
Friend Humphrey	Oliver Steele
James Gould	Robert H. Payne
John I. Wendell	John Groesbeck
Andrew Kirk	John Trotter
Conrad A. Ten Eyck	Charles D. Gould
Ira Harris	Arnold Nelson
Bradford R. Wood	Thomas McElroy

Phillip S. Van Rensselaer

Of these, Friend Humphrey and James Gould were to be members of the first Board of Management of the Albany Hospital in 1849.

The first faculty of the College was comprised of:

Ebenezer Emmons, M.D., Professor of Chemistry and
Natural History

James H. Armsby, M.D., Professor of Anatomy and Physiology

David M. Reese, M.D., Professor of Theory and Practice
of Medicine

Alden March, M.D., Professor of Surgery

Henry Greene, M.D., Professor of Obstetrics and Diseases
of Women and Children

David M. M'Lachlan, M.D., Professor of Materia Medica
and Pharmacy

Amos Dean, Esq., Professor of Medical Jurisprudence

James H. Armsby, M.D., Dean of the Faculty *(Figure 8)*

The circular in no way identifies Dr March, other than Professor of Surgery, therefore, it can be concluded that the first dean of Albany Medical College was Dr. Armsby. As Dr. March appeared the leading force behind the establishment of the College, and the preceptor and senior of Dr. Armsby, it is logical to assume that he would have been the first dean, but for whatever reason, this was not the case — the circular lists Dr. Armsby. However, the first circular advertising Albany Medical College is dated 1838 and it was not until the following year that the New York State Legislature granted the College the right of incorporation. Further support for the position that Dr. Armsby was not the first dean of Albany Medical College are the dates shown on the seal of the College, 1839 and 1873. The earlier date gives firm evidence that the founders of the College recognized 1839 as the year in which the College was established. A logical question then is what was the status of the fully organized but unincorporated school of 1838?

FIRST CLASSES AND COURSE OF STUDY

With the exception of the charge for material for dissection, which were advertised in the circular to be in abundance, the total annual fee for student attendance was $98.00. Of this amount $68.00 was the total

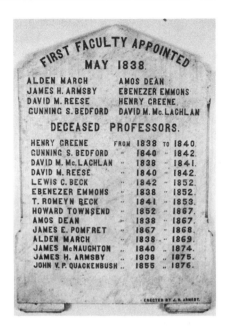

FIRST FACULTY APPOINTED
MAY 1838.

ALDEN MARCH	AMOS DEAN
JAMES H. ARMSBY	EBENEZER EMMONS
DAVID M. REESE	HENRY CREENE
CUNNING S. BEDFORD	DAVID M. Mc. LACHLAN

DECEASED PROFESSORS.

HENRY CREENE	FROM 1838 TO 1840.
CUNNING S. BEDFORD	" 1840 " 1842.
DAVID M. Mc. LACHLAN	" 1838 " 1841.
DAVID M. REESE	" 1840 " 1842.
LEWIS C. BECK	" 1842 " 1852.
EBENEZER EMMONS	" 1838 " 1852.
T. ROMEYN BECK	" 1841 " 1853.
HOWARD TOWNSEND	" 1852 " 1867.
AMOS DEAN	" 1838 " 1867.
JAMES E. POMFRET	" 1867 " 1868.
ALDEN MARCH	" 1838 " 1869.
JAMES McNAUGHTON	" 1840 " 1874.
JAMES H. ARMSBY	" 1838 " 1875.
JOHN V. P. QUACKENBUSH	" 1855 " 1876.

ERECTED BY J. H. ARMSBY.

(Fig. 8) This marble tablet, erected by Dr. J.H. Armsby, records the original faculty.

charge for attendance at all lectures; $5.00 matriculation fee; $5.00 for admission to the dissecting room; and $20.00 covered the charge for graduation. A further breakdown of the $68.00 fee for attendance at lectures is provided in the circular as follows:

Chemistry and Natural History	$11.00
Anatomy and Physiology	11.00
Theory and Practice of Medicine	11.00
Surgery	11.00
Obstetrics	11.00
Materia Medica	8.00
Medical Jurisprudence	5.00

One explanation for the differing fees is that the $11.00 fee was for lectures given five days each week; the $8.00 fee was for lectures given four days each week; and the $5.00 fee for Medical Jurisprudence which lecture was given twice weekly.

Requirements for candidates for an M.D. degree were that the applicant be at least 21 years old; could submit proof that the applicant had studied medicine and surgery with a respectable practitioner for three years; attended two full courses of lectures, the last of which was at Albany Medical College; had satisfactorily passsed an examination before the faculty; and had prepared and submitted to the dean a thesis on some medical subject. It was not necessary for a student to have attended demonstrations in the dissection laboratory to complete the course. Thirteen students graduated in 1839 and as the act of incorporation is dated February of that year, it is assumed that they were granted the degrees of Medical Doctors. The theses of the thirteen graduates are preserved in the archives of the College and five of the subjects were: Bloodletting, Dysentery, Nervous System, Urinary Calculi and Angina Pectoris.

The circular recommends 19 textbooks for use in the course of study but does not state that the entire 19 must be purchased or used. "Ray on Insanity" was one of the texts to be used in conjunction with the course in Medical Jurisprudence. The significance of this text in the course of Medical Jurisprudence undoubtedly went beyond the title.

LANCASTER SCHOOL BUILDING

The main building, exclusive of the wings, was described as being 100 feet long, 50 feet wide and three stories in height *(Figure 9)*. Of this, the anatomical theater occupied a 50 foot by 50 foot area which extended two stories in height and provided amphitheater seating to accommodate 400 persons *(Figure 10)*. The theater was roofed by a domed sky light. A museum occupied a second area 50 feet by 50 feet and 26 feet high *(Figure 11)*. The museum was surrounded by a circular gallery eight feet in diameter from which the specimens could be viewed. The dissecting rooms are described as spacious and convenient although the number of such rooms is not stated. The building also included a chemistry laboratory and "other rooms, large and commodious and well adapted to the purpose for which designed."

Clinical lectures were delivered for the students on Saturday and occasionally surgical operations were performed, which could be viewed by the students. No fee was charged against the Almshouse under the provision that the students be permitted to attend. During the winter months, it is stated that as many as 500 to 600 "inmates" lived in the Almshouse. Judging by the size of the building, which stood on the present grounds of Christian Brothers Academy, conditions must have been extremely crowded. No mention is made of the area in the building in which the patients were treated or operations performed. Needless to say, conditions must have been primitive.

The 1839 circular clarifies this situation by stating that these medical procedures were performed in the anatomical theater of the College. This statement erases the grotesque picture of an Almshouse inmate undergoing amputation of a gangrenous limb while an assortment of fellow inmates and students observe the sights and sounds with varying degrees of interest and horror.

Dr. March may not have been the first dean of the faculty, but he certainly was the star member. The credentials of none of the faculty are listed in the circular other than the fact that they possessed medical degrees or legal training as is the case with Amos Dean whose name is

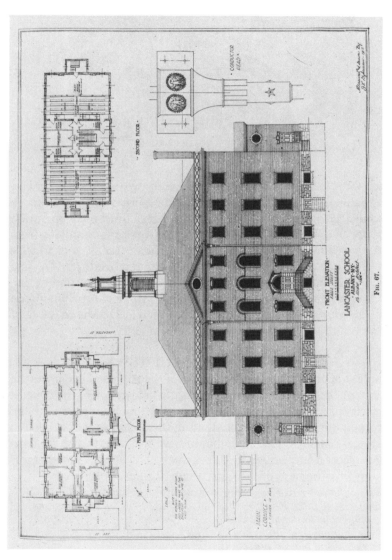

(Fig. 9) Philip Hooker's original architectural plan for the Lancaster School.

(Fig. 10) The Albany Medical College (Eagle Street) amphitheatre.

suffixed with "Esq." By contrast, approximately two pages of the circular are devoted to a detailed list of the operations performed by Dr. March subsequent to January 1, 1837 and the number of times each operation was performed. The total is an impressive 156 operations ranging from amputations and tonsilectomies to the repair of fractures of various limbs. The age of specialization was yet far removed. In 1870 one professor was simultaneously Professor of Ophthamology and Orthopedic Surgery—a most unusual combination. Rather surprisingly, one of the procedures included in the list performed by Dr. March is that of acupuncture.

ALBANY AS A COLLEGE TOWN

Ample support is given in the circular for the choice of Albany as the location for the College. Albany was at the crossroads of the state; it possessed sufficient population to provide student support for the school, and the incidence of accidents in the area was high enough to provide case studies. Excellent board was available to the students ranging in cost from $2.50 to $3.00 per week. And last but not least was the moral environment of the City which was described thusly:

> *It is not however, like New York and other overgrown Atlantic cities, filled with all those seductive and vicious allurements and fascinations so dangerous to the habits and morals of young men, and free from the contaminating influence of which, so many derive a ruined character and blasted prospects.*

In short, Albany was not the place of fast women, slow horses and strong drink—the ruination of many a man. Either the author of the circular had led a sheltered life or the City changed radically during the ensuing twenty-one years. On May 17, 1859, Dr. B.P. Staats, of the Albany Medical Society told the Albany Board of Excise Commissioners that he:

. . . was always in favor of prohibition, but we must take the law as it is. Last year over 600 persons sold liquor in this city, and we have one rum-seller for every twenty-five male inhabitants. During the past twelve years, 85% of the persons committed to the penitentiary were intemperate people; only 15% sober persons.

On the brighter side it could have been said that Albany now provided an excellent location for the medical study of alcoholism. This fact was not cited in catalogs of later years.

FELLOWS AND BOARD OF VISITORS

The 1838 circular contained two listings of individuals; one of which was identified as "Fellows of the College," and the other, "Board of Visitors." The "Fellows" were privileged to attend all meetings of the faculty and examination of candidates for the degree of M.D. In addition, they were entitled to visit the facilities of the College and attend all public lectures and courses of instruction. The "Visitors" had the privilege of visiting the Anatomical Museum, Dissecting Rooms and, as with the "Fellows," of attending all public lectures and courses of instruction. Seven pages, 25 through 32, in the circular provide a listing of specimens contained in the Anatomical Museum and provide an indication of the importance placed on the museum.

1839 ADMINISTRATION AND FACULTY

In 1839, the College issued a "Catalogue and Circular of the Albany Medical College." Foremost in the catalog was proudly displayed the act of incorporation signed by John C. Spencer, secretary of state, and dated February 18, 1839. The act of incorporation was comprised of ten sections, the first of which stated that Daniel D. Barnard, Samuel Stevens, John Taylor, Friend Humprhey, "and their associates are constituted a corporate body." Section III lists 23 trustees of the corpo-

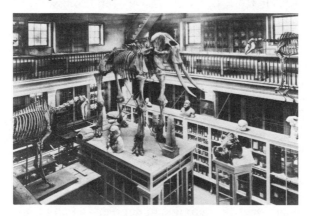

(Fig. 11) The Albany Medical College (Eagle Street) museum.

ration. In addition, Section III indicated that the Mayor and Recorder of the City were included as trustees. Recognizing the vagaries of election, the names of the latter two trustees were not listed. Section IV specifies that the trustees are empowered to appoint professors of the College as necessary and could remove the professors by a two-third vote. The aforementioned vagaries of election effected the only change in the Board of Trustees as noted in the 1838 circular, the Hon. Jared H. Rathbone, Mayor, having replaced the former Mayor, Hon. Teunis Van Vechten as President of the Board of Trustees.

In 1839 a major change was made in the faculty; Alden March, M.D., is recorded as president of the College and Professor of Surgery; the latter post which he held in the 1838 circular. Dr. Armsby is listed as professor of Anatomy but no longer Dean of the Faculty, a title which was not to reappear until the academic year 1875-76 when the title of president was changed to that of Dean. Dr. Armsby performed a dual role as he is also indicated as Registrar of the College. A small but interesting note is that when Dr. Armsby was Dean of the Faculty in 1838, his title and name appear at the bottom of the faculty list, but when Dr. March became President, his title and name are at the top of the listing of the faculty as would be expected.

The circular expressed gratitude to Dr. Greene who resigned the position of professor of Obstetrics and Diseases of Women and Children to be replaced by Dr. Gunning S. Bedford. The title was shortened to Professor of Obstetrics. A name of particular significance to Albany Medical College was the addition of Thomas Hun, M.D., Professor of the Institutes of Medicine. Dr. Hun's title may be confusing until reference is made to a dictionary. There the term "institutes" is defined as, "an elementary principle," however, the use of the word in this connotation is obsolete, hence, the possible confusion. In modern terminology, Dr. Hun's title would have been Professor of the Elementary (basic) Principles of Medicine. While writing of that time may appear to be rather "purple" to modern taste, it was in many instances ingeniously concise. For example, in the catalog of 1841, a procedure performed before the class is described as follows: "Wound dressed— finger bitten off in affray." Here the ingenuity is displayed by the use of the word affray which is defined as "the fighting of two or more persons in a public place, to the terror of others." In one word *affray,* we learn that the finger was bitten off, not by a wild animal but by a person in a fight involving at least two people, the fight took place in public, and the viewers were horrified. Not bad for one word.

Having been incorporated and thereby granted the right to confer the medical degree on successful candidates, the College organized a Board of Curators who were five in number and all licensed doctors. They were Doctors Peter Wendell, Platt Williams, Barant P. Staats,

Samuel White and Thomas C. Brinsmade. The students were obliged to stand before this Board and satisfactorily respond to questioning in an oral examination.

1839 STUDENT BODY AND COURSE OF STUDY

The circular lists the names of 68 students "Attending the First Course" and, even at this early date, the student body was not provincial. Seven states and two foreign countries, Canada and Poland, are given as the homes of the students. That Henry Cartier should have come from Canada is understandable as Albany is only 200 miles from the Canadian border, but that Arthur Gutowski came from Poland to attend a school in existence only one year is a tribute to public relations or extreme crowding in Polish medical schools. Sad to relate, Albany Medical College could not lay claim to a graduate from Europe for many more years and Gutowski's name does not appear in subsequent listings of graduates.

Opposite each student's name in the listing of the student body is the name or names of their preceptors. Doctors March and Armsby predominate in the category serving as preceptors for 22 of the 68 students. Preceptors were not required for students who were already recipients of M.D. degrees or those who restricted their studies to anatomy or chemistry and who would not be candidates for the M.D. degree. Why a holder of the M.D. degree would enroll and attend a second course is perplexing unless it was to enrich his knowledge of medicine. Of the 68 students listed in the circular, 13 are listed in the 1840 catalog as having graduated. In view of the requirement that a student complete two full courses of lectures before graduation, it follows that the College must have offered two full courses of lectures in the academic year 1838-39. The requirement that a student attend two full courses of lectures presumably of the exact same content is strange. The only rational explanation is that those who established this requirement believed in learning by rote and that a student would absorb the information imparted more thoroughly when subjected to it a second time. It must have been a tedious experience for the more perceptive students.

The same 19 texts are listed as recommended for study, but board went up from the $2.50-$3.00 per week range, shown in the 1838 circular, to $2.50-$3.50 and so did tuition. Tuition increased to $70 per year and the increase is accounted for by the $5.00 for the new lecture series, Institutes of Medicine, given by Dr. Hun. The catalog is completed by the listing of the 182 operations performed by Dr. March during the preceding year of which 66 were of a different procedure. The Anatomical Museum continued to grow and a listing of additional exhibits is included at length in the catalog.

A paragraph of curious content appears at the end of the circular which states that:

> *Dr. March and Armsby will give private instruction in the various branches of Medical Science, as usual, during the year. Students will have free access to the College Museum and its collections, and have opportunities of witnessing in practice of Dr. March a great variety of surgical cases and diseases.*
>
> *Terms of office tuition for the year, $75.*

At first blush,this might be understood as a fee for performing the service of preceptor to students, but if this was the case, why would free access to the Museum and witnessing surgical cases be offered as a further inducement, as enrolled students of the Colelge would have these privileges. The conclusion must be that for the same fee charged for attendance at College lectures, Doctors March and Armsby would instruct students in their office(s). It almost seems as if they were competing with the College and using space in the College catalog to advertise the fact. Why a student would choose this alternative route to medical education and what the advantage might be is not apparent. This offer appeared in the catalogs of 1838, 1839 and 1840, but does not appear thereafter.

1840 CATALOG

In the 1840 catalog the names of Archibald M'Intyre, Isaiah Townsend and John V.L. Pruyn were added to the Board of Trustees and those of John I. Wendell, Andrew Kirk, Israel Williams, George Dexter and John Davis were removed. The faculty also had its changes; Doctors Beck and McNaughten replaced Doctors Reese and Bedford. Dr. Beck's title was Professor of Chemistry and Therapeutics, and Dr. McNaughton became Professor of Theory and Practice of Medicine. The addition of Dr. McNaughton to the staff is extremely significant as he was to become president of the Faculty in 1869 on the death of Dr. March. Dr. McNaughton had been a professor at Fairfield Medical College when he joined Albany Medical College. As a courtesy to his students at Fairfield, he requested that those students, so desiring, would be admitted to Albany Medical College with full credit for their studies at Fairfield. His request was granted. Dr. Armsby while remaining as Professor of Anatomy, was given the additional title and responsibility of Registrar. Dr. Emmons' title was changed to Professor of Materia Medica and Natural History,and Dr. M'Lachlan became Professor of Obstetrics and Diseases of Women and Children. Four changes were made in the Board of Curators; T. Romeyn Beck, M.D. and Mason D. Cogswell, M.D. were added, replacing Doctors White and Brinsmade who had served but one year. The listing of "Fellows" and "Visitors" of the College is not contained in the 1840 catalog or any thereafter. The reason for the discontinuation of the listing is not stated and whether the privileges extended to these groups were also discontinued is not known. However, these privileges might have been continued in another form as provision is made in the catalog for students who have completed two full courses of lectures in Albany Medical College or other medical college to attend any lectures they desired for payment of fee ranging from $5.00 to $50.00. The determination of the fee for an individual depended upon where he had attended the previous course of lectures, a somewhat strange reason for the difference in fee.

The fee for attending a series of lectures remained at the previous year's figure of $70 and continued unchanged until 1853, when it was reduced to $60 per term and offered at the bargain rate of $100 for two terms if paid in advance. In 1859, the fee per term was increased to $65, but the same bargain rate for advanced payment held. Prices were stable and inflation was not yet a factor. The reasonable price for board remained at the affordable $2.50-$3.50 level until 1844 when surprisingly it was advertised to be available at a lower rate of $2.00-$3.00 per week. No mention is made of quality or quantity of food offered. Perhaps the number of roasts and beef steaks was reduced accordingly.

ENROLLMENT TRENDS 1840-64

In the 1840-41 academic year, student enrollment increased by five students from the previous year to total 73 students. During the first twenty years of its existence, student enrollment in the College averaged approximately 88 students per year. (The figure for student enrollment is not available for seven of those twenty years and, therefore, the average is based on the thirteen years that are available.) During this period, the greatest number of enrolled students was 122 in the academic year 1841-42, and the lowest was 30 students in 1863-64. It is difficult to explain the low enrollment in 1863-64 because this was the early period of the Civil War and a time when physicians would normally be in demand to attend the armies in the field and those with war injuries.

During the same twenty year period, graduating students averaged 31 per year with a widely varying high and low of 64 and 17 respectively. Just as the tuition of today contrasts vividly with that of "the good old days," so does the rate of student attrition. During those twenty years, only 35 percent of entering students successfully achieved graduation. Some of the 65 percent who did not graduate were the students who were conspicious by their previous achievement of a medical degree and who may have enrolled with the goal of broadening their education in specific areas only. By comparison with modern entrance requirements, admission requirements to the College during the early years were extremely lenient, and many may have been admitted who had neither the perserverance or mental skills to complete the course of study. Some few may have withdrawn because of the unquestioned boredom of listening to the same professors cover the same material twice in the same year. Not to be entirely discounted was the final oral examination before the board of curators, a more severe and dour group is difficult to contemplate, and not a few students may have been frightened out of their wits when confronted by those inquisitors.

FACULTY TRENDS

The faculty remained stable during the period 1840-64 with the most frequent change being the shifting of professors from one field to another. When T. Romeyn Beck, M.D. joined the faculty, he received two assignments, Professor of Materia Medica and Librarian. Dual assignments were given to Dr. Thomas Hun in 1844 when he also served as Registrar in addition to Professor of the Instututes of Medicine. That same year, Dr. Armsby became Curator of the Museum and was relieved of his duties as Registrar but was held to the task of Professor of Anatomy. In 1853, Howard Townsend, M.D. joined the faculty and had the dual responsibilities of Professor of Obstetrics and Registrar. It seems as though the role as Registrar descended on the junior member of the faculty who was required to "double in brass" to establish his endurance. That same year, Ezra S. Carr, M.D. became Professor of Chemistry and Pharmacy.

ANATOMICAL MUSEUM AND LIBRARY

The Anatomical Museum continued to be advertised in the catalog with detailed listings of acquisitions and recognition of the donors. The importance of the Museum is indicated by the appointment of Dr. Armsby as Curator. In 1849, it was reported that Dr. March during a trip to Europe, "obtained a very perfect collection of diseases and injuries of the hip joint," which made a valuable addition to the Museum. In addition to the growth of the Museum, the College developed a library which consisted of some 2,000 volumes in 1849 and grew to 5,000 volumes in 1857. At least a portion of the cost of the library was underwritten by a grant of $15,000 received from New York State in 1844 which was to be used to improve the building, anatomical preparations, chemical apparatus, and books. The following year an additional grant of $1,000 was again received from New York State.

CARE FOR THE POOR

The same offer of free medical advice and operations to the indigent continued to be made with the provision that the advice be offered or operations performed before the class on Saturday while classes were in session. In 1849, the offer was amended by the addition of the word "really" before indigent and both words were italicized. The opinion must have been that some who could have afforded the service were pleading false poverty. One hundred years, more or less, would pass before qualification as an indigent would be more precisely established, but someone in Albany Medical College was already working on the determination of that category of society.

THE UNIVERSITY OF ALBANY

In 1852, there was an apparent effort to broaden the College into a university. The 1852 catalog advertised as part of the "University of Albany" a department of law and a scientific department. The Department of Law was staffed by the Hon. Ira Harris, LLD, Hon. Amasa J. Parker, LLD, and Amos Dean, Esq. Fee for a full terms' attendance was $40 and three terms were required to complete the course of study. It may be just coincidence that the three term fee totalled $120, the same as the bargain rate for two years at the Medical College. The Scientific Department offered a wide array of subjects which included; Scientific and Practical Agriculture, Civil and Mechanical Engineering, the Mechanics Arts, Astronomy, Chemistry and Physical Geography. No faculty is identified for this Department and the fee for attendance is not stated. This was indeed an ambitious effort and few universities of present time could rival this diversity of curricula.

For whatever reason, the Scientific Department of the university did not succeed and is not mentioned in the catalog of later years. However, a Department of Chemistry is listed in the catalog for several years but this too was discontinued, leaving the Law Department as the only department in the ambitiously naive University.In 1858, the University of Albany had grown to sufficient stature to list the President of the University in the catalog. He was Thomas W. Olcott. The Department of Law which had previously been identified only with three professors now had a President of the Faculty, the Hon. R. Hyde Walworth. There seems to have been some confusion as to how the Hon. Mr. Walworth chose to be addressed; the 1865 catalog identified him as the Hon. Reuben H. Walworth.

In 1869, the growing importance of the University is indicated by the appearance of the University of Albany title on the cover of that year's catalog and the indented title of the Albany Medical College beneath it. The Department of Law was still relegated to the last page where it was listed as a Department of the University. Many questions remain unanswered concerning the University. Who was the motivating force behind its founding? Why was the Medical College identified in the University as a college and the Department of Law as a department and not a college? Who were the graduates of the Department of Law and why were their names not listed in the catalog as were the names of the graduates of the Medical College? If asked, doctors might have one opinion and lawyers another.

ADMINISTRATION AND FACULTY CHANGES

Membership in the Faculty, Board of Trustees and Board of Curators continued to change. In 1854, William A. Young became Recorder, ex officio, of the Board of Trustees. He was succeeded in that position by Alexander S. Johnson in 1857. That same year, U.G. Bigelow, M.D. became a member of the Board of Curators and in 1863, John V. Lansing, M.D. was added to the Board. In 1868, the number of Curators was increased to eight with the addition of Samuel H. Bailey, M.D., and James L. Babcock, M.D. That year Dr. Lansing resigned from the Board of Curators to become Professor of Materia Medica in the College.

In 1857, there were four changes in the faculty; Charles H. Porter, M.D., became Professor of Chemistry and Pharmacy, F.L.R. Chapin, M.D., was appointed Demonstrator of Anatomy and Assistant Curator of the Museum, Dr. Armsby remained as Curator of the Museum but his title of Professor of Anatomy was changed to Professor of Descriptive and Surgical Anatomy (shades of Professor of the Institutes of Medicine). Like several earlier freshman members of the faculty, when J.V.P. Quackenbush, M.D. joined the faculty in 1857 as Professor of Midwifery and Diseases of Women and Children, he too was saddled with the duties of Registrar. The faculty was unchanged in 1859 and catalogs for the years 1858, 1860, 1861 and 1862 are not available so changes in those years are unknown. It is known from the catalog of 1863 that George F. Barker, Ph.D., became Acting Professor of Chemistry, and, other than Amos Dean, he was the first member of the faculty who had a degree other than M.D. That same year H.R. Haskins, M.D., replaced Dr. Chapin in the dual posts of Demonstrator of Anatomy and Assistant Curator of the Museum where he had served since 1857. Jacob S. Mosher, M.D., was appointed Lecturer on Chemistry in 1864 and in 1865 he assumed the position of Registrar of which Dr Quackenbush was relieved. The variety of formats and varying content of the catalog may be accounted for by reason that the Registrars were responsible for their publication. The frequent transfer of the responsibility of Registrar opened the door to frequent rethinking of what the catalog should contain.

Four changes were made in the faculty in 1868: S. Oakley Vanderpoel, M.D. became Professor of General Pathology and Clinical Medicine; James E. Pomfret, M.D. became Professor of Physiology; and John V. Lansing, M.D., as noted earlier, became Professor of Materia Medica. That same year a new record for responsibilities was established by Dr.

Mosher when, in addition to his two previous assignments as Lecturer on Chemistry and Registrar, he added two more, Professor of Medical Jurisprudence and Librarian. His title of Lecturer on Chemstry was altered to Professor of Chemistry and undoubtedly indicates a well deserved promotion.

CIVIL WAR SERVICE OF GRADUATES

By 1864, Albany Medical College had graduated 840 students of whom 158 were Surgeons in the United States Army. That approximately 19 percent of all graduates were Army Surgeons may be explained by the fact that 1864 was the third year of the Civil War, and also that as Albany Medical College had been in existence only twenty-five years in 1864, most of its graduates were young men. Reflecting the effect of wartime inflation, board available to students had doubled being offered for $3.00-$5.00 weekly.

TRADITIONS OF FELLOWSHIP

There is little room for question that the men who comprised the faculty of the developing Albany Medical College were men of serious intent in whose lives there was scant time for distracting activity. Perhaps to provide an opportunity for relaxing in the company of their associates at the College and at the same time to discuss in a relaxed atmosphere developments in their profession, the Esculapian Club was formed in 1850. The Club members met bimonthly, during the winter months, before which meetings a scientific paper was presented by a member and discussed by all. The Club became a tradition in the College and continued until World War II when, due to the disruption of the time, it was discontinued. In the later years of the existence, members of the Club were leaders of the faculty and a very good index of the type of aspiring men whose spirit was responsible for maintaining teaching standards in an effort to improve the College. Dinners were served in the home of the host member or at the Fort Orange Club and the meals were sumptuous banquets, often prepared by special chefs or by a member with gourmet qualifications. Prominent in the membership of the Esculapian Club were Dr. Henry Hun, Sr., Dr. Elting, Dr. Gordinier, Dr. Archambeau, Dr. George Bloomer, Dr. Harry Judge and Dr. Sautter. Dr. Sautter, who was Professor of Dermatology, was a classic Hollander whose five feet height was equaled by his girth. He would spend great effort to assure the prime cuts of beef, the proper choice of wine, and even to supervise the preparation of food when he was host. Aside from the gastronomic pleasures of the dinner meetings, a strong sense of camaraderie was developed during these meetings and their discontinuation left a void in the social and professional lives of the faculty.

FINANCING THE COLLEGE

The catalogs provide no information concerning the finances of the College except for the acknowledgement of grants from the New York State Legislature, and the only discovered records of financing are those stated in the minutes of the meetings of the Board of Trustees. The minutes were transcribed in leather bound ledgers and provide a concise record of the meetings and magnificent examples of calligraphy. While the script is Spenserian and the letter "s" is written as one would form the small letter "f" in modern long hand, they are very legible. Sufficient information is contained in these minutes to provide the basis for supposition where otherwise only a blank would exist—such as what were the financial arrangements for the College.

Prior to federal and state funding of colleges and universities, the cost of establishing a college was generally met through the generosity of a group of wealthy individuals who banded together with the common interest of establishing a place of higher learning in their community. Another source of financing a college was church-related groups led by the clergy who to a large extent staffed the faculty. In other instances, individuals of great wealth such as Johns Hopkins or Andrew Carnegie single handedly provided the necessary funds. The funding of Albany Medical College does not fit into any of these three categories.

Doctors March and Armsby, while successful doctors, were young men at the time the College was founded and, therefore, were not sufficiently established to accumulate wealth, nor did they inherit family wealth. The same is true to varying extent of those who supported their effort. Dr. Armsby, through his lectures, was able to raise $10,000 to aid in the initial funding and the City granted free use of the Lancaster School for the first five years. The minutes of the first meeting of the Trustees of the College on April 14, 1838, are, as one might expect, primarily concerned with financing. At that meeting, held in the Mansion House, it was agreed that a corporation be formed for the purpose of obtaining funds for the school. The goal was to obtain $5,000 through the sale of corporate stock. Five hundred shares were issued with each share selling for $10.00. It was further agreed that all stockholders could attend lectures at the college without charge. This agreement may explain the meaning of the list of "Visitors," which appeared in the catalog of 1839, to whom free attendance at all lectures was offered. While funding was the primary topic,there was debate as to whether classes should be conducted in 1838 before incorporation was granted by New York State. That the decision was made to proceed anticipating legislative approval is apparent by the publication of the 1838 circular and the graduation of students in the spring of 1839.

That the stock was quickly sold by the committee for solicitation of funds may be concluded from the minutes of the third meeting held on August 7, 1838, which revealed that the money had been spent to improve the facilities of the Lancaster School. In fact, the funds were overspent by $1,104. No great concern was expressed, however, because the committee had not yet approached "citizens of known liberality" for contributions. Fund raising was already a developed skill with lists of possible contributors to worthy causes. The Board of Trustees had a list which identified 283 persons for the fund raisers to approach.

REMUNERATION OF FACULTY AND STOCKHOLDERS

One subject of the second meetng, held on May 2, 1838, explains in part how the faculty members were to be paid for their services. At that meeting, it was agreed that the faculty could retain the enrollments (tuition) which remained after a sufficient amount was deducted to pay stockholders five percent annual interest on their investment. As tuition during the following twenty years averaged $65.00 per session; and each year there were two sessions; and student enrollment averaged 88 students per year, the tuitions received averaged $11,440 per year. This figure is admittedly imprecise because some students did not enroll for both sessions, some students enrolled for only selected courses such as anatomy or chemistry, and some students paid in advance for two sessions and availed themselves of the reduced rate of $100 total for both sessions. After making allowance for these factors it is probable that the total amount received in tuition did not exceed $10,000. Nothing is available to indicate how this estimated annual income was divided among the faculty members; moreover, it is unlikely that entire tuition fees were distributed among the faculty.

Of the estimated $10,000, $250 was returned to the corporation to pay the five percent interest to the stockholders. As no provision is made in the later listing of disbursement in the minutes of the trustees meetings for such things as heating, lighting and custodial services of the building, it may be assumed that funds for these items were also deducted from tuition fees. Then there was the cost of medicine and dressings used in the demonstrations conducted on Saturdays for the education of the students and for which the patients paid nothing. As the first faculty had eight members, the average payment to each member probably did not average more than $1,000 after these deductions were made. However, indication that the sharing of the tuition may not have been arrived at by the simple process of equal division is the breakdown of the $68 fee for attendance at lectures in 1838 and simliar breakdowns shown in subsequent catalogs. Charges for five of the lectures was $11.00 each, and of the remaining two, the charges were $8.00 and $5.00. It is possible that the money was divided among the faculty members in accordance with the amount charged for the lecture for which each professor was responsible.

Also unaccounted for is the $10,000 that Dr. Armsby is reported to have received for lectures prior to opening the College and which he is said to have donated to the College. It is possible, though unlikely, that the full amount was used to defray the cost of preliminary organization which took place prior to the first meeting of the committtee on April 14, 1838, and is, therefore, unaccounted for in the minutes of that and subsequent meetings.

The over expenditure of funds noted in the minutes of the May 2, 1838, meeting may not have been offset by contributions of "citizens of known liberality" because on February 19, 1839, the Trustees authorized the negotiation for a loan of $1,200 to repay indebtedness of the College. That indebtedness could be traced back to the overexpenditure of $1,104 for improvement to the facilities of the school in 1838.

ARTICLES OF INCORPORATION

The second subject of the May 2, 1838 meeting of the Board of Trustees was the important one of drafting the articles of incorporation. The Board included men of sound business experience and others with excellent legal training; yet the articles, as proposed at that meeting, reflect some confusion or overly cautious regulation concerning control of the faculty. Two articles were proposed to govern the faculty in regard to appointments and dismissals and because these were the seeds from which much confusion resulted in 1914 to the point of almost closing the school, they are quoted here in their entirety. The first, Article VI, states the following:

> The said Board of Trustees shall have the power to appoint all such officers, committees, and employ all such agents and servants that they may deem necessary for the necessary and proper government and conducting the affairs and interests of said association—to fill the Departments or Professorships in the said College hereinafter mentioned with able and competent Professors, and generally to rent, purchase or otherwise procure all such necessary building or buildings, and other property and apparatus as may be necessary or convenient for the advancement of the objects of this association.

A second article covering the subject of the faculty appears in the draft as Article X—not VII as would be expected and, therefore, might be construed as an afterthought on the subject. It states:

> The Board of Trustees upon the recommendation of a majority of the Faculty shall have the power of removing any Professor or member of said Faculty, also by filling the vacancy by such removal, and also to fill all such vacancies as may occur by resignation, death or otherwise.

This article defines two additional subjects—the power of removal of members from the faculty, and the requirement of a majority of the faculty to recomend such action.

The minutes of the February 16, 1839 meeting contains the articles of incorporation as approved by the New York State Legislature and attested to by the signature of John C. Spencer, Secretary of State. The official articles of incorporatoin combine the substance of Articles VI and X of the draft copy into Article IV which states:

> It shall be lawful for the Board of Trustees to appoint the professors, and such other instructors as they may deem necessary, subject to removal by a vote of two-thirds of the members constituting said board, when found expedient and necessary.

The participation of the faculty is not mentioned in this article and, therefore, the power of appointment and removal resided solely with the Board of Trustees. Not included in the articles of incorporation is any provision for the structure of the faculty or description of the manner in which the tuition fees were to be divided.

On February 27, 1839, however, the Board convened for the purpose of reviewing and approving the by-laws which were, in effect, to govern the business of the College. Article IV of the by-laws provides for the structure of the faculty as follows:

> The Professors already appointed, and hereafter as they may be appointed shall constitute the Faculty of the Albany Medical College and shall have officer or officers, among themselves who shall be elected by the professors as they shall deem necessary and proper.

This by-law clearly grants the faculty the responsibility and authority to designate officers of the faculty and to select those persons to fill those offices. As it is not otherwise stated, it can be assumed that in the election of officers a simple majority would suffice. At that time, there were eight faculty members so that a 5 to 3 majority would have been necessary. It is through this by-law that the design of the faculty structure is granted to the faculty.

Article V of the by-laws, in effect, grants to the faculty the powers that would have been granted by Article X of the draft version of the articles of incorporation for it states:

> Vacancies in the faculty shall be filled by the Board of Trustees on the Nomination of a Majority of the Faculty, if the faculty see fit to make such nomination. Appointments and removals of Professors are to be made by resolution.

These articles of the by-laws clearly provide that the faculty had the authority to create the office of dean or president and by a two-third majority designate to the Board of Trustees the person selected by the faculty to hold that office. But it should also be recognized that by-laws can be amended by the Board of Trustees of a corporation without approvals other than those which the board has established. The articles of incorporation can be amended only with the approval of the granting legislature. A serious controversy was to result in 1914, from the interpretation of these articles and by-laws.

When the by-laws were approved on February 16, 1839, it was clear to the Trustees that the funds from the initial stock issue would be insufficient to conduct the affairs of the College. As a result, Article IX of the by-laws provided for additional stock sales in which the shares would be offered at $25.00 per share. However, Article X of the by-laws clearly indicates that the faculty would not be permitted to run wild with careless expenditure of the Corporation funds. It read as follows:

> *Whereas necessary expenses shall be incurred in behalf of the College not falling strictly within the meaning of "current-expenses" the Trustees reserve to themselves the right to direct the whole or some part of such expense as they shall judge to be just and equitable shall be borne by the faculty, out of current income and enrollments arising from the business of the College.*

In effect, the Trustees were stating that if they decided an expenditure was on the margin, the amount involved would be deducted from the faculty's salary and the Trustees were the sole arbitors of the decision. It would be interesting to see the results of such action on a modern corporation—academic or otherwise.

GRANT FROM THE LEGISLATURE

In 1841, the Trustees acknowledge receipt of $5,000 from a grant by the New York State Legislature. The funds were quickly put to the following use:

$ 740	Improvements to building
2,340	Improvements to Museum
900	Purchase of books for library
500	Purchase of chemical apparatus
520	Miscellaneous purchases at discretion of the faculty
$5,000	Total

That the Trustees did maintain a tight rein on the finances of the College is shown in the minutes of the meeting of Trustees held on July 13, 1842. In that meeting the request for the appropriation of $3,960 by the faculty for improvements to the College was discussed. In the breakdown of intended use of these funds, $150 was to be used "for the skeleton of the Elephant" and $1,500 for additional library books. The minutes are not specific as to whether the "Elephant" request may have been for the puchase of an elephant's skeleton or the repair of one already in the Museum. The Trustees approved the "Elephant" appropriation but reduced the "book" appropriation to $1,000. It may have been that the Trustees enjoyed visits to the Museum to stand in awe and marvel at the immense proportions of the skeletal elephant and in their mind's eye cloak it with muscle, flesh, and hide, but they had no great desire to research the dry medical texts. Two months later, on September 16, the Trustees relented, granting the additional $500 for the books.

And this gives rise to an interesting but unanswered question, what was the source for funding the $3,960 appropriation. The initial $5,000 received at the time of incorporation was spent, in fact overspent, for improvements to the building and facilities. The subsequent grant by the Legislature was likewise spent for improvements. The Corporation had received only four interest payments totaling $1,000. The minutes of the Trustees' meeting are recorded in a ledger which remains complete so that it is not possible that recording of meetings in which funds were received are lost. That the funds were spent is a matter of record so the conclusion might be that further loans were negotiated by the Corporation.

BOARD OF TRUSTEES PROCEEDINGS

A note of passing interest is recorded in the meeting of February 19, 1839 during which an election was conducted to determine who would be President of the Board of Trustees. The Hon. Teunis Van Vechten, Mayor of Albany, was elected by a vote of 12 to 1. In that election, Friend Humphrey received one vote and whether that vote was of his own casting is not recorded.

The meetings of the Board of Trustees were generally held twice a year, one being in the spring and the second in December. The contents of the minutes are dominated by approval to grant the degree of medical doctor to graduates who had successfully taken examinations and demonstrated their knowledge to the satisfaction of the Curators. The graduates who were awarded the degree are listed by name in the minutes of the meetings. In June 1856, it is noted in the minutes of the meeting that Mr. John Flickinger had passed the examination for his degree but had not completed the entire course of study, but the Curators recommended he be awarded the degree after six more weeks of study. The Trustees and Curators were concerned with the quality of application as evidenced by Mr. Flickinger's successfully passing the examination, but they also insisted on six more weeks of study to satisfy the quantity requirement. A precocious student was recognized but not fully endorsed on that basis alone. In other instances, the Trustees awarded the medical degree from Albany Medical College to persons who had completed a course of study at other medical colleges such as Columbia Unviersity. In a sense this may have been an honorary degree and based on the recipient's having achieved his degree from another recognized institution. In 1868, S. Oakley Vanderpoel, M.D., then the Professor of General Pathology and Clinical Medicine at Albany Medical College, was awarded the degree of Doctor of Medicine by Albany Medical College. Dr. Vanderpoel had attended lectures at Albany Medical College but had completed his studies at the University of Pennsylvania and was graduated from that University.

The minutes of the meetings during the period from 1839 to 1869 are somewhat inconsistent in that they treat some small business of the College in explicit detail, recording the disbursement of seemingly inconsequential amounts of money and trivial facts. An example of this is the approval of an expenditure of $207 to apply new lathing and plaster to the amphitheater, water closets and a laboratory. Yet the amount of rent paid to the City for the use of the Lancaster School after the five year grace period had ended in 1844 is not mentioned. It is possible that the city extended the rent-free period but that conclusion can be reached only by conjecture.

RELATIONSHIPS WITH THE UNIVERSITY OF ALBANY

A portion of the mystery of the appearance of the University of Albany's title on the cover of the catalog of 1869 and the advertisement of the Law Department in the 1852 catalog is explained in the minutes of December 24, 1860 *(Figure 12)*. In those minutes, the receipt of a communication from the University of Albany is acknowledged. In the communication, officers of the University explained that the articles of incorporation for the University provided for the "erection" of a Law Department and the establishment under the University of Albany, Albany Medical College as a co-ordinate Department of Medicine. The communication further states that while each Department would maintain a separate board of trustees, Albany Medical College would become a component part of the University of Albany. A motion was made in the meeting to apply to the Legislature for permission to amend the charter of the College so as to permit it to join the University of Albany. The application to the Legislature was subject to approval by a vote of the Board of Trustees. Unfortunately, nothing more concerning the merger is contained in the minutes, but from the content of the cover of the 1869 catalog it can be concluded that both the Trustees and the Legislature agreed and the merger was consummated some nine years later.

MORE TRUSTEES' MINUTES

In 1864, the first discordant note appears in the minutes and, ironically, the date was Christmas Eve, December 24. A resolution was proposed that Jacob S. Mosher, M.D., be appointed Professor of Chemistry after the removal of Charles W. Porter, M.D., who had been appointed to that position in 1857. The reasons for requesting Porter's removal was that he allegedly had neglected to perform the duties of a Professor; that he had gone into other departments; and was seeking other appointments. The situation was happily resolved either by the spirit of the date or because someone saw things differently than the accusation portrayed. In the same minutes it was noted that Doctor

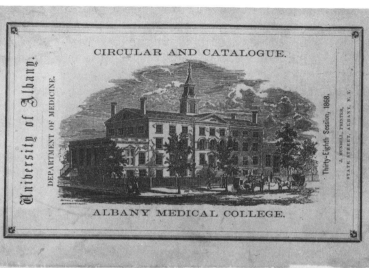

University of Albany.

1869-70.

DEPARTMENT OF LAW.

The Winter term of 1869 commences on the last Tuesday of November, and the Spring Term of 1870 on the first Tuesday of March, and each continues twelve weeks. The next Fall Term will commence on the first Tuesday of September, 1869, and will be followed by two successive terms of twelve weeks each.

Any three successive terms will complete the entire course, each term being independent and complete, as to the instruction embraced in it. The method of teaching is by lecture, examination, and practice in moot courts. Two lectures are given daily except Saturdays, and two moot courts held each week, at which causes are first argued by previously appointed disputants then discussed and decided by the class, followed by the views of the presiding Professor. Thus the law is taught both as a science and an art.

The immense *Law Library of the State* is open to the students, and all the terms of the *Supreme Court of the Third Judicial District*, and of the *Court of Appeals*, the highest in the state, are held in the city of Albany.

The fee for a single term is $50; for two terms $90; and for three $130; in each case payable in advance.

The Professors and leading topics, are as follows:

Hon. IRA HARRIS, LL.D., PRACTICE, PLEADINGS, EVIDENCE.
Hon. A. J. PARKER, LL.D., REAL ESTATE, CRIMINAL LAW, PERSONAL RIGHTS.
ISAAC EDWARDS, PERSONAL PROPERTY, CONTRACT, COMMERCIAL LAW.

Circulars are obtained by addressing ISAAC EDWARDS, Albany, N. Y.

HON. THOMAS W. OLCOTT,
President of the University.

(Fig. 12) This 1869-70 circular and catalogue shows the Department of Law and the Department of Medicine forming the University of Albany.

Porter was enlisting in the United States Army as a Surgeon and would serve for the duration of the War. Further, the Board expressed their high regard and appreciation of the worth and character of Doctor Porter, as a man and for his accomplishments as a successful teacher of Chemistry. No further explanation is given for the 180 degree turn from condemnation to praise nor is it indicated that Doctor Porter was permitted to confront his accuser or to personally refute the charges. Some person or persons must have had a different opinion of the doctor and it is unfortunate that the source and basis for vindication is not included in the minutes. Score one for the defense and Christmas Eve.

Little else of note appears in the minutes of the succeeding four years. In 1865, the Board agreed to sell $2,000 in bonds and to use the money in the Corporation's bank account to pay a bill presented by the faculty for repairs to the building. In 1867, the Board of Trustees held their meeting in the Mechanics and Farmers Bank. The College at that time had no Board Room and meetings were held where it was convenient for the members.

DEATH OF DR. MARCH

In 1869, Doctor Alden March died shortly after returning from a journey to New Orleans. On the evening of May 27, 1869, he visited at the home of his daughter, the wife of Doctor James P. Boyd. During the visit, he became so ill that it was decided that he should spend the night there rather than attempting to go home. During the night, his condition worsened. He continued to decline during three more weeks of illness, and apparently sensing his death approaching, he summoned his family and friends to his bedside and bade them farewell. Five days later he died. The nature of his illness is not known, but his 73 years is well beyond the normal life expectancy of that time. His was an amazing career. From ordinary circumstances he had risen to nationally recognized heights as a surgeon of skill and innovative ability. He had developed the technique of cosmetic surgery and instruments for the correction of hare lip, as well as the technique and instruments for removal of bladder stones *(Figure 13)*. The variety of operations which he performed ran the gamut of known procedures. Dr. March was the Professor of Surgery and Dean of Albany Medical College for 30 years, 1839-69. During those thirty year, 1,089 students graduated from the College with the degree of medical doctor. He had founded a medical college and a hospital by attracting other men of skill and professional and civic dedication to support him in his endeavors. In his administration, there is no evidence of any rancor between him and his staff or with the Trustees of the College. His leadership must have been even-handed and inspirational. In his will he bequeathed to the College the anatomical specimens which he had gathered during his life and $1,000 for the maintenance of his collection. In addition, Dr. March directed in his will that $1,000 be donated from his estate to Albany Hospital for the purchase of surgical instruments. In the thirty years since its founding by Dr. March, the College had not received any great endowments or substantial financial support. The College occupied a building converted for its use and had a precarious financial basis seeming to exist from "hand-to-mouth." There must have been occasions when a less resolute person would have become discouraged to the point of seeking a more free and financially rewarding life. While no monument or building has been dedicated to the Founder, in a sense Albany Medical Center stands as testimony to the energy, foresight, ability and dedication of Doctor Alden March.

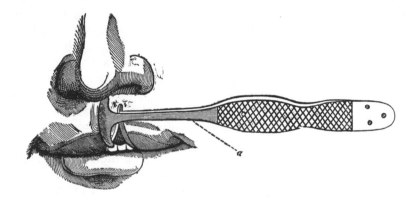

(Fig. 13) An instrument designed by Dr. Alden March for hairlip repair.

Development of the
Modern Hospital

The square, metal roadside sign bearing the capital letter "H" is a familiar sight to travelers directing those in need to the nearest hospital by the most convenient route. It is taken for granted that hospitals stand ready in any city to provide medical service in all seasons, night and day. A city without at least one hospital would be regarded as completely deprived. From its early days, there have been hospitals in the United States although they might not be recognized as such by contemporary standards. Those early hospitals must have been horrible places for patients, and for all except the most insensitive attendants if historical description of them is accurate.

Webster's New Collegiate Dictionary provides three definitions of the term which concisely trace the evolution of hospitals from primitive to modern times. The first, the historical definition is, "a place for shelter or entertainment of travelers, strangers, etc." The second, obsolete except for historical use is, "a charitable institution for the refuge, maintenance or education of needy, aged, infirm, or young persons." The third definition is, "an institution in which patients or injured persons are given medical or surgical care." These three definitions depict the evolution of hospitals from places of shelter for itinerants, refuges for the helpless, to the modern hospital, a place providing special medical and surgical treatment.

It might be expected that the early hospitals in the pioneer nation were reflections of the unsophisticated manners of population. However, hospitals in old established countries such as those in Europe, were equally crude or at best little better. They were few in number and of temporary existence, established in any convenient, empty building long enough to deal with those wounded in wars or stricken by epidemics. Hospitals in the early nineteenth century were places where those who were ill and destitute could find shelter, rudimentary care, and in most instances, a place to die. As recently as 1830, hospitals in England required two sums to be paid by those who had any money before they would be admitted. The first was to cover the cost of the care and food provided, and the second was to offset the cost of burial by the hospital should relatives or friends not claim the body of the deceased patient. The attitude toward hospitals as being but one step before the grave has prevailed amongst the elderly even into the twentieth century.

MOST HEALTH CARE WAS HOME BASED

Prior to the development of anesthesia and modern medical procedures, there was little that could be done for a patient in a hospital that could not be done in his home. Before the development of anesthesia and recognition of the dangers of contagion, the patient was more certain of recovery in the comfort of his own home. There, at least, basic cleanliness was provided along with nourishing food and the solicitous attention of his family. The family doctor would visit the home and would examine the patient and prescribe treatment and medicine. The doctor could have done no more for anyone who was hospitalized because the extent of the doctor's curative powers was limited by his personal knowledge and black bag of medicines. Births and deaths occurred in the home in most instances, except for the traveler or the indigent who had no home to shelter him or friends to attend to his needs. Even had hospitals been able to provide better care, there was still the problem of getting there. Roads were poor and horse and wagon was the only means of conveyance. To those who lived beyond the vicinity of the hospital, transportation would have caused long and cruel suffering. As recently as 1865, when Lincoln was assassinated, he was not taken while still alive to a hospital, but was carried into a house across the street from the scene of assassination where he could be offered some degree of privacy in death. Doctors were in attendance and nothing more could have been done for him in a hospital than was performed in the confines of a small bedroom in a humble home.

If at all posible, the mentally retarded were not committed to hospitals or asylums for the insane because in the early 1800's, existence there was frequently worse than that afforded to a jailed criminal. The criminal could attend to his bodily needs and general cleanliness but frequently the insane were incapable of such self-care and the asylums were understaffed or indifferent.

HOSPITALS IN ALBANY

The first formal hospital in Albany was built by the British prior to the Revolutionary War to provide for their soldiers who were garrisoned in Albany. *Munsell's Annals of Albany* relate that the city fathers requested permission to allocate to the Crown another plot of land for the erection of the military hospital which then occupied an area which had possibilities for commercial use. The request was couched in conciliatory tones by the representatives of a government which just eleven years later rose in successful revolution.

In 1785, we are told that a heated argument took place in Albany concerning the use of a hospital as a theater for a group of touring comedians. "A large and respectble part of the community" vigorously objected to the use of the hospital for such purpose. The dispute was resolved, perhaps to the satisfaction of neither side, to permit the touring performers to use two rooms of the hospital for the performances. We hope that the patients were able to view the entertainment without inserting coins in a box for the privilege.

While the citizens of Albany were concerned over the misuse of the hospital, they did not display great concern over its complete removal when the City government decided to lock the door and close it down. This occurred in 1808 when the Common Council ordered "the old hospital" to be sold at auction. The Common Council did a lively business in closing hospitals according to the "Annals of Albany," which state that the "South Hospital" was closed in 1832 and the "North Hospital" had been closed sometime earlier. Albany was not without a hospital at that time, however, because in the same passage it is noted that, "the Lancaster School House on Eagle Street was still used as a hospital." That same year, 1832, Dr. March recommended that temporary hospitals be established in the City to cope with the cholera epidemic which had again struck the population. Incidentally, the Lancaster School House Hospital must also have been closed between 1832 and 1839 because in the latter year it was loaned to the Albany Medical College for use once more as a school. The picture presented of hospitals of that time is confusing and inconclusive; one might see hospitals as numerous as gas stations of today and closing with the frequency of high risk businesses.

DR. MARCH'S CALL FOR A PERMANENT HOSPITAL

When on January 11, 1830, Dr. Alden March delivered a lecture in which he presented the many reasons for the establishment of a medical college in Albany, he also cited the needs which Albany had for a permanent hospital. He stated that Albany then had a population of "upwards of twenty thousand" and, in comparison with other cities, a large portion of Albany's population consisted of foreigners: destitute and friendless, many of whom were susceptible to all diseases, "which flesh is heir to" and were dependent on public charity for relief. Following this appeal for aid to the helpless, Dr. March made a startling statement in comparison to the present concept of society's obligation to the indigent. He said, "there seems to be a kind of moral obligation on their part," (the destitute and friendless) "to repay the public by affording a classical school in medicine to the young and inexperienced part of the medical profession." If the foregoing statements of Dr. March are correctly understood, he envisioned the hospital as a place of refuge for the indigent sick who would repay those who afforded them medical assistance with the opportunity to gain experience through the treatment of their ailments. The hospital would fulfill two purposes: the first, meeting society's obligation to the helpless, and the second, providing a valuable adjunct to classroom lectures. Dr. March reinforces this concept by concluding ". . . there ere long our city will be able to boast of a well-conducted Medical College and Hospital, institutions favorable alike to the interests of Science and Humanity."

There is little room for doubt that Dr. March's first priority was for the medical college and the second for a hospital which would serve as an adjunct to the medical college. His reasoning was in keeping with the times. There were some well-regarded medical colleges in the nation but few hospitals of equivalent stature and none in Albany. (Because of the significance of Dr. March's lecture in the eventual formation of the Albany Medical Center, the lecture is included in Appendix A of this book.)

TEACHING HOSPITAL CONCEPT

Dr. Armsby's address before the Albany Medical Society in November, 1852, further reinforces the conclusion drawn from Dr. March's lecture in 1830. Dr. Armsby said concerning the hospital, "But the amount of that good, will by no means be limited entirely to the sick and diseased who may be the immediate recipients. The good incidentally flowing from it may even equal that which is its direct result. I refer to the means and sources of instruction which it affords to those who are acquiring a medical education." Dr. Armsby continued in this vein, citing the many advantages of a hospital available to medical students where they could "learn, at the bedside of the sick, the symptoms as they actually presented themselves, and trace the effect of remedies as they are administered." These statements of Dr. Armsby, together with those of Dr. March, leave no room for doubt that these two men, who were the leaders in the efforts to establish a medical college and hospital, regarded the hospital as a teaching adjunct to the college. After establishment, the two institutions have moved forward together and the result of the alliance is Albany Medical Center.

Nine years elapsed after Dr. March's lecture before the Medical College was founded, and nineteen years passed before the hosptial became a reality. Dr. Armsby described the movement to establish a hospital as "sleeping for many years with occasional intermissions of activity." Albany was not as backward as one might think, however, because only three major hospitals were in existence at that time. They were located in cities which had enjoyed the greatest prosperity and growth: New York, Philadelphia, and Boston.

THE ESTABLISHMENT OF ALBANY HOSPITAL

The intermittent and diverse efforts to establish a permanent hospital in Albany coalesced in 1849 when a group of influential citizens petitioned the Legislature of New York State for permission to incorporate for the purpose of founding a hospital. Permission was granted on April 11, 1849 to the following incorporators:

Marcus T. Reynolds	Joel A. Wing	Stephen Van Rensselaer
John L. Schoolcraft	Clark Durant	John C. Spencer
Erastus Corning	John Taylor	Abel French
Amasa J. Parker	Barent F. Staats	T. Romeyn Beck
Greene C. Bronson	Franklin Townsend	James P. Boyd
James D. Wasson	Stephen O. Shephard	Herman Pumpelly
William James	Dyer Lathrop	Ralph Pratt
Erza T. Prentice	Thomas W. Olcott	Thurlow Weed
Arthur G. Root	James Gould	Jacob Ten Eyck
Samuel Pruyn	Friend Humphrey	Charles B. Lansing

Seven months after incorporating, the incorporators held a formal meeting on December 24 in the office of Marcus T. Reynolds for the purpose of discussing the financing of the hospital and to consider the proposed by-laws formulated in earlier informal meetings. It is interesting to note the date of the meeting, December 24, the Eve of Christmas. It may be only coincidence that many other meetings of the Trustees of the Medical College and subsequent meetings of the Governors of the Hospital also took place on December 24. Today many businesses are closed on this date and most people make an early departure for home and festive celebration. Not so with the Trustees and Governors who must have been sober-minded men who adhered steadfastly to the work-a-day routines of well ordered lives following the axiom of, "Do not leave undone for tomorrow what you can do today."

FUNDING THE NEW HOSPITAL

The sound financing of the proposed hospital was of paramount importance because it was intended as a permanent establishment and, therefore, the financial plan had to be one which could support a lasting institution as compared to the transitory earlier hospitals in Albany. The ad hoc committee recommended that twenty thousand dollars be raised as a founding fund to maintain the hospital until additional financial aid could be expected from other sources such as the State Legislature or the Federal Government. The committee further reported that the initial fund could be more readily raised if some tangible inducement were offered to the donors. Benefits would vary according to the amount subscribed: $25, $100, $140, $200 and $1,000. A subscription of $25 would permit the subscriber admission to the hospital once during the year of subscription. The admission could be used by the subscriber or anyone that he would sponsor. A $100 subsciption would extend the same benefit to the subscriber for a five year period. A subscription of $140 entitled the subscriber to recommend the admission of a patient at all times during the year. The $200 subscription granted the subscriber the right to recommend one patient's admission to the hospital during each year of the subscriber's life. The $1,000 subscription allowed the subscriber to recommend a patient to the hospital at any time during the life of the subscriber. In other words, for $1,000 a subscriber had the privilege of maintaining one patient in the hospital every day of the subscriber's life. That plan might well be the earliest form of hospitalization insurance. Even with allowances for inflation, this must be regarded as the bargain of all times.

HOSPITAL COSTS IN THE MID 19TH CENTURY

The offering of these inducements was based on sound reasoning and research by the committee, whose immediate goal was to raise $20,000 for the hospital and, only incidentally, to function as a philanthropy.

At that time, life expectancy for a male was 51 years. Calculating that many donors would be at least 40 years old at the time of subscription, a lifetime membership would provide coverage, on average, for eleven years. The members of the committee probably calculated that most persons under 40 would not be financially able to subscribe the amount for lifetime coverage. The cost of daily hospital care and the duration of the stay were based on the statistics of the New York City Hospital. In 1843, the New York Hospital had 228 patients on average each day during the year; the average stay of the patients was five weeks, four days, and four hours. The Hospital's cost per patient was $2.69 per week or 38¼¢ per day. It is amazing to think that a patient could receive food, lodging, nursing care, and the attendance of a doctor for 38¼¢ per day, until these facts are placed in perspective. A workman received pennies an hour for his labor, the food offered was common fare sufficient only to keep body and soul united, the beds were in a large room heated by a coal stove and illuminated by candles, there was no x-ray to peer into the body or cardiography to record the action of the heart, and an assistant attending physician received $100 per year.

Using these statistics, the committee calculated that the average patient stay of 39 days and four hours at 38¼¢ per day would cost the hospital approximately $15. To this, the committee added $10 to the average patient cost to protect the hospital from bearing the unrecovered expense of a decent burial should no relative or friend claim the body. As all of the foregoing is based on averages, it may be morbidly concluded that the average patient was expected to die without relative or friend who would offer $10 to see the deceased decently "laid away." It was also stated that a subscriber was not entitled to request admission without charge for any person who could afford to pay other than the subscriber or members of his family. If these calculations appear to be mercenary, it should be recognized that the committee was proposing to establish a hospital which would provide the best care available, and offering free admission to those cases requiring immediate attention regardless of ability to pay. They recognized that many charity patients would be admitted, and any funds not used by the subscribers would be available to defray the cost incurred by those who were without means. The City's location on a main avenue of travel, the Hudson River, and the starting place of the Erie Canal, provided a constant stream of travelers journeying to the west. Many of the travelers were immigrants who had been physically weakened by slow voyages from Europe and poor nutrition during their lives in their native lands. As a result, their need for medical care could be assumed to be high and their ability to pay for care low. The committee recognized this and in their financial planning prudently made provision for that contingency.

PATIENT QUALIFICATIONS

Ironically, the committee specified that some persons were to be denied admission to the hospital, specifically those who fell into the following categories: those judged to be incurable unless there were symptoms which the attending physician or surgeon was capable of relieving; those who were insane; those who were suffering from small pox, measles, or any infectious disease, or any malignant or contagious fever. The final arbiter of who would be refused admission was the "Visiting Committee" or three members appointed by the Board of Governors.

Persons suffering from accidents could be admitted immediately without further qualification. The Visiting Committee was to be notified of every such case. Section 8 of the by-laws provided for the admission of patients without tickets (non-subscribers) but who were of sufficient means to pay for treatment. The Visiting Committee was empowered to determine the fee. The Visiting Committee was intended to be the prime and immediate overseer of the management of the hospital. The necessity of devoting considerable amounts of time to this duty may have been the reason that the Committee was appointed to serve for only three-month periods. Precedence for admission to the hospital when there was room shortage was clearly established: first, emergency cases so judged by the superintendent; second, patients recommended by those subscribers who have not previously used their subscription rights; third, the patient recommended by a subscriber who has not used his privilege for the longest elapsed time; fourth, when the previous three precedents have been exhausted, the determination shall be made by lot. In the event a patient could not be admitted, medicines should be given as well as any other attention that was possible.

BOARD OF GOVERNORS

Governors from members of the corporation were elected by the subscribers to serve on the Board for one year. Notice of the date and place of balloting was advertised in the local newspaper. The elected governors then were to elect a president, vice president, secretary, and treasurer from the Board. Should a governor when elected refuse to serve or fail to attend two successive meetings, that person would be dropped from the Board and a replacement elected by the standing governors. No physician or surgeon was eligible to be a governor.

The first Board of Governors of Albany Hospital, elected by the vote of 71 subscribers, was conducted in the office of the Albany Gas Company and the result was announced at the Board meeting held in July, 1851. The Governors were:

Marcus T. Reynold	John Taylor
Erastus Corning	Andrew White
Ezra T. Prentice	James Stevenson
Franklin Townsend	Joel Rathbone
Friend Humphrey	John B. James
John C. Spencer	John V.S. Pruyn
John Townsend	Robert H. Pruyn

The elected Governors then chose from their group the following officers:

John C. Spencer, President
Ezra T. Prentice, Vice President
Joel Rathbone, Treasurer
Franklin Townsend, Secretary

FIRST HOSPITAL BUILDING, STAFF AND BOARD OF VISITORS

In 1851, the Governors opened the hospital to patients. The site was an inauspicious former private home still standing on the corner of Dove and Lydius Street (now Madison Avenue) *(Figure 14)*. However, the following facts are recorded. The Governors were aware of the inadequacy of the building for use as a hospital and, as a result, did not purchase it but leased it for five years. A major shortcoming of the building was its location; for at that time it was rather remote from the densely populated area of the City. When the hospital relocated in 1854, the house was given to a still active charitable society named

Home of the Friendless for the balance of the lease which expired May 1, 1855.

The Lydius Street house was again used for medical purposes in 1857 when $1,500 was contributed by the New York State Legislature and $1,500 by the Albany Hospital Corporation to equip the building for use as a small pox hospital. Because of the highly contagious nature of the disease and ignorance concerning the control of infection, patients suffering from it were not admitted to the new Albany Hospital. With the opening once again of the Lydius Street location, the Pest Hospital, which had become too small, was closed.

The attending physicians of the hospital were *(Figure 15):*

Surgeons	Physicians
Dr. James McNaughton	Dr. Joel Wing
Dr. Alden March	Dr. Thomas Hun
Dr. James Armsby	Dr. Mason Cogswell
Dr. John Swinburne	Dr. Howard Townsend

Both surgeons and physicians served the hospital without any fee. As they were all members of the Albany Medical College faculty and were permitted to bring students into the hospital when attending patients, the Governors may have considered this sufficient reward for their services.

On November 1, 1851, the Governors appointed the first Visiting Committee:

(Fig. 14) The first Albany Hospital (1851)
at the corner of Dove Street and Lydius Street (Madison Avenue).

Alden March   Jas. H. Armsby

James N. Naughton   Thomas Hun   John Swinburne

Joel A. Wing   Mason F. Cogswell   Howard Townsend

(Fig. 15) The first Albany Hospital staff.

M.T. Reynolds
R.H. Pruyn
Franklin Townsend

On September 4, 1851, the Governors met and authorized the issuance of certificates of membership to subscribers. The certificates are quite similar to stock certificates of the present time. The Governors also decided to apply to the Federal Government for funds to cover the cost of attending to mariners who received the services of the Hospital. The Visiting Committee was allowed, at its discretion, to authorize the superintendent of the Hospital to give money or clothing to patients who were being discharged and lacked these necessities. The Governors admonished the Visiting Committee and the superintendent to exercise great caution in their generosity.

SUPERINTENDENT BYGATE AND STAFF

Four days later on September 8, the Board again convened for the purpose of appointing by election a superintendent to the Hospital. The candidates were Richard Bygate and G.J. Constock. Mr. Bygate won by a vote of 8 to 2 and thereby gained himself a position which paid $750 annually. Included for the payment of $750 was the service of Mrs. Bygate as matron. It was apparently left to the discretion of Mr. Bygate the amount of the income that would be given to Mrs. Bygate for her portion of the work. That same year, Dr. A.T. Woodword was appointed House Physician and George E. Benson, Assistant House Physician and Apothecary. Mr. Benson received $100 annually for fulfilling both roles; an interesting contrast with the amount paid to Mr. and Mrs. Bygate for their work as superintendent and matron.

Dr. Woodword served but three months and his resignation was accepted at a meeting of the Governors on February 3, 1852. After accepting Dr. Woodword's resignation without recorded comment, the Board heard a report by Dr. Alden March concerning his labors as Attending Surgeon. At this time the board, through committee, approached the City Government to ask financial help in providing medical care for the needy.

SECOND HOSPITAL BUILDING

The house at Dove and Lydius Street was an expedient location of the hospital until another building could be found. On March 11, 1852, negotiations were opened with the City for the purchase of the former jail located on the corner of Eagle and Howard Streets, a new jail having been built by the City in 1848 *(Figure 16)*. This was a convenient location opposite the Albany Medical College which occupied the former Lancaster School on the opposite corner of the intersection,

(Fig. 16) The second Albany Hospital (1852) at the corner of Eagle and Howard Streets.

and more centrally located in the City. The sale was consummated on May 29, 1852, for $9,000 and renovation started shortly thereafter. That same year, the Hospital received $1,587.29 from New York State as its portion of the $2,500 appropriated by the Legislature for the financial relief of hospitals in New York State.

In an address delivered before the Albany County Medical Society in November, 1852, Dr. Armsby provides an interesting insight to the financing of the New York Hospital and Massachusetts General Hospital in comparison with Albany Hospital. Massachusetts General Hospital and Insane Asylum had cost $500,000 for buidings and facilities and had investing funds of $200,000 and an annual income of $17,000. A striking comparison with the $20,000 that the Governors had established as the financial goal of Albany Hospital in 1849. By comparison with Massachusetts General, the New York City Hospital also had a modest financial base. Its funds were derived from the following sources:

$12,500	New York State
15,500	U.S. Government for care of disabled seamen
8,000	Paying patients
100	Articles sold
750	Tickets of admission to medical students
700	Subscription
$37,550	Total

From its inception, Albany Hospital was financially vulnerable. The subscriptions were payable over a period of time and the capital fund of $20,000 would not be paid to the Corporation for several years. The subscriptions were actually pledges to pay with interest of five percent due on the unpaid balances. However, it was unlikely that failure by a subscriber to pay would be contested by the Hospital Corporation with legal action. One such action was considered for a sum due but the Governors declined to act because of the conviction that such action would be unseemly. In 1854, the Hospital received $500 from the estate of Miss Margaret Ten Eyck to be used for "the care of the destitute ill."

SEARCH FOR GOVERNMENT AID

Because the Hospital operated in part as a charitable institution providing free medical service to the poor of the City, indigent travelers, and seamen working on river boats, the Board of Governors turned to the City Government, the State Legislature and the Federal Government for financial relief. The Common Council members of the City were conducted on a tour of the relocated Hospital on October 31, 1854 with the intention of obtaining some payment from the City for the care of its poor. It was explained to the touring Councilmen that had the Hospital not received the ill who could not pay, those patients would have been housed in the Almshouse which was maintained by the City. As a result of hospital care many of these people were cured and able to work and support themselves. If they went to the Almshouse, cure was doubtful and they would continue as a burden to the taxpayers. This was a cogent argument and in February of the following year, the Council met for the purpose of discussing some relief to the Hospital.

An appeal for funds was also directed to the Federal Gvoernment so that the Hospital would be compensated for the care of mariners, and finally the appeal for continuing support from the residents of Albany was made. Subscribers who had not yet completed their pledges were encouraged to do so.

Work progressed on the former jail to make it suitable for hospital use. In December, 1854, the Treasurer reported that several of the "mechanics" who had worked on the renovation had not yet been paid. Times were hard for the people and the Treasurer pleaded their case to the almost insolvent Corporation. An effort was made in January, 1855, to obtain funds from the several railroads which terminated in Albany and from the Peoples Line, Steamboat Association. It was explained to these prospective donors that free medical care would be given to their employees who met with accidents while working. On May 1, 1855, the Treasurer reported that $572.15 was on hand and the Hospital would be shortly confronted with a due bill for $400. It was not an easy beginning but, providentially, money became available to enable continued service to the community.

EARLY SERVICE STATISTICS

Financial problems not withstanding the Treasurer's comprehensive report for the years 1851 through 1855 proved that the Hospital was providing a high level of service. The content of the report was presented to the stockholders in a pamphlet and much of the information was reprinted in a local newspaper. It provides the most comprehensive facts concerning the Hospital of any known.

Following are some of the tabulated statistics:

Persons admitted to the Hospital

1851-52	126
1852-53	170
1853-54	187
1854-55	222
1855-56	169
	874

The average number of patients admitted between 1851 and 1856 was 174. For comparative purposes, the New York City Hospital, serving a much larger population, maintained an average of 228 patients per day in 1843. Using figures presented in a subsequent chart, the Albany Hospital provided an average of 6,293 patient-days during the five years reported.

Nativity of Persons Admitted 1855-56

Ireland	103
United States	45
Scotland	5
Germany	9
England	5
Unknown	2
	169

This chart would indicate that by comparison with other nationalities, the Irish were a sickly lot. However, in their defense it must be recognized that many of these people had emigrated from Ireland to escape the Potato Famine in 1845, and were probably physically weakened from lack of nutrition. Also, the Irish were the most numerous of the immigrants of that time and, following the historical pattern, found employment in only the most physically demanding and dangerous work.

Age of Persons Admitted 1855-56

6 months	1
Under 10 years	3
10 - 20 years	33
20 - 30 years	56
30 - 40 years	43
40 - 50 years	20
50 - 60 years	9
Over 60 years	3
Unknown	1
	169

If the figures from this chart were shown as a graph they would form an almost perfect bell curve. As persons reached maturity, they had a greater need for hospitalization than during youth or old age. As life expectancy was 51 years, any years beyond that would have been considered old age.

Result of Treatment 1855-56

88	Cured
18	Relieved and improved
11	Died
7	Discharged as incurable
4	Operations performed
2	*Eloped
15	Improved
9	Unknown case not given
15	Remaining at time of report
169	

*Does not indicate a romantic escapade.
Probably signified, "up and left."

A significant footnote to this chart is that during the first four years of existence, the Hospital recorded a death rate of nine percent of admitted patients and this declined to seven percent during the last reported year, 1855-56. However, these figures must be considered along with the fact that, in 1855-56, seven patients were discharged as incurable and many more were not admitted to the Hospital because they were judged incurable before admission.

A chart was included which listed the sex of the patients treated during the five years which the report covers, as well as the total number of days of treatment and the cost. For comparison purposes, the chart has been extended to a further column to indicate average cost per day of treatment.

	Males	Females	No. of Days	Expense	Cost/Patient-Day
1851-52	82	44	6,381	$5,100.45	$.80
1852-53	113	57	6,710	4,118.76	.61
1853-54	133	54	6,121	4,015.54	.65
1854-55	146	76	6,837	5,862.75	.85
1855-56	105	64	5,416	3,559.12	.65

COSTS OF OPERATION

It may be recalled that the New York Hospital average cost-per-patient day was only 38¼¢ as compared to 71 ⅕¢ cost-per-patient day in the Albany Hospital. The difference may be accounted for by the New York figure having been reported for 1843 and the Albany average represented a period eight to thirteen years later. During that time, there was a general inflation throughout the nation. The eighty-cent figure in 1851-52 may be explained by the need for experience in the new hospital but similar reasoning cannot account for the eighty-five cent high in 1854-55.

An interesting record of the purchase of supplies and services is contained in the report.

Items of Expenditures	1851-52	1852-53	1853-54	1854-55
		Years and Amounts		
Sugar, molasses, tea, coffee, etc.	$ 252.98	$ 262.87	$ 256.94	$ —
Pork, beef, flour, butter	971.05	715.36*	901.18†	1,426.39
Cleaning hospital, etc.	227.40	—	—	—
Wood and coal	232.38	15.00	—	—
General expenses, fuel, etc.	305.50	660.58	1,053.77	—
Hardware and crockery	31.43	78.56	83.93	39.29
Liquors	22.50	26.13	—	—
Drugs, medicines, liquors, etc.	—	—	272.92	554.90
Drugs and medicines	109.16	351.83	—	—
Furniture, wardrobe, etc.	156.96	—	—	—
Vegetables	—	195.61	—	—
Servants wages	432.00	526.00	389.75	593.25
Superintendent and matrons salary	750.00	750.00	750.00	843.75
Furniture	1,669.00	536.90	—	562.31
Dry goods, stationery, etc.	—	—	80.24	60.53
Moving and cleaning hospital	—	—	56.75	—
Hay, feed, cartage, etc.	—	—	170.06	—
Groceries	—	—	—	355.25

Items of Expenditures	1851-52	1852-53	1853-54	1854-55
Furniture and carpeting	—	—	—	20.44
Sundry expenses	—	—	—	293.31
General expenses, fuel, etc.	—	—	—	1,086.08
Total	$5,160.36	$4,118.84	$4,015.54	$5,835.50

*includes cheese   † includes cheese and bread

A general accounting of expenditure for the period 1851-52 through 1855-56 is the following:

Lydius Street Hospital	$ 1,295.26
Furniture	2,768.30
General Expenses	13,115.90
Interest and Discounts	88.46
Superintendent	3,093.75
Hospital Building	29,530.75
N.Y. State Bank	.18
New York Central R.R. Bonds	2,992.50
Cash in Commercial Bank	709.6 1
	$53,594.71

The Hospital received grants from New York State totalling $11,817.21. These were increased yearly by small amounts from $1,500.00 to $2,835.65 between 1851 and 1855.

1851	$1,500.00
1852	1,587.29
1853	2,664.64
	1,000.00 (for dispensary)
1854	2,229.63
1855	2,835.65

The Treasurer's reports listed the donors to the Hospital Fund and the amounts contributed. The gifts ranged from $1,000, to $10. It also described donations such as butter, vegetables, groceries, pork, provisions, bread, sugar, cutlery, medicine, oysters, window shades, painting, pier table, furnace, bedsteads, hardware, books, carpentry, dry goods, gas fixtures, oil cloth, a blank book, clock and chairs. The nature of these gifts gives mute testimony to the manner in which the Hospital was regarded. A farmer brings butter or vegetables; the local butcher shop sends pork; a baker donates bread; a fish monger brings oysters; merchants deliver window shades, bedsteads, oil cloth, and dry goods; a painter donates his service as does a carpenter; grocers bring sugar and other goods from their shelves; a pier table and chair come from the furnishings of private homes. These are the sorts of gifts that are made to an institution which is truly regarded as a worth charity.

NOTES FROM BOARD OF GOVERNORS' MINUTES

In a sense, 1855 marked the conclusion of one period in the history of the Hospital and the beginning of another. The Hospital was six years old; it now occupied a substantial building in the heart of the City; it had achieved a reputation and recognition. The problems and excitement of founding the Hospital were subsiding. The Governors must have had more confidence in their decision-making, which had stood the test of trial. Hospital personnel had gained experience and the medical staff must have become more at ease in the now familiar surroundings in which they worked.

The minutes of the meetings of the Governors reflect a mood of "business as usual." Financial problems still plagued the institution and reports were maintained to the penny. Although the Civil War rocked the nation for four years, no mention of it is made in the record. The newspapers carried accounts of war wounded being treated in the Ira T. Harris Hospital in Albany, but the War apparently had no impact on Albany Hospital. The Ira T. Harris Hospital was near the site of the present Albany Medical Center.

One of the most common concerns of the Governors during the period 1855-69 was with the appointment and supervision of the superintendents of the Hosptal. Mr. and Mrs. Bygate, the first superintendent and matron, resigned their positions in 1857 because of the ill health of Mrs. Bygate. The Board had been well pleased with the conscientious performance of the Bygates and expressed the Governors' gratitude and regret at their departure. On June 18 of that year, the Board recorded the appointment of Mr. and Mrs. Jacob D. Eaton to serve as superintendent and matron at $750 annually, a lesser amount than had been paid to the Bygates.

The association of Mr. Eaton and the Board was not a happy one. The February 6, 1860 minutes contain a record very critical of Mr. Eaton. The Board found that Mr. Eaton had made a cash outlay of $6,834.33 for provisioning the Hospital. Unfortunately, Mr. Eaton could present vouchers for only $3,701.33 of the total amount. He accounted for the discrepancy by the fact that many purchases were made from street merchants who did not offer receipts for purchases. It was called to the attention of the Governors that Mr. Eaton had bought brandy, sherry wine, whiskey, St. Croix rum, ale and cider to the tune of $228.62 during the year. The Governors were further disappointed by the financial report that patient care costs had risen to $164 per patient as compared to an average of $127 during the preceeding four years. In an effort to curtail Mr. Eaton's generous purchasing practices, the governors restricted his purchase of fruit, oysters, game, wine and liquors to those which were made only by a written requisition of the attending physician or surgeon.

The Board's gimlet-eyed observation of Mr. Eaton was not restricted to his account book and expensive taste, for in October of that year, the Visiting Committee requested Mr. Eaton to remove all immoral and obscene books and newspapers from the Hospital. Life was to become dreary. A year later, Mr. Eaton and the better ways of life departed, and on November 12, 1861, the Bygates returned as superintendent and matron. A year later, the confused accounts kept by Mr. Eaton were straighted out and a satisfactory financial settlement was achieved with him. That the Governors ran a "tight ship" is attested to by the fact they authorized the exchange of the Hospital's cow for a supply of milk—presumably during the life of said cow. It is not recorded as to whether or not the cow was a pet of Mr. Eaton.

HOSPITAL USE OF ALCOHOL

That the Hospital did not remain entirely "dry" is shown by the acknowledgement of the Governors in 1864 of gifts of one barrel of ale, five gallons of rye whiskey and two gallons of bourbon whiskey and one barrel of flour. The latter was probably quickly rolled into the cellar and the former reverently closeted under lock and key. Obviously, the ratio of alcoholic beverages to patients had to be reduced, otherwise, with today's massive increase in Hospital occupancy, a pipeline would be required between the Hospital and a local brewery and distillery. However, it should be pointed out that the sedatives of today were not yet discovered.

Incidentally, the Medical College also had a use for whiskey, and from the contingency fund, the faculty authorized payment of $67.50 to Maloney & Co. for 30 gallons in 1866. Whiskey in this quantity could only have been for preservation purposes for both the living and the dead.

ADMINISTRATION CHANGES

Having restored stability to the financial records, the Bygates again resigned in 1864 and a Mr. and Mrs. Charles Bartram were appointed superintendent and matron. Their tenure lasted only until 1867 when they were asked to resign on request of Drs. March, Armsby, Vanderpoel, Pomfret, Mosher, Quackenbush, Boulware and Boyd, who complained that Bartram's ill health and mental infirmities interfered with good care of the patients. However, the game of musical chairs accelerated. On March 20, 1868, Mr. and Mrs. Ira W. Palmer were appointed superintendent and matron only to be replaced four months later by Mr. and Mrs. James Alexander. As a result, during its first 20 years, the Hospital had six superintendents; Messers. Bygate (twice), Eaton, Bartram, Palmer, and Alexander.

A somewhat puzzling fact can be resolved by a careful study of the minutes of the Board meetings during this period. The Assistant House Physician and Surgeon on appointment is consistently referred to as "Mr." In this recording of their resignations, the individuals are, with equal consistency, referred to as "Dr." The logical explanation is that the assistant was a medical student during his service and, after graduating and becoming a doctor, he resigned the position. It, therefore follows that the title of the position was a misnomer and the Mr.-become-Dr. was an assistant to the House Physician and Surgeon and not an Assistant House Physician and Surgeon.

A portent of the future for the medical profession took place in 1865 when the Hospital purchased its first insurance at an annual premium of $70. Three years later in 1868, the increased cost of the premium or increased coverage required an outlay of $120. The nature of the insurance is not disclosed but it probably was fire insurance; malpractice jeopardy was yet beyond the horizon.

Another subtle development took place in 1868 when Drs. Armsby and Vanderpoel recommended the establishment of a Department of Ophthalmic and Aural Surgery in the Hospital. The recommendation was implemented and Dr. Charles A. Robertson was appointed Surgeon in Charge.

The Changing
of the Guard

THE DEATH OF DR. MARCH

On June 18, 1869, the principal discussion at the meeting of the governors concerned the death of Dr. March. Though many others had contributed generously of money, time and professional skill to the founding of the Hospital, Dr. March must be recognized as standing foremost in these efforts as he did also in founding the Medical College. It was his lecture in 1832 which sowed the seeds for both institutions, and his effort which maintained the momemtum of the movement to fruition in 1839 and 1849. In acknowledgement of Dr. March's contributions, the Governors attended his funeral in a group, authorized the painting of his portrait and its display in the Hospital, and vacated his position as surgeon for one year. It is sad to note in retrospect that of the numerous memorials in the Medical College and Hospital none exists to testify to Dr. March, the one man best identified as founder of both institutions.

DR. JAMES McNAUGHTON

The by-laws of Albany Medical College granted to the faculty the authority to choose the officers of the faculty and in 1869, they exercised this privilege to select Dr. James McNaughton to succeed Dr. March as President of the College *(Figure 17)*. The motion was made by Dr. Armsby. It was a logical selection as Dr. McNaughton was the senior member of the faculty and had been the Professor of Medicine since 1840.

Dr. McNaughton was by birth a Scotsman, the son of Alexander McNaughton, a farmer and manufacturer. Dr. McNaughton studied medicine in Scotland, graduating from the Royal College of Surgeons of Edinburgh. After graduation the young doctor decided for some reason to leave Scotland and come to the New World. Passage to Canada was provided by serving as ship's surgeon on the Harmony which landed him in Quebec. In 1817, Dr. McNaughton came to Albany where he had relatives. He established an office in the City, which then had a population of 11,000. There he met Archibald

(Fig. 17)
Dr. James McNaughton

McIntosh, a fellow Scotsman, and later married his daughter.

Dr. McNaughton began in 1820 to teach Anatomy and Physiology at Fairfield Medical College, Herkimer County, N.Y., and continued to do so for the next twenty years while maintaing a practice in Albany where he was much interested in civic affairs.

A diary he kept in 1824 shows his intellectual curiosity as well as an itching foot and family ties in Scotland took him back to Great Britain on the American packet Columbia, which was captained by a man named Rogers. He visited medical clinics in London and then went to France, Holland, and Belgium. In his diary, he described medical museums in Brussels and Amsterdam, some of which he viewed with jaundiced eye. He commented that the medical school at Leyden in Holland had the same number of students as did Fairfield Medical College. True to his instinctive Scottish concern for money, he complained of paying duty on medical books which he apparently believed that, because of their subject, should be free of duty charges. His farewell to Europe was final because he had vowed not to return to Scotland until he had made his fortune. Doctors in America of that period seldom became wealthy.

Dr. McNaughton brought back to Albany a refreshed mind and memories that he would share with the more than 4,000 young men he is reputed to have prepared for the practice of medicine. He devoted time to the City's welfare in 1832 when, as President of its Board of Health, he was chiefly responsible for coping with the great cholera epidemic of 1832. In 1836, he was chosen President of the New York State Medical Society while still teaching at Fairfield Medical College. Fairfield Medical College closed in 1840 in part because of its inaccessibility to a hospital and in part because its faculty had been lured away by other institutions.

The teachers had, however, for years before the school's closing, demonstrated their loyalty to it. For the last ten years of its existence, the professors had taken over the financial problems of the school, having assumed all operational costs and retained only the amount of lecture fee as compensation. In 1836, the total assets of the Fairfield Medical School, buildings, grounds, apparatus, and library, were estimated by the trustees to be $19,000.

There is no question that Drs. Armsby and March were well acquainted with Dr. McNaughton. All three had practices in Albany, and were members of the Albany County Medical Society. However, Dr. McNaughton did not share in Dr. March's and Dr. Armsby's enthusiasm to found a medical college in Albany because he believed it would draw potential students from Fairfield Medical College to which he was loyal. Dr. McNaughton may even have been a member of the group that actively opposed the founding of the Albany College on the basis that there were already too many medical schools for the number of students in the area. But, being a realist, he knew that a good medical education must have the resources available in a city where a teaching hospital might, in time, be established.

As a result of the close acquaintance of Drs. March and McNaughton, it would be improbable that Dr. March did not know that Dr. McNaughton was available, as it were, to take a position in the Albany Medical College on the closing of Fairfield. Because of his education and travels abroad together with his 20 years of teaching experience, Dr. March undoubtedly regarded Dr. McNaughton as a valued addition to the Albany faculty. In reciprocal exchange, Dr. McNaughton saw Albany Medical College as having the potential of becoming a medical college associated with a hospital in a populated and accessible location—the characteristics of the ideal. In 1840, Dr. McNaughton was elected professor of Medicine at Albany Medical College. He was elected President of Albany Medical College in 1869 and simultaneously maintained his position of Professor of Medicine until his death in 1874.

CONTROVERSY REGARDING THE DEATH OF DR. MARCH

When, in 1869, Dr. McNaughton became President of the Faculty, he entered a maelstrom of contention in comparison to the administration of the late Dr. March. When Dr. March died in 1869, his life span was in excess of the normal male life expectancy and, therefore, his death would have been accepted as not premature or unusual in any respect. However, this seems not to have been the case. Doctor Armsby, Dr. March's brother-in-law, Dr. Boyd, his son-in-law, and Dr. McNaughton, then Professor of Medicine at Albany Medical College, were the attending physicians during his fatal illness and at the time of death. Dr. Edward Hun performed an autopsy and declared the cause of death to have been uremic poisoning. All four doctors were members of the faculty of Albany Medical College and, therefore, subordinates of Dr. March.

The October 1869 issue of the *New York Medical Journal* reprinted a pamphlet describing the "last illness" of Dr. March and the treatment provided to him by the attending physicians, as well as the post-mortem findings.

It was a strange custom of the time to have printed and distributed one's opinion and strong personal conviction on matters of public interest. The opinions were expressed in unequivocal terms and it is strange that there was not an exceedingly lively business in libel suits. It may have been that satisfaction was gained by the publication and distribution of an equivalently accusatory rebuttal. In accordance with this custom, two publications resulted explaining differing views concerning the circumstances surrounding the death of Dr. March.

DR. ROBERTSON'S CRITICISM
AND DR. McNAUGHTON'S REBUTTAL

Dr. Charles A. Robertson, then Ophthalmic and Aural Surgeon of Albany Hospital and Surgeon in charge of Diseases of the Eye at St. Peter's Hospital, in January, 1870 wrote, had printed and distributed a pamphlet titled, "Last Illness of Dr. Alden March—A Criticism on the Management of His Case." The publication was critical of the diagnosis, procedures, and autopsy report. Incidentally, the pamphlet was offered "With Compliments of the Author," or in other words, free of charge, and was presumably widely distributed. Why Dr. Robertson was so strongly and publicly critical of his associates is not clear. Dr. Armsby had recommended the establishment of the position in Albany Hospital which Dr. Robertson occupied.

The reply to Dr. Robertson's criticism was soon off the press. Dr. McNaughton composed the "Reply to Dr. C.A. Robertson's Review of the Report Concerning the Last Illness of Dr. Alden March." It, like Dr. Robertson's pamphlet, was reprinted in the *New York Medical Journal*. In his reply, Dr. McNaughton states that Dr. Robertson's pamphlet had been circulating in Albany since December 20, 1869 and had been scattered through the State. Dr. McNaughton's pamphlet dissects and challenges Dr. Robertson's logic and conclusions. He further accused Dr. Robertson of bearing ill will toward Dr. March and those who signed the report concerning his illness.

A few days prior to the distribution of Dr. Robertson's publication, he had addressed the students of Albany Medical College concerning his criticism which in turn had been earlier criticized in anticipation by Dr. Armsby. It was indeed a can of worms. As a result of Dr. Robertson's address to the student body, Dr. Lansing on December 22, 1869, recommended that Dr. Robertson be removed from the list of Summer Lecturers at the College. As might be expected, the resolution was accepted. The controversy was laid to rest or at least removed from public view into which it had been thrust by the publications.

DR. McNAUGHTON'S ADMINISTRATION

When the necessary shuffling of the faculty as a result of Dr. March's death, Dr. Armsby succeeded him as Professor of the Principles and Practice of Surgery. He in turn was succeeded by Dr. Albert Vander Veer as Professor of General and Special Anatomy. Dr. S. Oakley Vanderpoel became Professor of General Pathology and Clinical Medicine; Dr. John V. Lansing was appointed Professor of Physiology and Materia Medica; Dr. Henry Haskins, Professor of Surgical and Descriptive Anatomy; and Dr. Henry March, the son of Dr. March, was appointed Curator of the Museum which his father had been so instrumental in assembling.

In 1870, with the revamped faculty in place, a summer course of eight weeks of lectures was offered by the College. The subjects of the lectures and the lecturers were the following:

The Mechanism of Labor and the Application of Forceps
  J.V.P. Quackenbush, M.D.
Clinical Surgery
  James Armsby, M.D.
Diseases of the Skin
  S. Oakley Vanderpoel, M.D.
Insanity, Its Forms and Diagnosis
  John V. Lansing, M.D.
Jurisprudence of Medicine
  Jacob S. Mosher, M.D.
Diseases of Male Organs of Generation
  Henry Haskins, M.D.
Tumors
  Albert Vander Veer, M.D.
Diseases of Women
  William G. Wheeler, M.D.
The Diseases of Children
  James L. Babcock, M.D.
Ophthalmology
  Charles A. Robertson, M.D.
Physical Aid of Diagnosis
  Edward R. Hun, M.D.
History and Curator of the March Museum
  Henry March, M.D.
Ophthalmic and Orthopedic Surgery
  George T. Stevens, M.D.

Surgical Dressings
    D.M. Stimson, M.D.
The Microscope and Laryngoscope
    John M. Bigelow, M.D.

FACULTY RIVALRY

The hiatus in the controversy of the early years of Dr. McNaughton's administration ended in April, 1870 and an extrememly disruptive series of incidents ensued. To place the cause of the controversy in context, it should be recalled that the financial compensation for teaching in the College was based on a division of the tuition fees. The fee for some courses such as surgery was $15.00 per student and ranged down to $7.50 per student for other courses. When Dr. Armsby was unanimously elected by the faculty to Professor of Surgery, the Professorship of Anatomy was vacant. The faculty became divided over the appointment. Three members favored the appointment of Doctors Albert Vander Veer and H.R. Haskins to share the position, and three other members of the faculty promoted the appointment of Doctors E.R. Hun and Daniel M. Stimpson to share the post. After a discussion with Dr. Armsby, who apparently headed one faction, the opposing faction proposed a compromise by selecting one doctor from each of the two panels and the two would then share the professorship. However, the countering suggested settlement was that three of the candidates, not two, be appointed to share equally in the duties and remuneration. Dr. Hun declined to share in the "troika" arrangement, and the atmosphere between the two factions became frigid, with harmony completely nonexistent.

To compound the bitterness between the two factions of the faculty, an article was printed in one of Albany's newspapers which highly praised all of the Professors of the College except Doctors J.V. Quackenbush, S.O. Vanderpoel, and Jacob S. Mosher who were not even mentioned. This added generous amounts of salt to the wounds of those who felt offended.

Enter the student body which, by a petition, expressed its dissatisfaction with the public acclamation of some of their professors and the complete neglect of recognition for others. Two interesting questions present themselves here. First, who prompted the newspaper article? Such things do not usually come from the blue. Second, what prompted the indignation from the student body which might normally receive such an article with nonchalance. Heat of this degree is generally not of spontaneous origin.

At this point, the controversy became extremely vindictive with the students as the victims. The academic fitness of the students for graduation was determined by the faculty examining them in study groups starting with the group previously designated as Group 1 and working down successively to Group 5. For some obscure reason, Dr. Armsby requested that the order be reversed and that the first group to be examined would be Group 5 and the last Group 1. Again, for an obscure reason, two students held in disfavor by the Armsby faction were in Group 1, the last to be examined. The reason for the reversal of the order of examination was argued against by the other faction who seemed to favor the targeted students, but Dr. McNaughton resignedly stated that, as usual, Dr. Armsby would have his way in the matter. This seems to have placed Dr. McNaughton astraddle the fence; he recognized the contentious character of Dr. Armsby, but yielded to him without specifying a reason.

If an examining professor found a student deficient, he would place a black ball in the box; and the presence of two such objects required that student to stand for a second examination before the Curators. The need for an appearance before the Curators was construed as a blot against the candidate for the degree and placed his character in question. Dr. Armsby knew that there were sufficient members of both factions of the faculty to insure two black balls for any candidate. Could this have been the reason that he requested that the order of examination be reversed so that the two students who were held in disfavor could be sent before the Curators without jeopardizing others? In any event, the Quackenbush, Vanderpoel, Mosher faction probably interpreted the manipulation of the order of examination in that way. As a result, and a particularly devastating one, almost all students of that class were "black balled."

Subsequently, Drs. J.V. Quackenbush, S.O. Vanderpoel, and Jacob S. Mosher resigned from the faculty. Again the popular penchant for publication of grievances was not resisted and the resigning members went to press. Their resignation and a description of the sordid mess was published. Dr. McNaughton was presented with a copy of the "resignation" publication as a member of the Board of Trustees and not as President of the Faculty as courtesy dictated. Dr. McNaughton then went to press and resolved the matter by accepting the resignations without regret. He did, however, express regret that so many students were harrassed without cause because of the controversy. A second examination was conducted and the matter placed aside. Dr. McNaughton closed his statement by saying in regard to the resignations, "I do not think it necessary to notice the rest of their wordy, gossiping, resignation paper."

"It is an ill wind that blows no good." Doctor Thomas Clark Durant *(Figure 18)*, one of the incorporators of Albany Hospital and a graduate of Albany Medical College in 1840, made a gift to the College of $15,000, to be invested and the income to endow the March professorship in 1870. His generous offer was prompted by the controversy and

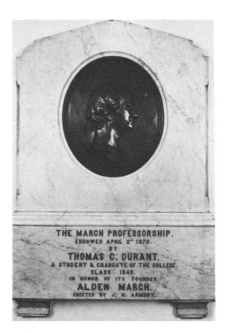

THE MARCH PROFESSORSHIP,
ENDOWED APRIL 2" 1870.
BY
THOMAS C. DURANT.
A STUDENT & GRADUATE OF THE COLLEGE,
CLASS 1840.
IN HONOR OF ITS FOUNDER
ALDEN MARCH.
ERECTED BY J. H. ARMSBY.

*(Fig. 18) A bronze and marble
placque commemorating the
endowment of the
March Professorship
by Thomas C. Durant.*

resignations. In his letter, he expressed gratitude to the remaining faculty and to the institution.

Dr. Durant practiced medicine for only three years after which he turned to the worlds of high finance and railroad building. He built the eastern half of the first transcontinental railroad, the Union Pacific. During the later years of his life, he worked to implement a plan to open the Adirondacks to tourism by building summer places and connecting them by a series of railroads, steamboats and stages.

DEATH OF DR. McNAUGHTON

Dr. McNaughton remained as President of the College and Professor of Medicine until June 12, 1874, when he died of a heart attack in Paris, France. He had been traveling abroad with his wife and two daughters when fatally stricken. His administration had started with two major controversies, neither of his making. To his credit both were resolved with no permanent damage to the reputation or effectiveness of the College. During his administration, the faculty had increased in numbers and in growth of the curriculum. Following is a listing of the faculty as shown in the catalog of 1873-74.

Faculty 1873-74 Catalog
James McNaughton, M.D.—President of the Faculty
    Theory and Practice of Medicine
James H. Armsby, M.D.
    Principles and Practices of Surgery and Clinical Surgery

Edmund R. Peaske, M.D., L.L.D., New York City
Disease of Women
William P. Seymour, M.D., Troy, New York
Obstetrics and Diseases of Children
Meredith Clymer, M.D., New York City
Diseases of the Nervous System and the Mind
John V. Lansing, M.D., Registrar of the College
Physiology and Clinical Medicine
Albert Vander Veer, M.D.
General and Special Anatomy
Henry R. Haskins, M.D.
Surgical and Descriptive Anatomy
George T. Stevens, M.D.
Ophthalmic and Orthopedic Surgery
John M. Bigelow, M.D.
Material Medica and Therapeutics
Maurice Perkins, A.M., M.D., Schenectady, New York
Chemistry and Toxicology
Hon. Ira Harris, L.L.D., President of the Board of Trustees
Medical Jurisprudence
William Hailes, M.D.
Demonstrator of Anatomy
Willis G. Tucker, M.D.
Assistant to Professor of Chemistry
Henry March, M.D.
Curator of Museum

ALBANY MEDICAL COLLEGE JOINS UNION UNIVERSITY

During Dr. McNaughton's administration, another milestone was reached by Albany Medical College when it became a member college of Union University. On April 10, 1873, the New York State Legislature approved the incorporation of Union Unviersity. This act joined Union College, Albany Medical College, Albany Law School and the Dudley Observatory into one body. Thomas W. Olcott, Dr. Armsby and Henry R. Pierson represented the Medical College in the negotiations which preceded the act of incorporation. It was agreed that each institution would be somewhat independent, but all would work for the good of the institution. This goal was stated in the catalog of Albany Medical College in 1874 in these words, "The principle underlying this union is that each institution shall seek to advance the well being of all, and all to cooperate for the well being of each." The President of Union College at the time of incorporation was Rev. Eliphalit Nott Potter, D.D., S.T.D., who was also Professor of moral philosophy and Lecturer upon the Evidences of Christianity. It might be assumed that the purchase of whiskey by the Medical College in multi-gallon quantities ceased forthwith, but there did remain the understanding that the various incorporators would remain "somewhat independent."

The elusive "University of Albany" was no more.

DR. ARMSBY ELECTED PRESIDENT OF COLLEGE

Seventeen days after Dr. McNaughton's death, on June 29, 1874, Dr. James Armsby was elected president of Albany Medical College. The appointment was made on a motion offered by Dr. Haskins. Dr. Armsby had been a member of the faculty for thirty-five years since the inception of the College in 1839. It is difficult to assay the man because at times he was the center of controversy as in the resignation of Doctors Quackenbush, Vanderpoel and Mosher and in the circumstances surrounding Dr.March's death. Yet he was steadfast in purpose and certainly loyal as testified to by his long and, apparent, harmonious association with Doctor March during the period prior to founding the College and the thirty years that he served with Dr. March after the College was founded. He was apparently willing to serve in a secondary capacity, but he seems to have had a liking for the limelight as demonstrated by his frequent addresses to groups concerning the Hospital and the College. It might have been assumed that he would have been elected president of the College to succeed Dr. March as he was, to a degree, a co-founder of the College. Yet when Dr. McNaughton was chosen, he continued to work with the same zeal that had carried him through the preceding thirty years. Had he been self-seeking, it might be expected that he would have withdrawn from the College on some pretext such as the demands of his practice. Instead in the manner of a grand gesture, he waived his salary and requested that it be returned to the College funds.

It is probably that he was a man steadfast of purpose and, as is often the case with that characteristic, he was equally of strong opinion which placed him in contention with his associates. Though he was sometimes at odds with others, he willingly acknowledged their contributions as evidenced by the numerous marble tablets which he had erected in recognition of their achievements. There is no evidence that his skill as as surgeon was outstanding and he spent the great part of his teaching career as an anatomist. However, there is sufficient evidence to suggest that the success of the College and Hospital was in large part due to his efforts.

DEATH OF DR. ARMSBY

Dr. Armsby's administration was the shortest of either of his predecessors and the shortest of any of his successors to date. He was President of the College from June 29, 1874, to December 3, 1875, just seventeen months. His death occurred on the day following the death of Ira T. Harris who, at the time of his death, was Chairman of the Board of Trustees of Albany Medical College and a member of the Board of Governors of Albany Hospital. Mr. Harris had been a servant of both institutions for many years, having been on the Board of the

College since its inception in 1839.

The science of logic in the rules of causality holds that, the cause of the cause is the cause of the thing caused. In observance of this rule, the cause of Dr. Armsby's death was the death of Ira Harris. It was reported in the *Albany Journal* newspaper that Dr. Armsby had, on the day preceeding his death, taught a class at the College and appeared to be in good spirits and normal in all respects. After leaving the College, he had attended several patients of his practice and then stopped at the home of Mr. Harris to offer his condolence to the family and pay his respects to the deceased. The room of the house in which Mr. Harris' remains were in repose was, for obvious reasons, quite cold and Dr. Armsby remained there with the deceased for a long period. On returning to his own home, Dr. Armsby complained of feeling chilled and after working on his papers, he retired for the night. The next morning his condition had become serious and he died that afternoon of congestion of the lungs—pheumonia. He was buried from the North Dutch Church. Born in 1810, Dr. Armsby was sixty-five years old at the time of his death.

DR. ARMSBY'S ADMINISTRATION

As noted earlier, Dr. Armsby's administration was the shortest of his predecessors and, perhaps for that reason, the least notable. During this time a regulation was enacted that imposed a fine of $10.00 to be paid by any member of the faculty who failed to fill his assigned lecture hours. The money received from the fine was given to the College library for its improvement. This regulation suggests that some laxity may have been growing in the faculty's responsibilities to the students. The total expenditure to the faculty for its service in 1874 was only $5,291.24, so a $10.00 fine was probably not regarded lightly.

The minutes of the faculty meeting of January 16, 1875 record two items of interest. The faculty acknowledged the gift of drugs and pharmaceutical preparations by Messrs. Powers and Wrightman of Philadelphia. The drugs were of their manufacture and are the first recorded gift of such free samples received by the College. It was stated in the acknowledgement of the gift that this material would improve the ability of the Department of Materia Medica to impart instructions. The second item of note was the appointment as janitor of a Mr. James Heath to replace the deceased Mr. Joseph Knibbs. Mr. Heath was provided with rooms in the basement of the College and $25.00 per month for his service. Mr. Knibbs must have been a particular favorite of the students for they had a marble tablet erected in his memory *(Figure 19).* Their action may have been supported or even encouraged by Dr. Armsby who had a propensity for memoralization. The event was unique in the annals of janitorial service to the College and maybe

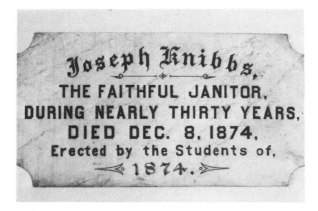

(Fig. 19) A memorial to Joseph Knibbs, devoted employee.

even in custodial history.

REV. ELIPHALIT N. POTTER, ACTING DEAN

An unusual series of episodes followed the death of Dr. Armsby. The deanship of Albany Medical College was first offered to Rev. Eliphalit Nott Potter, then President of Union University. The Rev. Potter would have been the first person to head the College who was not a doctor or who had not previously been a member of the faculty. Rev. Potter declined the post but was requested to temporarily perform the duties of the Dean, the faculty being seemingly unable to select another for the position.

On January 22, 1876, approximately seven weeks after Dr. Armsby's demise, the faculty met and appointed Dr. Samuel B. Ward to succeed Dr. Armsby as Professor of Surgery. At the same meeting, the faculty proposed the establishment of three additional professorships. They were; Professor of General Pathology and Public Hygiene, Professor of Diseases of the Mind, and Professor of the Diseases of Children. Doctors S. Oakley Vanderpoel and Dr. E.R. Hun respectively were selected to occupy the first two positions on the faculty. The third Professorship was to remain vacant until Doctors Vanderpoel and Hun could participate in the selection of the candidate. It may be recalled that Dr. Vanderpoel was one of the three faculty members who had resigned during Dr. McNaughton's administration.

BOARD ASSERTS ITSELF

Between December 3, 1875 and January 22, 1876, two appointments were made to the Board of Trustees to fill the vacancies left by Ira Harris and Dr. Armsby. The new appointees, one of whom was Dr. Vanderpoel and the other was Judge W.F. Allen, may have created a majority faction on the Board which had not existed prior to the appointment. The Board of Trustees in an, heretofore, uncharacteristic wielding of authority denied the faculty establishment of the three new chairs and informed the faculty that their authority extended only to the point of recommending new positions. The faculty submissively responded by claiming that their communication to the Board inadvertently omitted the word "recommended." The Board, in a further aggressive move, requested that all professorships be vacated.

REORGANIZED FACULTY

On February 8, the faculty responded to this request by stating that they had all been appointed by the Trustees; that the only position open at the time was Professor of Surgery; and that the faculty had maintained the high reputation of the College and had made many improvements at their own personal expense. Two days later the Board responded to the faculty by explaining that the request for the resignation of all professors was not to be construed as a reflection on the incumbents but rather to provide a more efficient organization of the faculty. The Board may rightfully have held that because four appointments were to be made, the time was appropriate to make a full reorganization of the faculty. However, subsequent events provide a basis for speculation as to whether this was the sole motivation for the request for resignations. On February 12, again just two days after the Board's prior communication with the standing faculty, the Trustees sent a communication to the faculty which contained the listing of the reorganized faculty. It was as follows:

J.V.P. Quackenbush, M.D.
  Professor of Obstetrics
S.O. Vanderpoel, M.D.
  Professor of Theory and Practice, and Clinical Medicine
John Swinburne, M.D.
  Professor of Fractures and Dislocations and Clinical Surgery
Albert Vander Veer, M.D.
  Professor of the Principles and Practice of Surgery
Jacob S. Mosher, M.D.
  Registrar, and Professor of Medical Jurisprudence and Hygiene
Maurice Perkins, M.D.
  Professor of Chemical Philosophy and Organic Chemistry
John M. Bigelow, M.D.
  Professor of Materia Medica and Therapeutics
Lewis Balch, M.D.
  Professor of Anatomy
Samuel B. Ward, M.D.
  Professor of Surgical Pathology and Operative Surgery
John P. Gray, M.D., LL.D.
  Professor of Psychological Medicine
Edward R. Hun, M.D.
  Professor of Diseases of the Nervous System

James P. Boyd, Jr., M.D.
  Professor of Diseases of Women and Children
Willis G. Tucker, M.D.
  Professor of Inorganic and Analytical Chemistry
William Hailes, M.D.
  Professor of Histology and Pathological Anatomy
Cyrus S. Merrill, M.D.
  Professor of Ophthalmology
Harrison E. Webster, A.M.
  Lecturer on Physiology
Henry March, M.D.
  Curator of the Museum
Eugene Van Slyke, M.D.
  Demonstrator of Anatomy

Dr. John V. Lansing had been Professor of Theory and Practice of Medicine and Clinical Medicine since 1875, and Registrar of the College. He immediately declined the new position offered to him as Professor of Materia Medica and Therapeutics. In his last act as Secretary of the Faculty, Dr. Lansing concluded the minutes by writing, "the 'late' Faculty then adjourned." Even at the time of apparent frustration, he was able to retain his sense of humor.

Indicative of the turmoil created by the reorganization and the effort to restore tranquility, the faculty met again on February 15, three days after the announcement of the reorganization. The purpose of the meeting was to appoint a new dean so that the proper business of the faculty could be restored. Dr. J.V.P. Quackenbush, newly appointed to the faculty, was elected chairman of the meeting and Dr. E.R. Hun, the son of Dr. Thomas Hun, was elected secretary pro tem. Dr. Swinburne made a motion that Dr. Thomas Hun be appointed Dean of the Faulty. Dr. Hun then held no position on the faculty, therefore, as would be appropriate, he was not present at the meeting.

Thus, the man who had declined to share in the Professorship of Anatomy, at the time it was vacated by Dr. Armsby's appointment to Professor of Surgery during Dr. McNaughton's administration, became Dean of the Faculty. Also, of interest is the fact that Doctors S. Oakley Vanderpoel, J.V.P. Quackenbush, and Jacob Mosher were once again faculty members. It may be recalled that these three had resigned after the running disagreements with others of the faculty in 1870. Doctor Quackenbush died in June of the year of his rejoining the faculty.

DR. JOHN SWINBURNE

The faculty member who advanced Doctor Thomas Hun's name for election as Dean of the College was the colorful Dr. John Swinburne. During his 69 years of life, he seemed to leap from one activity to another, leaving a trail of success and good will in his wake.

Born in 1820 in Denmark, Lewis County, New York, he was the ninth child and sixth son of Peter and Artemesia Swinburne. His education began in the public schools of the state, and as a young man, he taught in some of them. He developed an interest in medicine and chemistry while a student at Fairfield Medical College in Herkimer County. Coming to Albany, he studied medicine with Doctors Sweet and Armsby who were his preceptors. He graduated from Albany Medical College in 1846. He chose as the subject of his graduation thesis, "The Anatomy of the Neck." His selection of an anatomical subject may be a reflection of the effect on him of Dr. Armsby, who was at the time Professor of Anatomy. The subject and quality of the presentation was a factor in his becoming Demonstrator of Anatomy at the College in 1876. While serving in this capacity, he prepared many specimens for the museum, including that of Dr. Enson whose skeleton was exhibited because of its, "remarkable attenuation."

Dr. Swinburne served as physician at the Albany Almshouse for a number of years. At that time the Albany water system was very poor and the source of much disease such as diphtheria, commonly named "Albany Throat," and typhus which was identified as "Ships Disease." While attending the sick in the Almshouse, Dr. Swinburne treated 800 cases of typhus, and his ability is testified to by the fact that 785 of his patients survived that serious disease.

During the Civil War, Dr. Swinburne enlisted in the Union Army as a physician. He was taken prisoner of war during the Battle of Savage Station and, though eligible for parole as a physician, he chose to remain so that he could continue to care for Northern prisoners. At the conclusion of the War, Dr. Swinburne did not return to his former position in Albany Medical College but became quarantine health officer in New York City. He remained there for six years and his service was remembered by the naming of an island in the harbor in his honor.

Dr. Swinburne's adventurous spirit again came to the fore when during the Franco-Prussian War (1870-71) he went to Europe and served with the defeated French Army. He organized the American Ambulance Corps in Paris and his rewards for this service included the French Cross of the Legion of Honor and the Red Cross of Geneva.

On his return to the United States, he came to Albany and resumed his position on the faculty of Albany Medical College where he was appointed Professor of Fractures and Dislocations and Clinical Surgery. Dr. Swinburne, like many of his peers, was outspoken.

A controversy erupted in the faculty as a result of Dr. Swinburne's outspoken criticism of some of his colleagues on the staff. In a move to eliminate Dr. Swinburne from the faculty, some members petitioned the Board of Trustees to abolish the Chair of Fractures and Dislocations of which Dr. Swinburne was the occupant. Dr. Mosher, the Registrar, signed the request which would, in effect, pull the chair from under Dr. Swinburne. Doctors Lewis Balch, James Boyd, and C.S. Merrill, all professors of the faculty, countered the petition with a petition of their own. They cited the high regard in which Dr. Swinburne was held by the students. The request of the first petitioners prevailed, and the Chair of Fractures and Dislocations was abolished by a 17 to 4 vote of the Board. However, Dr. Swinburne, a survivor of the Civil War and the Franco-Prussian War, was not the type to withdraw from an engagement without thoroughly pursuing alternatives. He engaged an attorney who brought action against the Board claiming that the vote was taken without proper notice of all Board members, and requested that his client, Dr. Swinburne, be granted a writ of mandamus on the basis that a full two-thirds of the Board did not, in formal meeting, abolish the Chair. The Court found in favor of the Board, and Dr. Swinburne, no longer a member of the faculty, continued to care for patients in Albany, St. Peter's, and Child's Hospitals as related earlier.

Had he retired from Albany as a result of this rebuke he would have been justified. Instead, he remained in Albany and founded a free dispensary where he treated hundreds of persons with surgical problems. Partly in recognition of devotion to public well being he was supported in the polls and elected Albany's 55th mayor in 1882. Two years later he was elected to Congress. His contributions to the City of Albany, including his Professorship in Clinical Surgery at Albany Hospital, earned him recognition when Swinburne Park was named for him. At his death in 1889 at the age of 69, friends and citizens of the City joined his wife and four sons in mourning. Dr. Swinburne, like a diamond, had many facets; he was a physician, a military hero, a holder of high public offices and a benefactor of mankind both in his native country and abroad. He must be remembered as one of the illustrious graduates of Albany Medical College.

DR. THOMAS HUN

Dr. Hun's career marched to the cadence of a different drum beat than Dr. Swinburne. His primary endeavors were always centered in Albany where he founded a dynasty of three generations of prominent Albany doctors (Figure 20). Thomas Hun was born in Albany in 1808 and died there in 1896. The roots of his family were established in Albany in 1660 when Harmen Thomas Hun, his forebearer, came from Amsterfoot, Holland, a town near Amsterdam. Dr. Hun's grandfather built a house in Albany on Market Street, and worked as an agent for the Patroon, Killean Van Rensselaer. Thomas' father, Abraham Hun, was likewise an agent for Van Rensselaer and later occupied the same house.

Thomas Hun was in a sense "to the manor born." His family was one of the founders of the City and had performed, since their coming to

America, as agents for one of the most wealthy patroons. In addition, Thomas was the only son of Abraham Hun and Maria Gansevoort with all of the benefits which accrue to an only son. His mother also came from a recognized family. As a result, young Thomas was afforded the best education which the area could provide and, seemingly without pressure, made his own way. He received his early education at the Albany Academy and from there went to Union College in Schenectady. While a student there, he with Amos Dean, who subsequently taught Medical Jurisprudence at Albany Medical College, founded Kappa Alpha, the oldest undergraduate college fraternity in the United States. Something must have awakened his interest in medicine during his undergraduate years at Union College because after graduation in 1826, Thomas apprenticed himself for a year to Dr. Platt Williams who practiced in Albany and had served in the War of 1812. At the time, students were admitted to apprenticeship without the requirement of a college education. However, as noted, Dr. Hun had graduated from Union College.

After completion of his apprenticeship, Hun for the first time left the environs of the Albany area to attend the medical department of the University of Pennsylvania where he received his M.D. degree in 1830.

(Fig. 20) Dr. Thomas Hun

Albany Medical College was not founded until nine years later, otherwise he might have remained in Albany. After graduation, Dr. Hun returned to Albany to establish a practice which he maintained for three years before going to Europe to continue his medical studies. He took with him his knowledge of cholera, acquired by his service through the epidemic in Albany in 1832.

Evidence of his independent wealth is the fact that Dr. Hun remained in Europe for five years, which time was spent principally in Paris studying diseases of the nervous system. Upon his return to Albany, he accepted the professorship of the Institutes of Medicine in the newly founded Albany Medical College, a position he held until 1858.

He was active in the Albany County Medical Society and became President of the Society in 1844. In 1862, he was elected President of the New York State Medical Society. While practicing, he attended patients in Albany Hospital from its foundation; and later, also at St. Peter's Hospital, founded in 1869, and at Child's Hospital. In 1852, Dr. Thomas Hun wrote to the Governors of Albany Hospital, where he was then in charge of the Medical Department:

> *Very few persons suffering from acute disease apply for admission to the hospital. Most of the applicants are in the last stages of chronic diseases, who had been unwilling to leave their homes until they had exhausted their resources and the patience of their friends. In most cases I have refused to admit such persons, as not belonging to the class for which the hospital was designed. (Letter in AMC Library)*

It may be doing an injustice to Dr. Thomas Hun to quote this statement out of context and without further explanation of his position. Today such a statement would be intolerable. Perhaps we live in an age which is less, not more, pragmatic than that of Dr. Hun.

DR. HUN'S MEDICAL PHILOSOPHY

If this statement is accepted on face value, a redeeming virtue of Dr. Thomas Hun was his insistence on high standards, both for himself and his students. Witness his five years of financially unrewarding work in Europe after completion of formal study at Union College and Pennsylvania University and three years of practice in Albany. He told the students who came before him that the sciences in which we have arrived at ultimate laws are called certain sciences, but medicine is not one of these, since we have reached no ultimate law in medicine. Medicine must be perceived as an art. He continued, defining art as being founded on science and consisting in a "modification of nature so as to bring it into harmony with the wants of man." Here Dr. Hun appears to warn his students against satisfaction with the state of knowledge of medicine, and that they must continually strive for the ultimate perfection which is the objective of the true artist.

He described the practice of medicine as a trade, and maintained that "quackery consists not in using secret remedies, but in using them without discernment." Speaking of peculiar theories of medicine which might be applied to some unproven cures of today, Dr. Hun said, "A false theory is not merely absurd, but it is most pernicious. Its ideas become acts, its errors of speculation becomes errors of practice, and in medicine an error of practice is, for the most part, irreparable."

Carrying forward his belief that medicine was an art founded on science, in 1848, he told the Freshman Class at Albany Medical College:

> If you would become eminent in your profession, study well the theoretical branches. Learn the science of medicine before you attempt to learn, and still less to practice, the art. Undoubtably, the great physicians must be formed at the bedside, and not in the study, but you will profit in your bedside experience precisely in proportion as you come armed with science, which will enable you to comprehend what you see.

This statement was made at the time that Doctors March, Armsby, and McNaughton were urging the foundation of a hospital as an extension for the education of medical students at Albany Medical College. Dr. Hun concurred with that endeavor but admonished his student audience to prepare themselves well in the basic knowledge of medicine.

DR. EDWARD R. HUN

Dr. Edward Reynolds Hun, the son of Dr. Thomas Hun, was not the first son to serve on the same faculty as his father. Dr. Henry March, the son of Dr. Alden March, had been appointed Curator of the Anatomical Museum of Albany Medical College at the time of his father's death. Dr. Edward R. Hun, unlike Dr. Henry March, was to serve but a few years. He was thrown from a horse drawn carriage in 1876 and died four years later from the injuries sustained in the accident. The younger Hun gave promise of a brilliant career, having received his medical diploma from the College of Physicians in 1866. Like his father, he studied in Europe after receiving his M.D. degree. He returned to Albany where he established his practice. However, he too was interested in diseases of the nervous system and he became special pathologist at the New York State Lunatic Asylum in Utica. He wrote several papers on this emerging field of medicine. His death was mourned not only by relatives and friends but also by the many patients to whom he devoted much time in all three of Albany's hospitals. Dr. Edward Hun was born in 1842 and died when only 38 years old.

DR. HENRY HUN

Doubtless, Dr. Thomas Hun derived solace after the death of his son Edward from the fact that his younger son, Henry, had also chosen a career in medicine. Henry was born on March 21, 1854, and, like his

(Fig. 21)
Dr. Henry Hun

father and older brother, he too received his early education at Albany
Academy. From there he went to the Sheffield Scientific School of Yale
University from which he recieved a Ph.B. degree, and where, for a
time, he served as an instructor in physics. He then studied medicine at
Harvard University receiving his M.D. degree in 1879. It seems strange
that he had not studied at Albany Medical College until it is recalled
that this was prior to his father's being appointed Dean there, and
subsequent to his father's declining to share the Professorship of
Anatomy.

Following the same path as his father and brother, Dr. Henry Hun
broadened his medical background with two years of study in Europe.
In Paris, he came under the influence of Charcot, which augmented an
already present interest in neurology and mental diseases.

Upon his return to Albany, he was invited to accept the Professorship
of Nervous and Mental Diseases at Albany Medical College. He
occupied that chair from 1885 until his retirement in 1914.

Dr. Hun was active in the American Psychiatric Association and in
the American Neurological Association *(Figure 21)*. He followed in his
father's footsteps by becoming President of the Board of Trustees of
Albany Academy. He served the community as a member of the Board
of Trustees of the Dudley Observatory, and as a member of the Board
of Governors of Albany Hospital. He was Attending Physician at
Child's Hospital, and a Consultant to the Hospital for Incurables.

He organized the Department of Neurology at Albany Medical

College, and helped in the development of other aspects of the school's curriculum. He advanced the field of neurology by publishing an *Atlas of the Differential Diagnosis of Diseases of the Nervous System*. Its publishers, Southworth Company, of Troy, New York, described the second edition thus:

> *This book makes the diagnosis of nervous diseases not only plain for the neurologist, but simple and easy for the general practitioner. It consists of a series of diagnostic charts. On one side of the chart is an important symptom, such as motor paralysis, to be analyazed; on the other is a list of the diseases in which the symptom occurs. Between these two extremes, the beginning and the end of the diagnosis, are inserted a series of tests constituting the examination of the patient. By these tests all the possible diseases are divided into naturally related groups, which, with each additional test, grow smaller and smaller, until the actual disease in any given case, is revealed.*

Such a new approach to teaching was as revolutionary in its day as have been some later inventions and discoveries. It is particularly notable because of its meticulous attention to detail. Such attention was an intrinsic part of Dr. Hun's thinking.

Earlier in his career, in 1897, he organized a meeting of the New York State Medical Society to discuss in depth the problem of typhoid fever, via the topic of contaminated water. The discussion included the history of the typhoid germ outside the body, methods of disinfection of excreta of typhoid patients, and some points in treatment of the fever, as well as its bacterial diagnosis.

Dr. Hun approved the additional time that, after 1876, had been allotted to clinical medicine, and the fact that the teaching in specialties was almost entirely clinical. He was one of the first to hold clinics and conferences where a student presented a case previously assigned to him and postulated a diagnosis subject to criticism and correction by the teacher and the class.

Dr. Henry Hun was survived in 1924 by his wife, the former Lydia Maria Hand, a sister of Judge Billings Learned Hand of the United States Federal Court in New York, and by two sons, Samuel Hand Hun and Henry Hand Hun, and by a daughter, Lydia Hun Reynolds.

DR. HENRY HAND HUN

Henry Hand Hun followed his father in the practice of medicine, but chose surgery as his field. Like his father, also, he acquired his early education at the Albany Academy, and went from there to Yale University where he obtained the degree of Ph.B. in 1914. Four years later, he earned a medical degree from Harvard.

As an intern and for two years as a resident, Dr. Hun served on the staff of the Johns Hopkins Hospital. During World War I, he was a Lieutenant in the Medical Reserve Corps, but never was called for active service.

When he returned to Albany, he joined the faculty of Albany Medical College where he was an Instructor and Assistant in Surgery from 1920 to 1927. In 1928, he became Clinical Professor of Surgery.

Dr. Hun was genial and humorous and noted for his kindness and courtesy. Like his forebears, Dr. Hun made many non-medical contributions to Albany through public service. Clandestinely he paid tuition from time to time for impoverished students.

During World War II, Dr. Hun served as Lieutenant Colonel in the 33rd General Hospital in Africa and Italy. After the war, Dr. Hun resumed practice in Albany. He continued the family tradition of service to the community by sitting on the Board of Trustees of Albany Academy and as President of the Board of Trustees of the Home for Aged Men in Menands. In that position he succeeded Dr. Arthur W. Elting who had resigned at the age of 70, after having served the organization for ten years as President and twenty years as a member of its Board.

Dr. Hun held an honorary postion on the board of a local bank, and served as a Consultant in Surgery at the Veterans' Hospital.

When he died of a cerebral hemorrhage at the age of 78, on January 29, 1972, the medical saga of his immediate family closed. He left to a city much in his debt, the memory of a genial, compassionate and unassuming man.

ORDER RETURNS UNDER DR. THOMAS HUN

With the appointment of Dr. Thomas Hun as Dean of the College, the turmoil of the preceding period subsided and a period of tranquility ensued. A commencement program of January 31, 1877, provides an interesting insight into the quiet manners of the time. The program was printed on blue grey paper with a single fold to form a four page program. An elegant touch was added by a simple gold border on each of the pages. The ceremony, which started at eight o'clock in the evening took place in the quaintly named, Tweedle Hall. *Munsell's Annals of Albany* describes Tweedle Hall as a "grand pile" located on Pearl Street. Seven musical selections interspaced the events of the evening, and the now traditional Pomp and Circumstance was not included, the music being provided by one Porlate Orchestra. The commencement was opened and closed with prayers; the Invocation was given by Rev. Mr. Potter, President of Union University, and the Benediction was intoned by Bishop Doane. Dr.Thomas Hun followed the opening prayer, delivering the Annual Address from the Dean. One Horace T. Sprague, then read an essay. John A. Crowley gave the validictory address, and the Curators presented the "Report on Prizes." The top award was a $5.00 gold piece which, if not surrendered when Franklin Roosevelt recalled all gold, may still reside in someone's box of memorabilia. The program then listed the 37 names of the graduates. An obvious ommission from the program was the awarding of degrees which certainly must have been the highlight of the evening for the majority of those in attendance. The printed program concludes with a listing of the Class Officers, the Executive Committee for the evening and the names of the ushers. Almost as a footnote the program announced that there would be an Alumni Supper at 11:00 p.m., a late hour for those days.

FACULTY AND BOARD CHANGE ROLES

At the juncture of Dr. Armsby's and Dr. Hun's administration, the activities of the Board of Trustees and the faculty suggest that the two groups exchanged the roles that they had previously performed. Heretofore, the Board had concerned itself primarily with the financial affairs of the College and allowed the faculty a free hand in regard to staffing. As noted earlier, the board took a positive stand in regard to organization of the faculty, forcing the resignations and reorganization in 1876. Their admonition to the faculty restricting it to the role of only recommending appointments served notice of the Board's awakened interest in this respect. Approximately a year after that incident, the faculty took a positive role in the finances of the College. During the earlier history of the College, the faculty had been required to submit a list of proposed expenditures to the Board for approval and was then permitted, after paying the expenses incurred and interest on loans, to divide the tuition fees amongst themselves. There appears to have been a complete acceptance of these areas of responsibility with no intrusion by either group on the other's turf.

BUILDING PURCHASE AND SALE OF STOCK

In 1877, the faculty, at the suggestion of Dr. Vanderpoel, proposed that the Mayor of Albany grant the College a quit claim deed for the building and grounds which the College had occupied since its beginning in 1839. In exchange for the deed, the faculty proposed that the City be paid $12,000 for the property and $3,000 for rent which was past due. The proposal further stipulated that the buildings and grounds were to be used solely as a Medical College and Law School. The proposal was advanced in May of 1877 and the transfer was consummated on December 14 of that year.

The faculty then advanced another proposal, to wit that 387 shares would be offered to the faculty at $10.00 per share and the proceeds of the sale of shares be used to pay a portion of the mortgage necessitated by the purchase of the building. The shares were purchased in varying amounts by faculty members. The largest number, 379, was purchased by Dr. Albert Vander Veer. As further evidence of their continuing financial interest in the College, the faculty then sent a note to the Dean of Albany Law School informing him that the Medical College had paid to the City $3,559.52 in past rent for the building and grounds of which the Law School was a joint tenant. (The City evidently employed an able accountant who had corrected the Medical College's back rent by an increase of $559.52—precise to the penny.) The Law School responded by paying $1,186.34 for its third responsibility. The College's newly found financial acumen was exercised by its requesting a meeting with the Law School to establish what the latter's future rent would be. The Registrar of the College, Dr. Jacob Mosher, and Mr. Edward of the Law School agreed in writing on the amount of $300 for annual rent. The lawyers may have had their fill of the doctors when in 1880 they moved to a new location on State Street. In exchange for a quit claim on the Lancaster School property the Medical College paid the Law School $2,000.

CONTINUED EXPANSION

During the period in which the faculty was negotiating purchase of the property, a motion was made in an executive meeting to request that Union University place the American Veterinary College of New York City under the direction of Albany Medical College. The Veterinary College was a department of Union University. The rationale for this request was not expressed, and posterity is left to draw its own conclusions. Could it have been a counter move in anticipation of the Veterinary College's requesting dominance?

The desire for expansion, fiscal responsibility, and change became rampant. Dr. Vander Veer suggested in 1879 that there be an investigation of the feasibility of opening a School of Nursing under the aegis of the Medical College. There is small wonder that the Law School put some distance between itself and the Medical College.

In 1880, the title of the head of the faculty of the Medical School was changed from that of President to Dean to avoid confusion with the title of president, used to identify the head of Union University, of which the Medical School was one department.

STRICTER STANDARDS ESTABLISHED

The faculty continued to move forward in its effort to reform the College, and in 1879, students were required to complete two years of study before graduation. In 1880, the course of study was increased to three years. In 1882, the College encouraged other medical colleges to enact similar requirements for graduation. Does this mean that a student entering in 1879 and intending to graduate in 1880 was told he would not be graduated in 1881? Come the end of that year, was he then told that the new curriculum was extended to a third year? If the pleasure of anticipation is greater than that of realization, when finally receiving his sheepskin, his joy must have been overwhelming.

The faculty's influence was not restricted to intramural affairs; in 1880, they supported the enactment of legislation which would establish a State Board of Health. That same year, the faculty formally expressed their opposition to a movement to outlaw vivisection. A year later, in 1881, the faculty established new requirements for admission to the College. The new regulation stipulated that applicants either be graduates of recognized colleges, scientific schools or other medical institutions, or they were required to pass an admissions examination. The examination included the following subjects: orthography, grammatical construction, arithmetic, grammar, geography, and elementary physics. As a final hurdle confronting the applicant, the new requirement specifed that penmanship would be considered—a skill for which the medical profession is not renowned.

HUN ADMINISTRATION IN RETROSPECT

It is hazardous to draw definite conclusions concerning the Hun administration of Albany Medical College for sufficient reason. Dr. Thomas Hun was a private person. There are no printed copies of addresses which he delivered or even evidence that he indulged in open forums. The minutes of faculty meetings do not record his attendance or participation and in reading the records of those meetings, he is conspicuous by his absence. The second reason for hesitancy in passing judgment on the Hun administration is the seeming contradiction of direction. During earlier administrations, the Trustees had concentrated their guidance of the College in the narrow channel of finance and seemed content to allow the faculty free reign in staffing. It may be recalled that the curb was applied vigorously by the Trustees at the time just prior to Dr. Thomas Hun's appointment as Dean of the College, the faculty having been told that their powers of appointment ended with recommending—far short of appointment. As if to fill the void left by the Trustees, some of the members of the faculty took an active interest in the finances of the College. Through their initiative, the Lancaster building was purchased from the City and a portion of the mortgage was held by faculty members. The faculty, as if constrained by boundaries of the Medical College, suggested taking control of the Veterinarian School of New York and founding a nursing school as an adjunct to the Medical School: all of this prior to the game of Monopoly. As if to contradict conclusions that one might draw from the foregoing attempts at physical enlargement, the College experienced a volcanic academic improvement. The curriculum was extended from one year to three years. Entrance examinations were required, with the Regents of New York State in charge of conducting the examination. The faculty was increased from the initial eight, and sixteen at the time of Dr. Hun's administration, to forty-two members in 1890. The forty-two members were comprised of 13 professors, 1 emeritus professor and dean, 2 demonstrators, 3 lecturers, 15 instructors, and 8 clinical assistants. A uniform method of grading students was initiated that conformed to that used by the Civil Service Board. The maximum grade a student could attain was 10 and a grade of 7 was required to pass a course. Students were required to pass courses in surgery, medicine, obstetrics, specialties, anatomy, physiology, materia medica, and chemistry *(Figure 22)*.

A TIME OF ACCOMPLISHMENTS

The same year Dr. Thomas Hun died, his son, Dr. Henry Hun was selected to deliver the address to the incoming class of 1896. It is interesting to note that Dr. Thomas Hun had delivered the first introductory lecture to students of Albany Medical College at its inception on November 18, 1839. Again on October 3, 1848, Dr. Hun delivered the introductory lecture. In 1877, Dr. Thomas Hun addressed the graduating class as a principal speaker. He was published in the *American Journal of Insanity,* July 1846, and in 1863, his address before the Medical Society of New York was published. In a sense, the son was following in the footsteps of his father.

While the title of the lecture is verbose—"A Sketch of the Gradual Perfecting of the Methods of Medical Education in the Albany Medical College"—it should be read in its entirety to appreciate the ability of expression of the author. It traces the evolution of education in Albany Medical College and predicts that 10 years from that time, the methods of teaching would be improved but those then used met the requirements with a reasonable degree of completeness. In addition to the improvements identified earlier with the Hun administration, the lecture reported the fact that the following eight specialties had been added: ophthalmology, otology, laryngology, dermatology, neurology, psychology, gynecology, and pediatrics. Dr. Hun then cited what was to be the most spectacular achievement of his father's administration: through the generosity of Matthew Bender, a prominent resident and businessman of Albany, the Bender Hygienic Laboratory had been constructed at a cost of $22,000 *(Figure 23)*. The College faculty contributed $6,000 for the installation of fixtures for the use of Medical College students. Students and faculty were encouraged to perform research in the new Laboratory for the express purpose of original investigation. Through these efforts, Albany Medical College formally joined the profession in the growing effort to remove the shroud of ignorance which had impeded its progress from time immemorial. Dr. Henry Hun concluded his lecture by telling his audience that they had

SESSION OF 1878-79.
ALBANY MEDICAL COLLEGE.
MEDICAL DEPARTMENT OF UNION UNIVERSITY.
Order of Lectures and Clinics for November.

Hours.	Monday.	Tuesday.	Wednesday.	Thursday.	Friday.	Saturday.
9	Medical Jurisprudence & Hygiene. Prof. Mosher.	Med. Jurisprudence & Hygiene. Prof. Mosher.	Med. Jurisprudence & Hygiene. Prof. Mosher.	Theory & Practice & Clinical Medicine Prof. Vander Poel.	Theory & Practice & Clinical Medicine Prof. Vander Poel.	Chemistry. Prof. Perkins.
10	Anatomy. Prof. Balch.	Histology and Pathological Anat. Prof. Hailes.	Anatomy. Prof. Balch.	Histology and Pathological Anat. Prof. Hailes.	Anatomy. Prof. Balch.	Surgical Clinics. College.
11	Obstet. & Diseases of Women & Child. Prof. Boyd.	Materia Medica & Therapeutics. Prof. Bigelow.	Obstet. & Dis. of Women & Child. Prof. Boyd.	Medical Clinic. Prof. Bigelow.	Obstet. & Dis. of Women & Child. Prof. Boyd.	10 to 11:30 A. M. Prof. Swinburne.
12	Surgery. Prof. Ward.	Surgery. Prof. Van Derveer.	Surgical Clinic. Profs. Balch and Van Derveer.	Surgery. Prof. Van Derveer.	Ophthalmology. Eye Clinic. Prof. Merrill.	Albany Hospital. 11:30 to 1 P. M. Prof. Van Derveer. Prof. Ward.
3	Physiology. Prof. Webster.	Physiology. Prof. Webster.	Fractures and Clinical Surgery. Prof. Swinburne.	Theory & Practice & Clinical Medicine Prof. Vander Poel.	Chemistry. Prof. Perkins.	
4	Chemistry. Prof. Tucker.	Chemistry. Prof. Tucker.	Surgery. Prof. Ward.	Nervous Dis. & Psycholog'l Med. Prof's Hun, Gray.	Materia Medica & Therapeutics. Prof. Bigelow.	

(Fig. 22) The curriculum for the 1878-79 session.

(Fig. 23)
The first Bender Hygienic Laboratory on Lake Avenue as seen in 1909.

much more to learn than their predecessors but they had better facilitites for learning.

To conclude this attempt to peer through the veil of the Hun administration, meaning no disservice to those who attempted to enlarge the physical dimensions of the College, someone was working as industriously to improve the academic posture of the institution. No one member of the faculty or group is certainly identified with this movement; so, rightly or wrongly, Dr. Thomas Hun, the Dean, is recognized as the force who thrust the Albany Medical College into a height of excellence from which it could enter the 20th century. Had his successors the wisdom to avoid the excessive growth in faculty and staff, and the zeal to carry forward his entrance into the field of medical research, much of the travail of the 1910-14 period might have been avoided. To use an expression of the theater, Dr Thomas Hun's administration was a difficult, if not impossible, act to follow.

MEDICAL EDUCATION AT CENTURY'S CLOSE

The nineteenth century of medical history was able to close the curtain without apology to predecessor or successor for lack of accomplishment. Doctors, where once scarce, were abundant and the medical profession had attained a degree of regulation never before enjoyed. The doctor was no longer the precursor of the undertaker and hospitals were far removed from the dungeons of despair. Aspirants to the profession could no longer merely spend a hundred dollars, sit through two semesters of identical and probably boring lectures, and walk from the platform with diploma in hand amidst applause from relatives and friends.

During the nineteenth century, an applicant was required to cope with an increasingly more demanding curriculum which was expanded from one to four years. Tuition funds in hand was no longer the primary requirement for admission to most medical schools, the profession having encouraged legislation that required that the applicant not only have previous academic experience, but that the degree of learning be demonstrated by impartial State examinations. As a final test, the graduate doctor was required to pass an examination conducted by the State before being granted a license to practice medicine.

It is possible and even probable that nepotism had played a role in determining who became a doctor in the past, but the new regulation of the profession all but closed the door on that path of entry. As Dr. Henry Hun stated so well, students had more to learn but the facilities for learning had progressed equivalently. Medical schools at the turn of the century had awakened to the need for a more formal course of study than that provided by the preceptor-student relationship, with the school as an adjunct to the learning process. Too frequently under that education system the student could only attain the skills of preceptor and then only if the preceptor was sincere in his role as instructor.

Despite these advances, however, the more perceptive members of the profession could take satisfaction only to the extent that they did not make a comparison of medical education in this hemisphere with that in Europe where the truly great schools of medical education had developed. The European schools were not only places of learning for students, but they were the citadels of research which would enlighten the path to future medical breakthroughs.

It is impossible to conceive of a nation that is always first in everything and the United states is no exception. However, the unique characteristics of this nation have enabled it to be first in most achievements and, in others, second only for a short time. The Soviets had an early lead in space exploration only to be surpassed by the United States in launching outer terrestrial exploration and interplanetary travel. With similar vigor, the United States began a march in the nineteenth century toward medical education which would in the succeeding century place it in the vanguard of the world both in education and research.

ROLE OF JOHNS HOPKINS UNIVERSITY

The salient toward this goal of excellence was made by Johns Hopkins University, founded in 1896 by the man from whom it derived its name. Johns Hopkins, unlike other universities, was not required to build on a humble foundation but was structured in an orderly fashion with sufficient financial substance; and, being new, was free of tradition which can be meritorious or retarding. Because its entire faculty was being assembled for the first time, the members who constituted that faculty were chosen because of their demonstrated ability. Johns Hopkins was particularly blessed by being able to attract four giants of medicine; Drs. William H. Welch, William Osler, William S. Halstead and Howard A. Kelly, at the time that the University opened its school of medicine in 1893. All four were eminent in their field and became great teachers of medicine as well as practitioners. This was a first in medical education in the United States where, heretofore, many were excellent doctors but only incidentally educators.

Prior to the founding of Johns Hopkins Medical School, the better medical schools in the United States, judged by the standards of the time, may have reached 4 on a hypothetical scale of 5. However, with the foundation of Johns Hopkins the hypothetical scale was advanced to 10 which left much room for improvement for those who remained at 4. Their reach toward the horizon was not reduced but the horizon was moved further away.

THEOBALD SMITH

It was during those waning years of the nineteenth century that Albany Medical College's most illustrious son made his first of many great contributions to the advancement of medical science. It is ironic that the man who made discoveries equivalent to those of Pasteur, Koch, and the Curies remains unrecognized in the city of his birth and among most of the medical profession. The lay world is rightfully familiar with the scientists mentioned earlier, perhaps because their lives and discoveries were dramatized by Hollywood, but no limelight illuminated the name of Theobald Smith *(Figure 24)*.

Theobald Smith was born in 1859 of German immigrant parents, Philip and Theresa Smith, the name having been Anglicized from Schmidt. The family lived in the South End of Albany and young Theobald attended Holy Cross parochial school where he was a serious student interested in botany and music. From the latter interest he developed into a competent pianist and an accomplished organist. From Holy Cross School he went to Albany Free Academy, now Albany High School, where he graduated valedictorian with an academic average of 99.5%. Smith's father was a tailor and practiced his trade from a shop in the same building in which the family resided. He was

(Fig. 24) A bronze bas-relief honoring Theobald Smith mounted in the building bearing his name.

successful but not able to provide his son with the funds for a college education. However, a year after graduating from Albany Free Academy, Theobald was awarded a scholarship to Cornell University. While attending Cornell, young Smith earned some money by playing the pipe organ in a nearby church. He also became interested in working with the microscope which may have been a carry-over interest from his earlier interest in botany. He graduated from Cornell in 1881, a Bachelor of Philosophy. During his undergraduate years, Smith had a diversity of interests and was enthusiastic for science, music, engineering, literature; and, as a result, he almost chose a career in journalism because it would afford him the opportunity to pursue his wide ranging interests. A more mundane reason for his consideration of journalism was the ill-founded belief that such a career would lead to quick wealth.

Fortunately for medical science, Smith turned to medicine and on graduation from Cornell he entered Albany Medical College from which he graduated two years later in 1883. At the time Smith attended Albany Medical College, the course of study was three years. However, Dr. Smith accomplished the requirements in two years, some allowance having been made for his studies while at Cornell—few students came to medical school having already accomplished such academic achievement. Smith lived at home with his parents probably to reduce his expenses because, as was stated earlier, he could attend undergraduate school only after receiving a scholarship and it is improbable that any new found wealth had come his way in the interim. Tuition at Albany Medical College at the time was $200 for attendance at lectures and an additional $20 for matriculation and $25 for graduation. Smith may have already chosen bacteriology as his specialty as indicated by his choice of Dr. Hailes as his preceptor; Dr. Hailes then being Anthony Professor of Histology and Anatomy on the faculty of Albany Medical College. Courses in bacteriology were not yet offered in any medical schools in the United States but Smith pursued his interest in that field by doing independent research. He dissected cats so that he could perform a microscopic study of their internal organs. Graduating, as might have been predicted, at the head of his class, he wrote his thesis on Cell-Activity in Health and Disease.

DR. THEOBALD SMITH TURNS TO RESEARCH

Paul De Kruif in his book, *Microbe Hunters,* said that Dr. Theobald Smith was "the first, and remains the captain of American microbe hunters." He first earned that recognition by his work in the United States Bureau of Animal Husbandry in Washington, D.C., where he went, after graduation, with the recommendation of Professor Simon Gage. Dr. Smith was not interested in practicing medicine because he could not bear the frustration of diagnosing illness without knowledge of a cure. He had, perhaps unconsciously, dedicated his life to the pursuit of cures.

Dr. Smith was certainly not interested in financial gain because he could undoubtably have found more remunerative work than that offered by the Veterinary Division to which he was assigned at the time the cattle industry was faced with a calamitous disease which was causing the death of beef cattle by the hundreds. Dr. Smith willingly accepted the assignment to seek a solution to the problem which was devastating the herds. Four years later, he revealed the carrier of the disease as the common tick. This is the first time that insects were proven to be the bearers of disease. From this discovery other researchers were able to extend the proven theory to identify mosquitoes as the carriers of yellow fever and malaria. While these diseases were not as severe in the United States, they had accounted for innumerable deaths in tropical climates throughout the world. While Dr. Smith was solely responsible for identifying the theory of contagion through insects, he shared the recognition with an associate named Kilborne who co-authored the report with Dr. Smith.

Perhaps as a result of his work, Dr. Smith was offered what may be the first professorship in bacteriology in the United States, at the School of Medicine, which is now George Washington University. Dr. Smith remained in Washington until 1895 when he became Director of the Pathological Laboratory of the Massachusetts State Board of Health. While at that post, Dr. Smith did independent research on diphtheria and provided the basis for later immunization through the use of toxin-antitoxin.

DR. SMITH ACQUIRES A NATIONAL REPUTATION

C.W. Eliot, President of Harvard University, then offered Dr. Smith the Fabyan Professorship of Comparative Pathology at the Harvard Medical School and Dr. Smith accepted. Scientists throughout the world had recognized his achievements and traveled to meet with him. Paul Ehrlich, a Nobel Prize winner, observed Dr. Smith's work in diphtheria experimentation, and Ehrlich's associate, Otto, published a paper entitled "The Theobald Smith Phenomenon of Serum Sensitivity." In 1896, Dr. Smith published the first differentiation between the human and bovine tubercle bacillus. In 1908, Robert Koch acknowledged Dr. Smith as having called to his attention the difference between the bacilli which had motivated Koch to take up the same study. Seven years earlier, Koch had accepted the Nobel prize for his work but not until 1908 did he acknowledge Dr. Smith's substantial contribution.

Theobald Smith was, perhaps, indifferent to that slight and the absent renown he merited but which went to others. He willingly served on the Board of Directors of the Rockefeller Institute but declined to become the Director of the Institute when the position was offered to him in 1902. The reason for declining was that he had worked exclusively in animal pathology and he felt that the appointment of an animal pathologist to head the Institute "might eventually arouse adverse criticism." The fact that he had always worked with the lower animals may account for the absence of the popular recognition attained by others. But within the scientific profession, he was properly recognized as being among the leaders in bacteriological research.

In 1915, Dr. Smith left Boston to become Director of the Rockefeller Institute's Department of Plant and Animal Pathology at Princeton. While there, he continued to publish papers on a diversity of subjects ranging from medical economy and medical philosophy to pathology. It was during this time that medals and awards were bestowed upon him in belated recognition of his life achievements. The true satisfaction must have come to him through his personal knowledge of what he had contributed. In a letter written in 1933, he said, "We must not be discouraged if the products of our labor are not read or even known to exist."

In Albany, the place of his birth and education, he is practically unrecognized. Albany Medical College acknowledges Dr. Theobald Smith's achievement with a tablet on a research laboratory in the college complex. Also, to honor him the College has established the

Theobald Smith Annual Lecture. Chosen to lecture each year is a leader in the field of scientific research.

The College at the
Turn of the the Century

The eighteen years following Dr. Thomas Hun's death were years that can be described only with contradictory adjectives—success and near failure, growth and stagnation. The success was in the growth of the College, both in faculty members and graduates. During the first fifty years, 1839-89, the College had graduated 1,828 doctors or an average of 36.5 per year. There is no other explanation for the ".5" graduate except that it is a statistical oddity. During the following 19 years (1896-1914), an average of 43 students graduated each year. Student enrollment for the academic year 1896-97 totaled 210 students in the three year curriculum. The next year (1897-98), 244 students were enrolled, and the following year, the last in which only three years of study were required, enrollment declined to 154.

With the start of academic year 1899-1900, when the requirement for graduation was extended to four years, total student enrollment again declined sharply to 124 students. The number of first year students totaled 44 as compared to 34 in the previous year but second, third and fourth year student members declined to 25, 26 and 29, respectively. It is not unlikely that many students transferred to other schools where they could avoid the new fourth year requirement.

INCREASES IN FACULTY AND STUDENTS

During the next fourteen years, student enrollment grew steadily, with only one year recording a decline, until a to-date all time high of 258 students was recorded in 1914. Of the 258 students enrolled, 55 graduated that year.

Growth of the faculty was even greater, to the point that the word dramatic might be applied to the upward surge. During the previous fifty years, the College faculty had a total of only 45 professors on the staff. It was during Dr. Hun's administration that the staff had grown to 48 members. From 1897 through 1914, the faculty increased from 49 to 109 members: an increase of more than 200%. During the same period the student body had increased and the curriculum extended from three to four years. One can only conclude that the faculty had been

106

severely understaffed at the start of the period or was grossly overstaffed at its conclusion. In 1896-97, 244 students were taught by 49 faculty members. In 1913-14, the faculty had increased to 109, 60 more than 1896-97, while the student body was increased by only 14 members. There is no question that the College had grown in numbers and if growth is a constituent of success, then success was also present during this period.

SCATTERED RESOURCES AND FINANCIAL INSECURITY

Albany Medical College had never enjoyed the financial security present in an institution which has a firm base of endowed funds. From its origin, the financial structure was shaky with insufficient funds to undertake a plant expansion or even major improvement. The school was maintained to the point of remaining habitable, but it was the same building at the turn of the century that Alden March had obtained the use of from the City sixty-one years earlier. At that time, the excellent anatomical museum had provided an attraction to the perceptive student where he could see a wide variety of human organs that had been afflicted with diseases and disorders of mankind. These were an informative aid to diagnosis but provided minimal steps toward curative knowledge. The wired up skeletal remains of an elephant were of interest, but would have been more appropriate in a school of veterinary medicine. The College had cleverly shed the expense of maintaining a medical library by transferrring its library to New York State. The material was still readily available to the students but the library was not on the premises, a further diminution of the physical mass.

Laboratory facilities had been expanded after the construction of the Bender Hygienic Laboratory. Here again, while available to the students of the College, it was removed by several miles from the school and there were yet no commuter buses to carry students the several miles from classroom to laboratory benches. The Albany Hospital, started ten years after the College, had already moved to new buildings several miles from its previous location diagonally across the street from the College. With the preceptor process of education such an arrangement was acceptable as the formal classroom had been an adjunct to the student learning experience. Dr. Thomas Hun had seen the necessity to change the educational emphasis, which would place the burden of teaching on the school and increase the need for better teachers and expanded laboratory facilities. The College staff would have to become the educators and, to properly fulfill their obligation, they would have to make teaching the top priority for at least a core of the faculty.

The founders of the College had as their primary motivation the establishment of an institution for the education of men to become doctors whose knowledge and skills surpassed those of their contemporaries. Concurrent with their efforts to improve medical education, these men also had to support themselves and their dependents. The time that they spent in this pursuit was time taken from their practices and compensation of some sort was necessary to augment the reduction in income. From its inception, the College gave the faculty the student tuition after the cost of maintaining the school and payment of interest on loans had been deducted. No necessity was seen to build a development fund and it probably would have been impossible to do so even if the eventual need had been foreseen.

The last occasion that the Board of Trustees had given evidence of performing a dominant role in governing the College had been at the time of Dr. Thomas Hun's appointment as Dean. The succeeding years had been a tranquil period free of major internal strife and, as a result, the Board members were lulled into the role of spectators who would nod obligingly once a year to acknowledge the competency of the list of graduates presented by the faculty. The faculty, in turn, with a provincial outlook, viewed the progress of the school as satisfactory and placed no pressure on the Board of Trustees. The team moved at a comfortable pace and the drivers dozed at the reins.

FACULTY INVOLVEMENT AND FACTIONS

In fact, the faculty had taken a financial interest in the school beyond the receipt of lecture fees by purchasing $12,000 of the outstanding mortgage on the College. In 1912, the College listed present holders of interest in its mortgage as follows:

Dr. Albert Vander Veer	$ 3,790
Dr. Willis G. Tucker	2,500
Dr. Joseph D. Craig	500
Dr. William Hailes	830
Dr. James P. Boyd	1,250
Dr. John M. Bigelow	1,920
Dr. Leo H. Newman	500
Mr. Charles W. Russell	710
	$12,000

As a result, the College's indebtedness to some of the faculty went beyond their professional contribution and extended to gratitude for financial support. In the present time of monetary inflation and government subsidization, $12,000 is picayune but, at the turn of the century, $12,000 was not a trifle,

It is axiomatic that human nature does not change, and rare and even foolhardy is the person who refuses to accept a greater sum for services rendered in a business transaction. Therefore, it may logically be concluded that the faculty did not view with disfavor the increased student enrollment and resultant increased receipt of tuition fees to be divided among the faculty at their discretion. The entire arrangement was provided for in the by-laws of the College and with full approval of the Board of Trustees.

Patronage in the field of politics is accepted and provides in some measure the sustinance of political parties. There is nothing morally wrong with the patronage system if one of two equals is chosen as the recipient and the individual selected provides "a day's work for a day's pay." It is possible to conclude that a patronage system may have grown in appointment and promotion at the College.

The various professors of the faculty were empowered by simple majority approval to recommend appointment to, and advancement within the teaching staff. With a quiescent Board of Trustees the recommendation may have become pro forma. In a democratic institution there is never just one party or faction, the latter term being applied frequently by the newspapers to describe the condition which developed in the faculty during the years 1896 to 1916. As a matter of record, one Albany newspaper identified the two factions as the "Vander Veer Faction" and the "Hun Faction." The members of the Vander Veer Fraction were identified as Doctors McFarlane, Tucker, Root, Newman, Craig, Curtis and Merrill. The second faction was supported by Doctors Elting, Theisen, Sautter, Nellis, Van Rensselaer, Mereness, Murray and Sampson. It is impossible to imagine the continued existence of two parties with identical objectives and means of achieving those objectives. If such was the case the two would quickly dissolve to one.

However, if two factions exist, no matter how meritorious their objectives, if they are equally strong and persevering, then stalemate must be the result. This may have been the case in regard to Albany Medical College for the period between Dr. Thomas Hun and Dr. Thomas Ordway's administrations. Dr. Vander Veer's primary effort was to expand the student body and the physical plant. Dr. Thomas Hun worked to improve the teaching staff of the College through the addition to the staff of full time teachers who would be teachers first and practitioners secondly. An objective appraisal of the situation presents the conclusion that both were needed. Both improvements needed at the same time and the funds and effort needed to achieve simultaneous fulfillment were not available. It was as though the College were the only child of two strong willed and loving parents, one of whom saw potential in the child as a scientist, the other as a musician. In the tug to send him to a technical school or a school of music, the child may be emotionally torn and go in neither direction.

DR. ALBERT VANDER VEER

The brief biographies of the Doctors Hun were related earlier and testified to the character of the Huns and their unquestioned devotion to their profession and medical education. The Vander Veers are no less distinguished through three generations of doctors who served the Albany area as surgeons and builders of the medical institution. Dr. Albert Vander Veer was a handsomely robust man who radiated health, intelligence and confidence. He wore a full beard and had a benign appearance that belied his steadfast adherence to his convictions.

Dr. Albert Vander Veer was, as his name suggests, of Dutch ancestry, his forebears having immigrated from Olkmaar, Holland to America in 1639. Albert's father, Abraham Vander Veer, in 1828 built a tannery in what is now Rural Grove, Montgomery County, New York. It was in that county in the Town of Root that Albert was born on July 16, 1841. He acquired his early education in the Mohawk Valley public schools of Canajoharie, Union Free School in Palantine, and at the Canajoharie Academy. As a boy, he worked in a pharmacy of his native town and developed an interest in drugs. This interest carried into his professional and teaching years and he always advocated the use of pure and unadulterated medicine. In later years, evaluating the talents of different nations in the field of medicine, Dr. Vander Veer thought that the English and Italians excelled in gross anatomy, the Germans in bacteriology and pathology, the French in the beauty of their medicinal preparations, but that for the use of all kinds of drugs the United States took the lead.

It would be interesting to know why young Vander Veer chose medicine as a career. From his early experience, he might have turned to pharmacy, for which he had a liking. Then there was the tannery owned by his father and into which business he would probably have been welcomed. For whatever reason, medicine became his choice and at the age of eighteen Albert began his medical studies with Dr. Simeon Snow of Currytown, whose daughter, Margaret, he later married. With Dr. Snow he continued to mix drugs, a carryover from his boyhood experience. From Dr. Snow's office he went to Albany where he studied surgery with Dr. John Swinburne, and later became advisor at Ira Harris Hospital under the direction of Dr. Alden March. Although Dr. Vander Veer attended the series of lectures at Albany Medical College in 1861-62, he received his medical degree from Columbian College Hospital in Washington, D.C. He left Albany to become one of the "original hundred medical cadets" called by the Surgeon General to serve in the Federal Army during the Civil War.

After graduation, young Vander Veer was commissioned Assistant Surgeon to the 69th New York Volunteer Infantry and in June 1864 was promoted to Surgeon with the rank of Major. As a soldier, he emulated others in his family who had served in the American Revolution and in the War of 1812. Dr. Vander Veer was a front-line doctor and operated not far from the shooting at Fredericksburg, a battle which was a bloody disaster for the Union Army because of the poor site chosen for a full scale engagement with General Lee's Confederate Army. It was at the Battle of Fredericksburg that men entering the battle were marched past field hospitals to which the wounded had been carried, and surrounding the crude facilities were piles of amputated limbs. Because of the use of the minnie ball and the state of medical knowledge of the time, amputation was practically mandatory in most instances. Dr. Vander Veer quickly became experienced with the scalpel and bone saw.

After the war, he commented that military surgeons learned more than their civilian colleagues about the value of good nutrition, sanitation and fresh air in maintaining good health. He may have also added that the war provided him great opportunity to treat the ghastly wounds inflicted by minnie ball and bayonet. From the same experience he may have developed the outstanding manual dexterity and quickness which he later demonstrated. These abilities stood him in good stead when he entered civilian practice at a time when much surgery was performed in the home. The conditions prevalent there required that the operation be completed with as little delay as possible.

At the conclusion of the war in 1865, Dr. Vander Veer, after being mustered out of the Army in September, spent a year in New York City where he attended lectures at the College of Physicians and Surgeons and served at various dispensaries in that city. He returned to Albany in 1866 and established his practice there. In the same year he was elected to the Albany County Medical Society. For the next 61 years he participated vigorously in the projects of the Society. He served on numerous committees and presented papers on a large number of topics including varieties of cancer of the liver, arterial embolism, uterine surgery, preventable diseases and the future of electricity in gynecology. Dr. Vander Veer was generous in sharing his knowledge and published important monographs on abdominal surgery.

In 1867, a year after returning to Albany, he joined the faculty of Albany Medical College and began by teaching anatomy. However, as would be inevitable with his skills as a surgeon, he established a course in abdominal surgery to which he was appointed professor. For whatever reason, there were those who opposed the establishment of the course. Specialization had not yet emerged.

There are photographs in the archives of Albany Medical College Library, taken in the operating pit of Albany Hospital, which show Dr. Vander Veer, associates, nurses and members of the College's student body. Dr. Vander Veer, in the opinion of some, dominates the entire scene by his rather magnificent presence, which radiates confidence and high professionalism. When addressing the graduating class of 1880, he enunciated the high standards which he himself had observed and which he expected of others of his profession. He stated that the doctor might be required to render services to his patients beyond that of medical or surgical scope; he mentioned the suspicions and temptations to which doctors are subjected; and he warned against undue familiariy with patients, gossip, and false pride; and finally, on that occasion he emphasized the need for professional courtesy.

Dr. Vander Veer was aware of the need for improvement in medical education in this country and was unequivocal in his statements concerning his appraisal of the situation. In an address to the Alumni Association of Albany Medical College in 1882, he said, "Owing to the general low requirements for graduating, the number of doctors yearly let loose in the United States is fearful to contemplate." Two thoughts may occur to the reader of this statement; first, during his deanship of Albany Medical College, the curriculum was extended from three years to four and secondly, the number of students, after an initial down turn, climbed steadily. This effort to improve medical education took the form of extending the curriculum, but did not curtail the quantity of doctors being graduated during his administration. One may conclude that he was not referring to graduates of Albany Medical College specifically by his forthright condemnation of medical education. Further foundation for this conclusion is the fact that he was speaking to the Alumni of that institution.

In quest of further education, Dr. Vander Veer took leave of the faculty and his practice to travel abroad in 1874. One result of his study in Europe was the introduction of the Gamgee pad as an instrument for the administration of anesthesia. During his life time of medical practice, he accomplished many unique and outstanding surgical procedures. Among these accomplishments was his pioneering the use of the plastic jacket for the treatment of spinal curvature.

DR. ALBERT VANDER VEER'S ACCOMPLISHMENTS

He was appointed dean of the College in 1895 and served in that capacity until 1904 when he resigned in order to remain a regent of New York State because of a new law requiring that only one of the two positions could be held at one time, that of dean or regent.

Dr. Vander Veer had occupied diverse chairs on the Albany Medical College faculty. The first was that of General and Special Anatomy in 1869 when he first became attending surgeon at Albany Hospital. In 1874, he was called to a similar position in St. Peter's Hospital. In 1876, he became Professor of Principles and Practices of Surgery at Albany Medical College and in 1882, he became Professor of General and Clinical Surgery, specializing in abdominal surgery.

(Fig. 25) A bronze memorial to Dr. Albert Vander Veer.

In addition to teaching and maintaining an active practice, Dr. Vander Veer was very active in the affairs of Albany Hospital and made every effort to develop and improve the facility. Among other things, he was instrumental in the establishment of a school for nurses and was an advocate of the pavilion plan for hospitals. He served for many years on the board of governors of the Hospital and when he retired as attending surgeon, the Board created especially for him the position of Surgeon-in-Chief, which he held until his death. The Governors recognized his ability and wished to retain him for operative and consultation services.

He served the City and its population in ways other than as an outstanding surgeon. He, along with others, was instrumental in bringing a safe water supply to the City and improving sanitary conditions for disposal of waste. Dr. Vander Veer remained a man of extremely high vitality until the time of his death in 1929. Despite his tremendous burden of professional and civic activities, he still made time to vacation in the Adirondacks at his cottage on Big Moose Lake where he enjoyed life in the woods. Death came to him when he was 88 years old in his home on Eagle Street, attended by his three sons: Dr. Albert

(Fig. 26) A 1909 view of the Albany Hospital amphitheatre with, seated from left,
Dr. Willis Goss MacDonald, Dr. Albert Vander Veer, Dr. Samuel Baldwin Ward, Dr. Samuel Roseburgh Morrow.

Vander Veer, Jr., Dr. Edgar Albert Vander Veer, and Dr. James Newell Vander Veer. The man was legendary. A plaque in Dr. Albert Vander Veer's honor is mounted at the rear entrance to the Huyck Auditorium in the Albany Medical College *(Figure 25)*.

DR. WILLIS GOSS MACDONALD

From a biography of Willis Goss MacDonald prepared by Dr. Frank R. Maxon (AMC '39) the reader might rightfully conclude that Dr. MacDonald's life was fruitful, merry and short. It is fitting that his biography should follow directly after that of Dr. Albert Vander Veer because of the close relationship during their careers.

Following, in its entirety, is the biography written by Dr. Maxon:

"Willis Goss MacDonald was born in the Town of Richmondville, New York on April 11, 1862, the son of Sylvester and Louise Goss MacDonald. It is of interest that his great grandfather, Benjamin MacDonald, came from Edinburgh to settle as the first Scotsman in Coeymans, New York, establishing the first boat landing in that area. Benjamin MacDonald served in the Revolution, became prisoner of Brant's Indian warriors and was taken to Canada and imprisoned. He later was released. Dr. MacDonald's grandfather is described as a man of influence in Schoharie County.

"Sylvester and Louise Goss MacDonald provided Willis with a good education at the Cobleskill Free Academy from which he graduated in 1878. He later studied at the State Normal School in Albany, qualifying as a teacher. It was as a teacher in Berne and Central Bridge that he acquired the funds necessary to enter Albany Medical College in the Class of 1887. Details of his student performance are not specifically recorded, but it is noted that he was elected Marshall of his class in 1885. This gives forecast of his personal or organizational capabilities. His preceptor was Dr. Albert Vander Veer, a distinguished surgeon and one time president of the American Medical Association.

"For eighteen months following his graduation, Dr. MacDonald was house surgeon at the Albany Hospital under the direct tutelage of Dr. Vander Veer and his associates *(Figure 26)*. On completion of this assignment in 1900, he matriculated at the University of Berlin for special courses in surgery, pathology, and bacteriology. During this period he had the opportunity to act as assistant to famous German surgeons of that era, and rounded out his European training with exposure to the hospitals in London, England. It should be recalled that during the late 1890s and early 1900s young physicians and surgeons with academic and scientific professional aspirations gained distinction by European experience, particularly in Germany.

"On returning to Albany, Dr. MacDonald promptly demonstrated his diagnostic and surgical skills and rose rapidly in the academic rank in the surgical professorial steps. As far as can be learned from written records and comments by his peers, his success and recognition did not seem to arouse envy or indignation. Furthermore, one who had the opportunity to personally know numerous of Dr. Macdonald's students from their medical school days of the 1900s, was privy to recollections that attest to his personal attractiveness and diplomatic organizational capabilities as well as his surgical and teaching expertise.

"As examples of Dr. MacDonald's academic and scientific versatility, a list of representative publications speaks for itself.

> *Cholecystectomy: Removal Versus Drainage.* Albany Medical Annals, 1889.
> *Congential Umbilical Hernia: Abdominal Section Six Hours After Delivery.* American Journal of Obstetrical Diseases of Women and Children, 1890.
> *Open Treatment of Wounds.* Albany Medical Annals.
> *The Present Status of Ectopic Pregnancy—A Surgical Disease.* Journal of American Medical Association, July 25, 1896.
> *Non-Parasitic Cysts of the Liver.* New York State Medical Journal, 1908.
> *Tuberculosis: Curability by Koch's Method.* Albany Medical Annals, 1890.
> *The Treatment of Fracture of the Patella by Immediate Suture.* Medical News, July 30, 1898.
> *A Case of Spina Bifida Treated by Excision—Recovery.* Albany Medical Annals, 1899.
> *Operations in Imperative Surgery in Private Houses: A Demonstration of Surgical Technique.* American Journal of Obstetrics, 1904.
> *Rupture of the Spleen.* Albany Medical Annals, 1897.

"It is worthwhile to give special attention to Dr. MacDonald's paper on surgery in the home. At this time in history, techniques for many acute surgical conditions had been well developed; namely, for appendicitis, gall stones, fractures, empyema, to mention some examples. Efficiency of transportation to hospitals, however, did not exist at that time. For instance, a patient in rural New York or New England might be found by his physician, making a house call by horse or sleigh, to have appendicitis. The patient would face a trip to a railroad station on a horse drawn sled to await a train to take him to the nearest city with a hospital. He would then be trundled via a horse drawn ambulance over cobblestone streets to have his surgery in an operating room; altogether a time consuming and hazardous trip. The surgically trained doctor with nurse assistant and ready equipment could be more expediently transported to the patient *(Figure 27)*. As a matter of fact, this author, whose father practiced in Great Barrington, can recall occasions when Dr. MacDonald was summoned by his father to perform surgery in the home. The Boston-Albany Railroad provided frequent local trains making a quick trip from Albany to Pittsfield and then a short transfer on the New York Central that stopped at Great

Barrington was the route. One AMC student once described a trip to Altamont from Albany by horse drawn surrey with nurse assistant and containers of instruments and supplies to perform a cholecystectomy. I personally have seen octagenarian patients in rural Albany County, where I practiced in the 1940's, bearing abdominal surgical scars from operations performed in the home by doctors taught by Dr. MacDonald. In that particular era, this paper of Dr. MacDonald's was of timely importance.

"A list of representative examples of the various presentations and discussions concerning which Dr. MacDonald made himself available at Albany Medical College, Albany Hospital, County Medical Society meetings and at many State Society meetings demonstrates his wide sphere of interest. He was also in demand as a lecturer even in such distant places as Philadelphia, Pennsylvania; Atlanta, Georgia; and Richmond, Virginia. In Richmond, he gave the address to the graduating class of 1901.

"One of his local addresses was reprinted from the *New York Medical Journal* and *Philadelphia Medical Journal* consolidated from March 19, 1904. This was the opening address delivered at the inauguration of the 73rd course of the Albany Medical College. Dr. MacDonald gave a masterful discussion of medical education. The displacement of the preceptorships in favor of didactic lectures, the desirability of preliminary collegiate background, the problems of preparation for rural practice and its unattractiveness were discussed with keen insight and terms that could easily be modified to apply today. This quote from Dr. MacDonald's discussion of competition exemplifies his pragmatic approach:

> *Competition is an advantage in medicine, just as in business. The physician who is unable to cope with an honest and intelligent competition, had better sell books or divert his energies to farming. The law was not designed to protect either incapacity or laziness.*

His comments on curriculum are worth quoting for current consideration:

> *Assume a curriculum established upon the fullest individual demands of every department. The sum total of hours of instruction demanded in all departments would far exceed the limitations of a four year course of study — Limitation must be placed on every department of instruction measured by its conservative value as an element of substantial medical education.*

This dictum is applicable to today's medical academic scene.

"Dr. MacDonald's concern for public health is demonstrated by his steps to organize the South End Dispensary in Albany. This was staffed by Albany Medical College and Albany Hospital faculty, and it provided a rich field for teaching of clinical medicine as documented by tales of their experiences there from alumni who were Dr. MacDonald's students and who worked in this clinic which continued to be effective for many years even after his death.

"Despite his primary surgical interests, it is obvious that Dr. MacDonald had a broad understanding of medical problems of his day. In 1908, he was on the advisory board for the care of tuberculosis to the New York State Department of Health. His persistent organizational efforts to develop a sanitorium in New York State for the treatment of tuberculosis were effective. Raybrook Sanitorium was built in the Adirondacks, just a few miles southeast of Saranac Lake, where the Trudeau Sanitorium had already been established. A plaque in recognition of Dr. MacDonald's efforts in the establishment of this institution was mounted on the wall of the B Wing of Raybrook Sanitorium where he continued to serve on the Board of Trustees. I am informed by Mrs. Shirley Oehler, who is employed in the superintendent's office at that facility, now a correctional institution, that this plaque is still in place. There was also installed in another wing a second plaque in recognition of Dr. John H. Pryor of Buffalo who joined Dr. MacDonald in a combined effort to complete this tuberculosis sanatorium to care for 600 patients a year.

"In conjunction with these activities, it is apparent that he had always been one to get involved. He was, from time to time, on the nominating and disbursement committees of the alumni association, and appeared to have attended essentially every annual meeting. He was a frequent participant in the scientific programs.

"In addition, he regularly cataloged the surgical activities of the Surgical Service of Albany Hospital, presenting the experience with appropriate remarks and discussion. Stories of his continuous effort to improve surgical technique include one that gives an insight into an unexpected side of Dr. MacDonald. He had insisted on replacing glass drainage tubes with then modern flexible rubber drainage tubes, and had at his own expense provided a supply for the Albany Hospital operating room. Apparently, administrative attitudes have remained static. For when Dr. MacDonald would ask for a drainage tube at the operating table he would be handed one of the old glass tubes. (They hadn't been used up as yet.) Dr. MacDonald would gracefully drop it on the floor and continue so to do with others until he was provided with the rubber tube that he preferred, at which time a benign smile would beam from his pink cheeked, chubby face.

"Very early in his career, Dr. MacDonald demonstrated an interest in organized medicine. In 1889, he was secretary to the Medical Society of the County of Albany and served from time to time on various committees. He also became active in the Medical Society of the State of New York and was chairman of the business committee in 1899, and elected to its presidency in 1900. It should be noted he reversed the

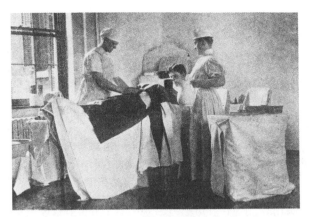

(Fig. 27) An illustration, from Dr. MacDonald's 1904 paper "Operations in Imperative Surgery in Private Houses: A Demonstration of Surgical Technique," showing the use of rubber sheeting.

usual order by later being elected to the presidency of the Medical Society of the County of Albany in 1908.

"During the Spanish-American War, Dr. MacDonald's practice was interrupted. He was commissioned as Brigade Surgeon in June 1898. He served as Chief Surgeon of the Second Army Corps, stationed at Fort McPherson, Georgia. On his return from military service, he is recorded in 1899 as participating in the program for the annual Albany Medical College Alumni meeting and taking charge of the South End Dispensary. As a result of his experiences during the Spanish-American War, he had apparently made a thorough evaluation of the care of those wounded and sick members of the military. This resulted in his conviction that the military should utilize women as nurses despite current public opinion. He championed their cause, describing women nurses as dedicated and adaptable as well as acceptable to all involved in military medical and surgical care.

"Early in his career, Dr. MacDonald recognized the importance of the pathology and bacteriology laboratories to the practice of medicine and surgery as well as teaching. He demonstrated this by frequent financial support to the Bender Laboratory for maintenance of technical and professional personnel. Furthermore, he, along with a few of his associates, was convinced that the old Albany Hospital at Eagle and Howard Streets had to be replaced by a more modern structure. Despite some oppostiion, the present site "way up on the hill" was selected and Dr. MacDonald gave generously of his time in shaping the plans for the original building and backed this with generous monetary contributions.

"It was also at this time that internecine strife occurred in the faculty of Albany Medical College. Descriptions of these problems handed down by word of mouth and documented by recorded disruptions in the medical staff paint a confusing scene. At this time, Dr. MacDonald's staunch loyalty did much to stabilize the Albany Medical College. Heresay from his contemporaries indicates that he was a formidable adversary in spontaneous debate.

"By virtue of his personal charm, Dr. MacDonald had a wide variety of friends in the Albany area. There is no question that he knew intimately many State legislators. His social contacts included many influential, well-to-do and colorful citizens. An insight into some facets of his social life is recalled from the reminiscences of his former students that I had the privilege of knowing. One can gather from his photographs that Dr. MacDonald enjoyed dining. It is well known that he and his friend, Mr. George Hawley, a successful and philanthropic businessman in Albany, arranged for sumptuous dinner parties at the Ten Eyck Hotel, then in its lavish years. He was also a member of the Fort Orange Club. Dr. MacDonald also received distinguished visitors from time to time and one of his students remembers the day when Dr. Charles Mayo stopped off in Albany to spend some time with him.

"Incidentally, one of the students who lived in his office residence on Eagle Street described a midnight scene following one of the social events in which Dr. MacDonald occasionally became involved. The student was awakened in the middle of the night by loud shouting in front of the office on Eagle Street. On arising and quickly dressing to see what was the problem, he found the portly figure of Dr. MacDonald wedged between the front and back seats of a hansom cab. Fortunately, this student was familiar with the construction of horse drawn conveyances, and the prompt use of a wrench permitted Dr. MacDonald's release. This experience was apparently well tolerated for he was up and off to the operating room at 7:00 a.m. the next morning following his usual cold bath. Dr. MacDonald took in his office with him not only students, but also a recent graduate to act as his assistant for extended surgical experience. This apparently was a rich academic experience and, more to the point, a deep personal experience from the daily contact with this exceptional man.

"At the peak of his illustrious career, Dr. MacDonald developed pneumonia on Christmas Day in 1910. At the end of five days he died at his home at 144 State Street, at age 47. He never married and there is no record of the details of his remaining family. Dr. MacDonald's reputation and popularity in the Albany area was such that the *Times Union* published his picture and a review of his career on the front page at the time of his untimely demise. This front page recognition of Dr. MacDonald by the local press is a most unique event for a member of the medical profession.

"On January 7, 1911, a meeting was arranged at the Historical and Art Society of Albany to start plans for an appropriate memorial to Dr. MacDonald. Over an extended period of time, various projects in his memory were considered. At the same time, contributions were being made by his colleagues and his patients. It came about on June 13, 1927 in the new Albany Medical College at its present site that the MacDonald Memorial meeting took place. This was a most dignified ceremony, including appropriate tributes to this gifted surgeon and teacher who had demonstrated influential versatility in the direction of medicine's role in the community of the day—thus, the plaque on the fourth floor of the Albany Medical College.

"Despite his dedication to medical and surgical teaching and practice in the Albany Medical College and Albany Hospital, not to mention his community involvement in health organization, and his travels to broaden his academic scope, he apparently maintained a close attachment to his home town. Prominently displayed in the park of the Schoharie County Town of Cobleskill is an impressive statue erected in memory of Dr. Willis G. MacDonald, who is recognized as one of its most outstanding citizens. It would seem that the distinction that Dr. MacDonald had achieved had not deprived him of the humility of maintaining his loyalty and concern for the community from which he had received his early education. It is apparent that Dr. MacDonald's combination of dedication, energy and intelligence along with his academic and technical skills and insight into the needs of his fellow men resulted in his being the ideal leader."

DR. SAMUEL B. WARD

The previous deans of Albany Medical College had died while holding that office and after each death there was a new beginning. There is little question that a succesor will be influenced by a predecessor for whom he has respect and may, to some extent, owe his position. Though there is no positive evidence of the fact, it is not unlikely that Dr. Vander Veer's opinion was sought in regard to who would succeed him as Dean. Therefore, it may be concluded that, while Dr. Samuel Baldwin Ward was his own man, he may well have sought the counsel of Dr. Vander Veer at times during his Deanship. And, indeed, it may even have been imprudent of him if he did not seek the counsel of a man of Dr. Vander Veer's experience and sagacity.

A biographer has written that unlike many physicians, Samuel Ward grew up in a family of comfortable circumstances. It would be interesting to review the statistics on which this conclusion is based. A medical education has never been inexpensive. Pursuit of a medical degree takes one down a long road and is without financial reward until the goal is achieved. In the times before grants and the financial aid available today, a pennyless student, no matter how brilliant and dedicated, was confronted by a blank wall in his quest for a medical degree. Fortunately, this was not the case for Samuel Ward who was born June 8, 1842 in New York City to Libbeus Baldwin Ward and Abbey Dwight Pratt Ward. He was educated in a private school and, at sixteen, graduated third in his class from Columbia University.

When the young man began to study medicine, Dr. Willard Parker of the College of Physicians and Surgeons was his preceptor. Like many other medical students, he entered the United States Army as a cadet in 1862. Commissioned by President Lincoln as Acting Assistant Surgeon in 1863, Samuel was stationed in Washington. He attended medical lectures at Georgetown University which awarded him a medical degree in 1864. He was then 22 years old. Unlike Dr. Vander Veer, the War having ended the year of Dr. Ward's graduation, it is unlikely that his experiences in the war extended beyond services performed in Washington.

Dr. Ward then gave evidence of the inadequacy of medical education in the United States as did many other of his contemporaries who had sufficient financial resources, by going to Europe to continue his medical studies. After his return to the United States he resumed contact with the College of Physicians and Surgeons where from 1867 to 1869 he was curator of the museum. The same year that he became curator he also accepted the Professorship of Anatomy at the Women's Medical College and New York Infirmary. He retained that post until 1870, when 28 years old, he became Professor of Surgery. Today, a doctor is unlikely to have progressed much beyond internship at this age.

Dr. Ward continued in that position for six years after which he moved with his family to Albany to become Professor of Surgery at Albany Medical College. This was at the time of Dr. Armsby's death and a period of turmoil between the faculty and the Board of Trustees. His addition to the faculty may have been the result of an effort to bring new people into the faculty and an attempt to ward off the growing provincialism in Albany Medical College. He served the institution faithfully for thirty-eight years until he retired in 1914 because of failing health *(Figure 28)*. His administration as Dean from 1905 to 1914 was a tempestuous period in the history of the school and the pressures of the position, torn between the two factions contending for control of the school, did nothing to aid his physical condition. The hammer blow was struck in 1910 when the Flexner Report was published.

A year after joining the faculty, Dr. Ward was admitted to the Albany County Medical Society and, like Dr. Vander Veer, was an attending member for thirty years. He eventually became President of the Society and delivered an address that dealt with "Medical Expert Testimony in

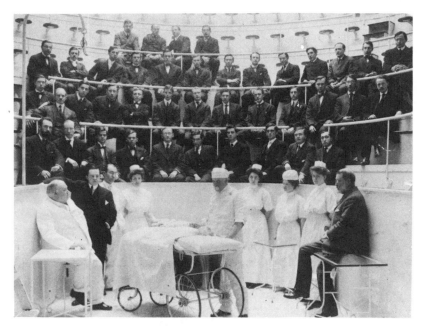

(Fig. 28) The Clinic at Albany Hospital in 1908 with Dr. Willis Goss MacDonald, Dr. Samuel Roseburgh Morrow, Dr. Samuel Baldwin Ward.

Courts." One case which he cited in his paper concerned testimony regarding a criminal abortion in which a woman died from shock when a trumpet-player of great lung capacity blew air into her uterus. In today's permissive society such things are discussed openly and are frequently the subjects of "sick" humor. However, as the scene is a very Victorian gathering of solemn men of medicine, the reaction must have been quite different. Dr. Albert Vander Veer, who was in the audience, was said to have been incredulous. It is a matter of record that he was strongly opposed to abortion but the question remains as to whether the broaching of the subject was the cause of his incredulity or the fact that anyone could have submitted her person to such outlandish treatment. The second case concerned medical testimony on the death of a child who fell from the balcony of a theater. In subsequent reviews of the erudite paper which Dr. Ward had presented, there is little question as to which case elicited the greater discussion.

While Dr. Ward was a staunch advocate of better medical education and for improvements in medical practice he signed a minority report to the Albany Medical Society on pending legislation relating to medical board examinations. The minority report held that such tests were unnecessary for graduates of properly adminstered medical schools. The fallacy in this position was the point of who would determine if the school was properly administered. Objective appraisal of one's self is difficult and frequently suspect. While this report was submitted some twenty-five years before the Flexner Report, it may have been typical of the attitude that moved the Carnegie Foundation to institute the study.

Dr. Ward was a man of diverse talents and interests. He was fluent in French and German, he learned surveying, he was a photography hobbyist and was skilled in the use of hand tools. He played cards well, entertained with grace and told amusing stories. In 1906, when speaking to the freshman class, he gave many points of advice such as: go to church, get enough sleep, do not cram for exams, and, among other admonitions, develop concentration. He concluded by saying, in the woods select a physically capable guide, but one "who would probably be killed by the shock if a new idea should chance to strike him." With his variety of interests and sense of humor, there is small wonder that he was well regarded by his students. It was his misfortune to have become Dean of Albany Medical College during a period of turmoil both within his faculty and medical education throughout the nation.

He died in 1915, one year after having resigned as Dean.

DR. HENRY LARNED KEITH SHAW

Energy and ebullience carried Doctor Shaw through sixty-seven years of life begun in Chaumont, New York, in 1873, and concluded in Albany in 1941. Along the way, much of his youth was spent in Canada and England. But his diverse education was begun in the United States.

In 1890, he was graduated from The Pennsylvania Military College, and three years later received a B.A. degree from Cornell University. In another three years he had been graduated from Albany Medical College to which he matriculated from Watertown, New York.

Thereafter, he spent a year as intern at St. Peter's Hospital in Albany before going for another year to the Utica State Hospital. That experience was followed by two years of graduate study in Munich and Vienna where he specialized in pediatrics. He described the years abroad in letters to friends and to the editors of the *Albany Medical Annals,* for the benefit of students who might go to Europe.

He delineated the pattern of German education which permitted boys as young as six years to enter a gymnasium where all preliminary education for medical school began and continued for seven years. At fifteen, a student took an examination which, if passed, allowed him to serve only one year in the army instead of the longer period normally required. Classes in the prescribed classical course convened for eight hours a day and produced much homework.

Upon graduation, the pre-medical student could attend lectures in any German, Austrian, Hungarian or Swiss university, having his credits transferred. Thus, he could study in many different places under noted teachers.

Foreigners did not need to take State examinations but were required to present a thesis and pass the examination for doctor of medicine before obtaining a degree. All examinations were oral.

In a letter from Munich dated March 27, 1899, Dr. Shaw reported that the German government did not recognize women physicians. Their male colleagues were required to sign prescriptions given by women practitioners, and to be responsible for operations performed by women.

Dr. Shaw described Vienna as a mecca for medical students. There he heard Nothnagel say that a physician should be guided by examining the patient and not by a history of the case.

In Vienna he sharpened his interest in pediatrics. He reported that milk inspection was strict in Austria, but eight out of ten children in the clinics suffered from rickets, called "the English disease."

While in Germany and Austria, Shaw became fluent in German. He translated into English a number of medical papers for publication in the *Albany Medical Annals,* and in England, in February, 1900, he wrote a report on the milk supply of European cities.

That year, he returned to Albany to practice and become an instructor in pediatrics at Albany Medical College. His advancement in rank was relatively rapid. When he had become Professor of Pediatrics, a colleague described him as perhaps the most publicized member of the faculty *(Figure 29)*. His national fame grew from his articles on child care in the *Sunday New York Tribune* and from his column, "The Happy Child," in *The Delineator* magazine.

His purpose for writing the articles was to persuade parents to practice measures of sanitation and good nutrition to decrease infant mortality. Although the infant death rate had fallen since 1898, it still was high a decade later in New York State. In New York City it had declined from 1,160 to 620 per 100,000 births; in Rochester from 584 to 340, and in Yonkers from 880 to 660.

With other physicans, Dr. Shaw worked to establish milk depots throughout the country. By 1907, twenty-one American cities had them. They emphasized Osler's dictum: "Not Providence, but dirty milk killed a baby." They taught mothers how to care for babies in summer and winter. Since the milk depots were established by private philanthropy, the medical profession strove to have them put under its supervision and transferred to public support.

Throughout his practice, Dr. Shaw stressed in various lectures that preventive medicine is the highest branch of the science. When he spoke to nurses, he admonished that they had an important role in persuading mothers to nurse their babies, not only to secure good

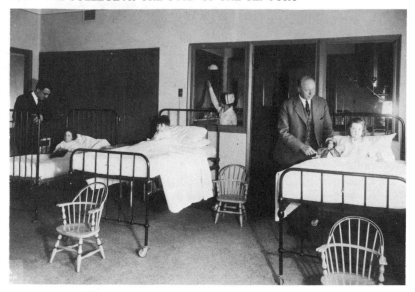

(Fig. 29) Dr. Otto A. Faust (left) and Dr. Henry L.K. Shaw, Professor of Pediatrics (right) in the Pediatrics Ward, circa 1930.

nutrition, but also to develop a close relationship between mother and child.

His hearers must have pondered his description of man's growth: One-third of his normal life is devoted to development. His long period of infancy and plasticity has enabled him to excel other animals because, the higher the intelligence of the adult animal, and the more complex its life activites, the longer is its infancy or period of development *(Figure 30)*.

At the beginning of the twentieth century, some of Shaw's audiences may have been startled by his contention that children should not be thought of as miniature adults, and that their early training should be adaped to their unripe condition. Persistently he stated that diseases in children follow patterns different from those of adults.

While he strove to prevent infant deaths by having regular and frequent bacteriological examinations of milk supplies, he was confronted by unexpected situations such as the one in which milk contained enough formalin to kill one hundred babies had it not been tested. Investigation discovered that the man who tested the milk did not know how to make an analysis for formalin.

At a meeting of the Albany County Medical Society on November 10, 1909, Dr. Shaw asked that the Society request the New York State Department of Agriculture to investigate the milk supply of Albany. He said that tests in other parts of the state had shown their supply to be dangerous to health, and that the Milk Committee of the County

Medical Society had reason to suspect the supply in Albany. His resolution was carried.

In a meeting at Albany before the New York State Nurses' Association, Dr. Shaw in October, 1911, talked of the needs of the nursing mother. She should learn of the importance in nutrition of fats, proteins, carbohydrates, mineral salts and water. Her diet should be generous in variety, but simple. She should get enough sleep. Since human milk is better for a baby than cow's milk, a mother who cannot continuously nurse her child should employ a wet-nurse when necessary.

Among Dr. Shaw's obiter dicta was: "The child and fresh air should be inseparable." He told members of the New York State Teachers' Association on November 20, 1911, that fresh air prevents disease, and that fear of night air is a relic of barbarism. He indicated that in some instances, fresh air may cure disease, and pointed out that a higher mortality among girls than boys may be traced in part to the fact that girls get less exercise than do boys.

Dr. Shaw established the rule that babies in St. Margaret's Home should have adequate fresh air. He was also closely concerned with the Open Air School in Albany.

It was one of thirty-five such in the country. Although proven tuberculous children were not admitted, first preference was given to those who were "pale," under-sized and of tubercular parents. Each morning the children were given breakfast of milk and cereal. At noon they consumed a hearty meal of meat, potato, a vegetable and dessert. In the afternoon, each child received a glass of milk. Each was provided with a tooth brush to be used twice a day.

Doubtless, Dr. Shaw had in mind the milk depots and the public school regulations he had observed in Germany. In Albany, however, it was not compulsory, as it was in Munich, that children in the public

(Fig. 30) A newborn weighing in.

schools bathe there once a week. In Albany's Fresh Air School a trained nurse took each child's temperature once a day.

In 1911, no regular physical examination of pupils was mandatory in Albany's public schools. Dr. Shaw worked to have the situation changed. He thought that physicians should be less indifferent to the health of children. When speaking before the Vermont State Medical Society at Burlington in October, 1913, he quoted John Burns, Minister of Health of Geat Britain, who had said: "Parents should be cleanly wed, the children nobly bred, wisely fed and firmly led."

At the same time that he strove to decrease infant mortality, Dr. Shaw advocated methods of contracepion. Reviewing in the *Albany Medical Annals,* William J. Robinson's *Fewer and Better Babies,* or, The Limitation of Offspring by the Prevention of Conception, he wrote that New York State laws which forbid any remedial discussion of the subject are the result of morbid sentimentalism and should be amended. He thought that Dr. Robinson's book would aid greatly in opening the eyes of those who had been blinded through ignorance and tradition. Today such ideas would raise no eyebrows, but when Dr. Shaw presented them, numerous persons considered them immoral.

On March 8, 1914, he read a paper on sex hygiene at the Second District Conference of Charities and Corrections in Albany. His theme was that parents should educate their children with assistance from the schools. He was aware that among children there is no total ignorance of sex. He commended to professional and lay readers Maude Glasgow's Life and the Law which presented sex hygiene and other topics from a female point of view.

Dr. Shaw's knowledge of hospitals in Europe proved useful when expansion of Albany Hospital became necessary *(Figure 31).* He approved of pavilion construction, but did not wish to see such a failure as the Wilhelmina Hospital in Vienna. Comprising forty separate buildings set far apart, it had been built without consultation with physicians. Nurses had to travel between sections, as did the medical staff who did not change their coats, and thus spread infection from area to area.

As he advanced in rank from instructor to professor of pediatrics at Albany Hospital and in the Medical College, Dr. Shaw participated in many professional organizations in the Community. For five years he was Director of the New York State Division of Child Hygiene. He founded the Society for the Study and Prevention of Infant Mortality which became the American Child Hygiene Association. He also founded the Central New York Pediatric Club. He was active in the American Academy of Pediatrics and in the Albany County Medical Society. He served as pediatic consultant to Greene County Memorial Hospital, Catskill; Vassar Brothers' Hospital, Poughkeepsie; Little Falls

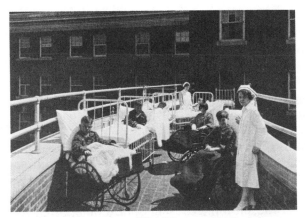

(Fig. 31)
Convalescent children receiving sunshine and fresh air on the outdoor runway.

Hospital; Glens Falls Hospital; and Mary McClellan Hospital, Cambridge, New York.

He found time to translate from the German the seven volumes of Pfaundler and Schlossman's *Diseases of Children*. It added a useful item to the armamentarium of American and English pediatrics.

In common with other native Americans who had ties of friendship in Germany and Austria, Dr. Shaw experienced some traumatic moments when the United States entered World War I. But he did not hesitate to join the Medical Reserve Corps of the War Department. Stationed first at Madison Barracks, New York, he was later transferred to Fort Oglethorpe, Georgia, where he became effective in the field of army intelligence. At the close of the war he related to the Albany County Medical Society some details of his work.

During his early days in the Army, he wrote to the editors of the *Albany Medical Annals* an appeal to physicians to join the Corps. He said that of the 176 doctors in Albany, forty-six had received commissions and forty-one were in active service. Fourteen had been rejected for disability, age or other sufficient cause.

One hundred and forty-eight members of the Albany County Medical Society were in service. Its new service flag was shown for the first time at a meeting in February, 1918. The stars represented William D. Allen, Erastus Corning, Frederick Crounse, Albert M. Dickinson, Joseph Lewi Donhauser, Malcolm Douglas, Edwin L. Draper, Arthur W. Elting, Emanuel M. Freund, Nelson K. Fromm, Louis H. Gaus, Henry Gillen, L. Whittington Gorham, Philip C. Hacker, Eugene E. Hinman, Clinton P. Hawn, John E. Heslin, Thomas M. Holmes, William M. Keeling, William G. Keens, Joseph A. Lanahan, H. Judson Lipes, Howard E. Lomax, Andrew McFarlane, James E. Maloney, Clarence E. Mullins,

Joseph P. O'Brien, George W. Papen, Jr., George B. Randall, H.L.K. Shaw, John F. Southwell, and James Vander Veer.

Returning to a peace-time schedule, Dr. Shaw resumed private practice at 149 Washington Avenue, and teaching at Albany Medical College. His third and fourth year students spent thirty-three hours in formal pediatric clinics. They were taken to inspect dairies, and they worked in the outpatient departments of Albany and Child's Hospitals and saw children at St. Margaret's Home.

Dr. Shaw became an associate editor of the *Albany Medical Annals,* and continued to write professional articles on pediatric subjects. He was appointed by Governor Charles Evans Hughes to the Board of Managers of the Training School for Girls at Hudson, New York.

He and his wife, the former Susanne Sturtevant Burrell, took time for a cruise to the West Indies in 1939. The Shaws, with their two daughters, presided at notable eggnog parties each Christmas season.

Colleagues retain vividly their memories of Harry Shaw as a jovial companion at meetings of the Esculapian Club, or seeing him descend backwards down the steps waving his hands in farewell to the children and, sometimes, missing the last step, almost making a backward somersault.

DR. KENNETH DANIEL BLACKFAN

Another graduate of Albany Medical College who attained international recognition and fame was Dr. Kenneth Daniel Blackfan. Eulogizing Dr. Blackfan after his death on November 29, 1941, Dr. E.A. Park enumerated the qualities of friendliness, simplicity and directness. These attributes had made him an oustanding pediatrician, researcher and administrator.

He was born on September 9, 1883, in the village of Cambridge, New York, where for many years, his father, Henry S. Blackfan, had practiced medicine. In 1901, directly from high school, Kenneth matriculated at Albany Medical College. Four years later, he was graduated at the head of his class, and spent the next year working in pathology at Albany Hospital under the direction of Dr. Richard M. Pearce, and in bacteriology at the Bender Laboratory.

Thinking that he wished to practice general medicine, Dr. Blackfan returned to Cambridge to work with his father for three years. But the field of pediatrics, beginning to be considered a specialty, attracted him, and he accepted an appointment as Resident in St. Vincent de Paul's Foundling Hispital in Philadelphia. There he came under the influence of Dr. David L. Edsall and Dr. Samuel M. Hammill.

In 1911, on the recommendations of Doctors Pearce and Hammill, Dr. Blackfan was invited to become house officer in the newly organized Washington University School of Medicine in St. Louis, Missouri, to which Dr. John Howland had been called as Professor of Pediatrics. One year later, when Dr. Howland accepted an invitation to the Johns Hopkins University Medical School, he took Dr. Blackfan with him as resident physician.

At Johns Hopkins, Dr. Blackfan quickly became noted as a clinician, administrator and teacher. He might have begun there his role as investigator, had not Dr. Howland insisted that a resident physician confine his activities to the hospital wards and not spend time in the chemical laboratory.

Nevertheless, Dr. Blackfan's ability was so conspicuous that in 1920, he was invited to become the Professor of Pediatrics in the College of Medicine at the University of Cincinnati. There he remained for three years until called to the chair of pediatrics at the Harvard Medical School.

For eighteen years at Harvard, Dr. Blackfan's talents had full play. His first interest was to cure his patients and to reassure their parents by his cheerfulness and air of optimism. His colleagues described him as an acute observer with a memory that helped him to apply his experiences with common sense. He understood human nature intuitively, his coworkers believed; as an administrator, he almost always chose the right person for a given place.

Dr.Blackfan considered teaching an important duty. He inspired his hearers to attempt an approach to his own skill and knowledge. His ability to deal with untoward circumstances and difficult persons was augmented by a subtle sense of humor.

At Harvard his research contributed much to medical progress. Previously he had collaborated with Dr. Walter Dandy in investigating hydrocephalus. Later, with Dr. Hamilton and others, he did chemical research that made possible the use of magnesium sulphate to reduce hypertension in acute hemorragic nephritis. At the time of his death, his *Atlas of the Blood in Childhood,* created with his associate, Louis Diamond, was ready for the press.

That book, and the four-volume report on the White House Conference on Child Health and Protection, which Dr. Blackfan edited in 1932, are still useful. Though he never studied abroad, his name was known and respected in Europe. He was General Secretary of the Fifth International Commission on Nutrition sponsored by the League of Nations at Berlin in 1932. He was a corresponding member of the Royal Society of Medicine of England and of the British Pediatrics Association.

He belonged as well to many pediatric groups in the United States. From 1937 until the end of his career, he was a member of the Commission on General Medical Eduation.

Surely it can be said of Dr. Blackfan that the good he did lives after him.

DR. WILLIS GAYLORD TUCKER

The seventh dean of Albany Medical College was Dr. Willis Gaylord Tucker. He was born October 31, 1849 in Albany, acquiring his basic education from the Albany Academy where he studied for eight years. While at the Academy he came under the influence of Dr. Jacob S. Mosher, and from this association he may have developed his inclination toward medicine as a vocation. Graduating from Albany Medical College in 1870, his goal was not to practice medicine but to teach chemistry. Unlike the deans who preceded him and were first and foremost medical doctors or surgeons, he remained primarily interested in chemistry. Pursuing this interest, he was instrumental in founding the Albany College of Pharmacy in 1881. He began teaching there, and in 1906, was appointed Dean of that College. Simultaneously, he taught chemistry at Albany High School, Albany Academy, the Academy for Females, and at St. Agnes School. His teaching career at Albany Medical College extended 44 years from 1871 to 1915 where he served at different times as a teacher, registrar, and finally dean. From these facts it may be concluded that he was primarily an academician and, as such, his views concerning education were founded on sound experience in that field, more so than that of his predecessors.

It may be recalled that Dr. Ward was of the opinion that the medical school should be the sole judge of the worthiness of a candidate to practice medicine. In 1908, Dr. Tucker expressed a dramatically opposite view to that of the then Dean, Dr. Ward. As a member of the New York State Board of Regents, he suggested that examination for licensing should be nationally uniform, that the competence of examiners should be listed, and that a competent board of examiners should be comprised of experts and men skilled in teaching. The examiners should be compensated for their work and none should be on the faculty of a medical school. This process of testing would produce uniformity in the quality of medical education in the United States and, was therefore, in accord with the objectives of the Flexner Report issued four years later. However, when the Flexner Report was issued in 1910, Dr. Tucker did not agree with the wholesale closing of the smaller schools advocated by Abraham Flexner even though he admitted that some of the teachers were not superior, some of the equipment not the best, and some results not entirely satisfactory. He held that some small schools gave as good an education as do large ones, and that the student of average ability and small financial income needs more help than does his equally impoverished but brilliant fellow. While this attitude was not an endorsement of Flexner, it does come close. This attitude might be explained by several circumstances in Dr. Tucker's career as an educator; he taught in both public and private schools and thereby came in contact with financially affluent students and those less fortunate. He was educated in small schools himself and as a result was probably more familiar with the ability of a small school to produce a competent graduate. Also, he was a member of the faculty for many years of one of the small schools which was threatened by the Flexner Report. While intellectually honest, he was a product of his environment and influenced by personal experience.

Dr. Tucker, in addition to his many academic commitments, was active in improving the sanitary conditions in the City and at the turn of the century became a member of the Albany Sanitary Bureau. Earlier he had analyzed 36 of the 39 public wells in the City. Only three met his criterion of good, five were "fair," thirteen "doubtful," and fifteen "bad." The last group he said should be closed. Pure water had been a scarce commodity in Albany and the City was notorious for its contaminated supply. He was equally critical of pharmacists, taking them to task for thinking of themselves as shopkeepers rather than professional persons. He admonished that they should be compensated in proportion to their skill and education. He urged them to take steps toward abolishing cut-rate drug stores, proprietary prescriptions, and quack nostrums.

Dr. Tucker was a man of energy and diverse interest and was competent in all of his fields of endeavor. Unfortunately, when he became Dean of Albany Medical Collge the situation there was in chaotic disarray. The faculty had split into two factions and each was successful in frustrating any attempts of the other to get the school moving. The physical plant was outmoded and now removed from the Hospital so that students were at a pronounced disadvantage for clinical and laboratory facilities. The finances of the school were never better than marginal and insufficient to rectify the school's shortcomings.

THE FLEXNER REPORT

In the midst of all of the ills which had been growing since the turn of the century, the Flexner Report, issued in 1910 by the Carnegie Institute, struck an almost lethal blow to the struggling College. The Flexner Report, formally titled "Medical Education in the United States and Canada, A Report to the Carnegie Foundation for the Advancement of Teaching," was written by Abraham Flexner and copywrited in 1910. Dr. Abraham Flexner had been commissioned by the Carnegie Foundation to make an on-site examination of medical schools in the United States and Canada and then issue a comprehensive report of his findings and evaluation. He reported that at the time of his survey of Albany Medical College, there were 94 members of the teaching staff of whom 16 were professors and 78 in other grades of the faculty. The Professor of Chemistry, the Associate of Physiology, and the Director of the Bender Laboratory were non-practitioners. The financial resources of the College were only sufficient for maintenance purposes, with the income from tuitions amounting to only $20,276 per year. This money was largely distributed among the faculty and their interest in the school did not extend much beyond the income to be derived. The College had but $10,000 as the nucleus of a building fund.

In regard to the laboratory facilities, Dr. Flexner stated that the Bender Laboratory was at a considerable distance from the school and had insufficient funding. The laboratory was practically self-supporting through work performed for the Board of Health and similar sources. The College, after equipping the laboratory for the use of students, contributed to its support only sufficiently to keep it going. As a consequence of the meager financial support, there was little research in progress. In addition to the shortage of laboratory facilities, the College included no course in pharmacology, the course in histology did not include embryology, and only a small amount of demonstrative work in physiology. In short, Flexner stated that the laboratory branches had been slighted in pursuit of the policy of paying annual dividends to the faculty.

On the positive side he found that the medical school building had good laboratories for chemistry and physiological chemistry and the usual dissecting room with a few charts, models, etc. Otherwise, the equipment was found to be scant. Flexner stated that the main clinical reliance was Albany Hospital in which 200 beds were available of which 75% were for work in surgery. The report stated that, in general surgery, students could only "look on." The students had no access to obstetrical wards and only students serving as externs were allowed to observe cases. Other institutions furnished supplementary material in obstetrics, pediatrics, mental diseases, etc. The school was using two dispensaries. The one at the Hospital was unimportant; the South End Dispensary had a fair attendance and was conducted in an orderly manner.

The Flexner Report appraised medical education in New York State in general as being overly productive and causing even adjoining states to suffer from the plethora of its productivity. This statement may have been made in frustration because of New York State's unrealized potential for high quality education. The report then states that, "Its vast hospital and university resources should make it (New York State) the Berlin or Vienna of the Continent." The Flexner Report was obviously aiming at a reduction in quantity and improvement in quality. The Report then went on to state, "We have now suggested two results that the medical schools in New York must attain; (1) they must make doctors in sufficient number; (2) they must actively participate in the advancement of medical science."

> *Of the eleven medical schools now existing in the State only the bona-fide university departments can expect to survive; outside of New York City, Syracuse University alone has just now a chance. The schools of Buffalo, Albany, and Brooklyn belong to the past. None of these three has yet even emerged from the fee dividing stage. Syracuse with a smaller total fee income than any of them, devotes every dollar to the development of the fundamental branches and has fairly earned support from outside.*

REACTION TO THE FLEXNER REPORT

This was a rather devastating report coming from an objective review. One can imagine the consternation which it produced. Dr. Ward, then Dean, wrote to Dr. Flexner in an aggrieved tone and stated that the on-site review of Albany Medical College was performed in a very perfunctory manner. He concluded by stating that he believed the criticism to be unjustified and asked for and received a second review. The Report remained unaltered.

However, Dr. Ward's reaction had some justification in view of other facts revealed in other portions of the report which stated that the City of Cincinnati had, at the time, twenty active medical schools. If, as Dr. Flexner contended, New York State was causing a "plethora" of doctors in adjoining states, then Cincinnati was producing doctors for its area in the abundance of locusts in the seventh year. Again to measure Albany Medical College in perspective with some other medical colleges a review of some of its contemporaries would place it high on the scale. For example, Dr. Flexner described the laboratory facilities of one medical school founded in 1906 by a stock company in the following note:

> *At the date of visit, there was no outfit at all. Subsequent reliable reports credit the school with a vat containing four cadavers in a room without other contents, a simple outfit for elementary chemistry and twenty brand new microscopes, but no material to use with them.*

Small wonder that Dr. Ward objected to the low appraisal of Albany Medical College.

Yet there is no denying that medical education in the United States and Canada was in need of improvement. Many schools were founded primarily as business ventures with as little investment as possible and a will-o'-the-wisp existence. When one area was financially "milked," the itinerant "professor" moved to another fertile area to organize another diploma mill. In 1910, there were 155 surviving medical schools in Canada and the United States from 457 previously recognized. New York State which earlier had 43 schools was then down to eleven. It was not without need of justification that the Flexner Report pointed a long finger.

There can be little doubt that the Flexner Report shook Albany Medical College to its foundation and the reverberating shock waves radiated throughout the City. This was no quiet appraisal circulated within an intimate group, but rather an authoritative evaluation which was published and circulated nationally. The newspapers gave further disclosure to the Report and even lay circles were concerned. And certainly the students must have been aware of the event and somewhat apprehensive of the shadow that was being cast upon their hoped for diplomas. Even if others had interest in the school of only a pecuniary nature, they too must have been shaken by the castigation implied by the Report and the potential termination of future monetary gain. However, immediate change was not possible as the nature of the criticism was not such that could be quickly rectified. The College had never enjoyed any substantial endowment and there was only $10,000 in the building fund at the time of the Report. Another factor that would retard action was the contiuing division of the faculty into two factions pulling in opposite directions and the inherent suspicions of the others' motives. No one had an imposing financial interest in the institution and it would have been financially painless to accept the situation as irrevocable, arrange the transfer of the students to another school, dismiss the faculty, sell the equipment to satisfy the small mortgage and close the doors. There is no reason to assume that the area hospitals would have been inconvenienced by the termination because the hospitals were sufficiently staffed and independent of the College in all respects. As the Report stated, there was a plethora of doctors in the State as well as adjoining states so that lay persons had no immediate reasons to protest the closing.

On the reverse of the coin there was a large, active group of alumni which had taken up practice in the City and other areas of the State. Then too, this was an institution which had survived and flourished for seventy-one years and had developed traditions and a good reputation. And finally, those men who were most influential in the affairs of the College were men of reputation for success and not of a nature to abandon a struggle and turn from a challenge. In fact, their very willingness to assume many burdens and to work in many areas may have been the subtle cause for deterioration described by the Flexner Report. All three Deans from 1896 through 1915 were men who had given substantially of their time and abilities to improve the health and sanitary conditions of the City through service on committees of the Albany County Medical Society and other civic groups. Each was recognized nationally for his abilities in his field of specialization and each spared no effort to broaden the knowledge of others through the presentation of papers and speaking engagements.

PLANNING FOR A NEW BUILDING

Concurrent with the preparation and release of the Flexner Report an effort was being made to relocate the College in the area now known as University Heights and proximate to the new location of the Albany Hospital. At that time, the County was planning to construct a new penitentiary, thereby vacating the old building which was adjacent to the Albany Hospital. Letters were sent to all doctors in the area asking them to intercede with the Board of Supervisors so that the vacant penitentiary buildings and grounds could be deeded to the College for expansion and relocation. On December 10, 1910, a meeting was held in the College building to which all City doctors were invited so that the plan could be further explained and to receive their suggestions. Less than one year later the *Albany Sunday Telegram* announced that the legislature had agreed to transfer the 12 acre property and penitentiary to Albany Medical College if a satisfactory arrangement could be made between the Board of Trustees and the County government. The architectural firm of Fuller and Robinson Company was engaged to survey the penitentiary building to determine if it could be altered to fulfill the needs of the College. Their report, submitted to Dr. Vander Veer, who, though no longer dean was still a dominant figure in the College, was that the expense of renovations would make the project impractical. It cited the need to cut numerous new openings from the building in addition to other extensive changes. The proposed former alterations had no doubt been attempted by the inmates on several occasions. The consideration of the use of a jail for medical purposes was not unique, the Albany Hospital having originally occupied a former Albany jail.

For one reason or another, in 1913 the County Board of Supervisors declared that the penitentiary could not be vacated and transferred to the College for sometime into the future. As an alternative the City offered property on Delaware Avenue which would be immediately available, on the condition that the Medical College would erect a building on the premises within three years. That this alternative was considered acceptable is proven by architectural plans for the new school which identify the building as being on Delaware Avenue. The plans were extremely optimistic in view of the College having but $10,000 in the building fund at that time. The drawings detail an imposing two story building extending approximately 215 feet in length and 45 feet in depth with three wings each approximately 45 feet on each side. The new building, in addition to other features, was to include two impressive amphitheaters, laboratory rooms and dissecting rooms. Unfortunately, the plans were never realized. Fortunately, neither was the site on Delaware Avenue; otherwise, the physical merger of the College and Albany Hospital would not have been possible with the convenience to both interests afforded by the present location. It is surprising that there was a momentum for such ambitious plans amidst all of the internal turmoil and the near condemnation by the Flexner Report.

PROPOSED FACULTY REORGANIZATION

In 1908, two years prior to the issuance of the Flexner Report, Doctors Albert Vander Veer and Willis Tucker were appointed as a Committee of two to propose a plan for the reorganization of the faculty. The plan was developed, printed, and circulated for consideration. In substance it proposed the creation of an executive faculty comprised of the nine members of the faculty who held full professorships. The executive faculty would vote on administrative affairs and other members of the faculty would be consulted at the pleasure of the executive faculty. In an effort to control the growing number of faculty members, the number of professors not members of the executive faculty was not to exceed five; the number of clinical or adjunct professors was not to exceed 12; and lecturers not to exceed 15. Upon submitting the report, the committee requested comments on the proposal. Indicative of the deadlock and intransigence of the competing factions, no action was taken and the committee withdrew the proposal.

POST FLEXNER REFORM

The situation remained unchanged and on November 12, 1911, the *Albany Sunday Telegram* announced that the Board of Trustees had appointed a committee to report on reorganization of the faculty and securing of a new site for the College. The committee consisted of Supreme Court Justice Chester, Albany Mayor McEwan, Robert H. Pruyn, Charles Gibson, and the Rev. Charles A. Richmond, Chancellor of Union University. The *Times Union* and *Albany Journal* also carried reports of the action in further detail. They reported that the committee was empowered to make recommendations in four areas, specifically to:

1. Investigate faculty conditions.
2. Make recommendations to departmentalize College courses.
3. Recommend complete reorganization of various courses with one doctor at the head of each course.
4. Make recommendations for a permanent paid faculty in accordance with the Board of Regents that held that no medical school would be recognized without at least six full-time faculty members.

It is more than likely that the Trustees were jolted into action by implications of the Flexner Report and by members of the faculty who could attract their individual attention.

In 1912, at the Board's annual meeting, the by-laws of the College were amended and the most significant change was that nine departments should be established. These were:

1. Anatomy
2. Physiology
3. Pathology and Bacteriology
4. Medicine
5. Surgery
6. Therapeutics, including Pharmacology and Materia Medica
7. Obstetrics
8. Chemistry and Toxicology
9. Neurology

FACTIONALIZATION

Another factor which was undoubtably instrumental in forcing action by the Board of Trustees was a document signed by Drs. James P. Boyd, C.S. Merrill, Hermon C. Gordinier, Howard Van Rensselaer, Thomas Ordway, Arthur W. Elting, and John A. Sampson. There was either a reportorial error or a change of allegiance, because one Albany newspaper had earlier identified Dr. Merrill as a member of the Vander Veer faction and this document was the work of those supporting Dr. Henry Hun's views.In brief, this protest to the Board opposed the recommendation presented to the faculty and adopted June, 1911 whereby three professors were added to the faculty. It was alleged that the professorships were relatively unimportant and created so as to establish a majority to support certain positions. The document requested that the Board take actual and not nominal direction of the college and to consider a reorganization of the teaching corps. It concluded by stating, "A house divided against itself cannot stand," shades of Lincoln's comments on the separation of the States.

ACADEMIC STANDARDS CHALLENGED

In May of 1914, the house of cards did indeed begin to collapse. Doctors Gordinier, Elting and Sampson sent a letter to the Board of Trustees calling their attention to the decline in scholarship. The letter cited the fact that approximately 50% of the graduates had that year failed to pass the State examination to qualify them to practice in New York State. In addition, the State of Pennsylvania refused recognition of a diploma from Albany Medical College. Dean Tucker replied shortly thereafter, to the accusation with a printed refutation. The message from Dr. Tucker was addressed to students and friends of the College and asked them not to be misled by the accusatory statement. As the letter from the three doctors was sent to the Board of Trustees, one may wonder how its contents were disseminated to the extent that an almost public refutation was necessary. Whatever the cause of the ill-famed publicity, the Dean did not deny the high percentage of failure. He stated that the failure rate would have been reduced had the students who failed the two year State examination been refused by the College to be permitted to continue their studies before successfully completing the two year examination. As to Pennsylvania's refusal to recognize the Albany Medical College diploma, Dean Tucker stated that this was not an unusual situation as many states did not have reciprocal agreements concerning recognition of credentials.

An interesting sidelight on the appraisal of academic achievement at the College is provided by a review of the catalogs. Beginning with the 1907-08 catalog there was a statement made concerning the successful achievement of license to practice by Albany Medical College graduates. This statement was repeated each year thereafter up to and including the 1911-12 catalog. Three quarters of a page of copy was devoted to that subject in the catalog including a comparison of Albany graduates to those of other major medical colleges. The following year there was what some might interpret to be an ominous omission of such claims. There can be no question that the entire gamut of accusations from the Flexner Report of 1910 to the claims and counter claims of 1915 must have had a disturbing effect on the concentration of the student body. Had such things occurred during the latter years when students are more assertive there is no end to speculation as to what might have happened.

FACULTY CHANGES AND RESIGNATIONS

The minutes of faculty meetings during 1914 and 1915 are filled with resolutions and approval of appointments to the faculty and changes of titles of members of the faculty. It was almost like a game of musical chairs. The whirlwind of changes climaxed in May, 1914. On May 24 there was an announcement in the newspapers that the College planned a campaign to raise $150,000. The following day a report appeared stating that the Board of Trustees had, with regret, accepted the resignations of Doctors Albert Vander Veer, Samuel B. Ward, James P. Boyd, Cyrus S. Merrill, and Henry Hun. All would be appointed Emeritus Professors of the College. Dr. Vander Veer had served on the faculty for forty-five years and Dr. Hun for thirty-one. With the exception of Dr. Hun the reason given for the retirement of the group was that they had reached or exceeded the age limit for faculty membership. Dr Hun is said to have earlier expressed a desire to resign from the faculty. The timing of the resignations was appropriate, it being spring and the end of the academic year. But it does appear more than coincidence that Doctors Vander Veer and Hun should have tendered their resignations simultaneously.

This wave of resignations was followed by others. Doctors Gordinier, Bernstein, Ayer, Keeton, Elting, and Van Rensselaer resigned. These resignations were for a variety of reasons, some not associated with protest over the control and lack of direction of the College. Dr. Sampson had also resigned, but he and Doctors Gordinier and Elting reconsidered their resignations and were willing to accept new positions on the faculty if management of the College was altered.

Among the changes required for their return was the agreement that six instructors as specified by the Board of Regents would become full time instead of dividing their time between teaching and private practice. Another requirement was that there be a closer association between the College and Union University.

CONTINUED IN-FIGHTING

Anonymous criticism of the administration of the College broke in an article in the *Knickerbocker Press* quoting "a prominent physician who refused to permit his name to be used." The physician stated that the College was governed by a Board of Trustees that did whatever it had been told to do, not being aware that the Medical College had become a proprietary school owned by individuals. The article continued by reporting that the Albany County Medical Society would dismiss from the Society and impose professional ostracism on any physician who discussed medical affairs with a newspaper reporter. Others claimed that promotion within the faculty was arbitrary and additions to the faculty were most frequently made from the alumni.

With justification, the opposing opinion was that the Board of Trustees had abrogated its authority for years and had looked to the faculty to administer the school and control its finances. Prior to the regulation requiring six full time instructors, the school had been able to survive upon tuition fees. With the new regulation except for the other expenses all tuition fees were required for the full time instructors. Other teachers were called upon to make personal sacrifices to staff the faculty and keep the College open.

As a sidelight on the resignations it is interesting to note two letters received by the faculty. The first letter recorded in the June 17, 1914 minutes of the Faculty Meeting is from Dr. Henry Hun and was addressed to Dr. Craig, then registrar of the College. It stated; "Mr. Luther Tucker informs me that the Trustees of the Albany Medical College have elected me an Emeritus Professor. I have not been officially notified of my election but when I am I shall decline it. And I forbid you to put my name in the catalogue as an Emeritus Professor."

Ten days later on June 27, a letter from Dr. Albert Vander Veer also directed to Dr. Craig was recorded as follows; "I desire to acknowledge commuication of June 20, 1914 from the Board of Trustees of the Albany Medical College notifying me of their action in appointing me Emeritus Professor in Surgery. I beg of you to extend to them my thanks for the honor conferred."

The readers of these dramatically opposite attitudes are free to draw their own conclusions as to what prompted the differing reactions to the intended honorable recognition of services rendered.

BOARD OF TRUSTEES ASSERTS ITSELF

The Board of Trustees, after years of seemingly lethargic interest in the comings and goings of the faculty, had been goaded into action. After due deliberation the Board requested that the entire faculty of the College resign so that on selection of a new Dean he would have full free rein in restructuring and appointing members of the faculty. On March 8, 1915, Dr. Root of the faculty directed a lengthy reply to the request for resignation. The statement by Dr. Arthur Guernsey Root, Professor of Diseases of the Throat and Nose, cited how the faculty had been responsible for the finances of the College and the maintenance of the professional standards of the College without the help of others. He also stated that the present faculty had all been appointed within the by-laws of the institution whose Board of Trustees was now demanding their resignations.

The Board was not swayed by Dr. Root's erudite argument and on March 11, the Trustees formally again requested the resignations. Dr. Willis Gaylord Tucker, then Dean, made a resolution which was accepted by the faculty to tender their resignations effective June 1, 1915.

Period of Development

ALBANY HOSPITAL IN 1896

Today an aerial view of most hospitals with the exception of those recently built would appear as a series of blocks of varying dimensions and heights thrust together by the hand of a playful giant. The architecture runs the full spectrum from neo-Grecian to modern functional. This architectural diversity can be explained by the fact that they are growing institutions and are a series of additions reflective of the time in which they were built and the funds available for their construction. In 1896, the Albany Hospital, then located on the corner of Howard and Eagle Streets was essentially the same functional oblong cube that had housed the Hospital since 1851 and earlier served as a jail. A cupola sat on top of the former jail like a small derby on the head of a fat old man. Two additions were made to the jail structure, but these only reduced the ventilation and natural light entering the original structure.

The building had been renovated at the time of its conversion from jail to hospital, but since that time no extensive renovation had taken place. These were times before Federal and State grants and support for the hospital was dependent on charitable contributions, payment from the few who could afford the cost of hospitalization, and token payment from the City for the indigent sick.

Those who could afford payment for hospitalization were afforded reasonably suitable accommodations and were probably well satisfied with what was offered. The healthy were unaware of the conditions that existed in the Hospital and provided no impetus for change. Fortunately, the doctors who comprised the medical staff were cognizant of the need for improvement.

CRITICAL REPORT OF HOSPITAL CONDITIONS

On July 1, 1896, the following communication was presented to the board of Governors of the Hospitals and signed by Doctors A. Vander Veer, Henry Hun, and C.S. Merrill who headed the medical and surgical staffs:

To the Board of Governors of the Albany Hospital:
Gentlemen,

Your medical staff feel much hesitation in making any suggestion which might be construed into a lack of appreciation of the valuable aid and material comfort freely given to the sick of Albany, and its vicinity, by the institution under your charge. At the same time we cannot blind ourselves to the serious (its) defects and disadvantages. The building which has been in use for a hospital for nearly fifty years, was not originally constructed for this purpose at all, and although much ingenuity was displayed in remodeling the original structure, and much additions to it, yet we respectfully submit that since the hospital began to be used as such the whole subject of hospital construction has been so thoroughly studied out and that so improved that nothing but a new structure, created for the purpose can possibly fulfill modern requirements. It will be impossible ever to light, ventilate and cleanse this old building as modern sanitary requirements show to be necessary.

Ever since the importance of light and fresh air in the treatment of disease has been recognized it has been the custom to build wards on the pavilion plan, so as to have them exposed to light and air on all sides. The Albany Hospital, being in great part a remodeled jail, with thick walls and small window space, and with its subsequent addition joined to each side of the original building. Moreover, its location has now become very unfortunate. Howard Street is largely occupied by stables, the consequent odors, flies, and vile language from which are a constant detriment to the welfare of our patients. Eagle Street is from daybreak the thoroughfare of milk wagons, ice-carts, and market wagons, on their way to the public market, and throughout the day one of the noisiest streets of the City.

In this connection we would also call your attention to the fact that, although an effort was made in 1894 to render the Howard Street wing safe, despite the settling of its foundation further since that date we would suggest that an expert examination, to ascertain whether it is now in an entirely safe condition, would be advisable.

With the growth of Albany in population, and more especially as a medical center, our hospital accommodations have become inadequate. During the winter season just past the wards were so crowded that the cubic air space to each patient was reduced at times to 900 square feet while 1700 square feet is what should be allowed, and statistics show that such reduction means necessarily, and increased mortality. The Hospital is contantly overcrowded. It will be observed that 1200 patients were treated last year. This necessitates a change of 25 patients weekly and the maximum time allowed to each patient is something over 20 days so that as soon as a bed becomes vacant, by death or otherwise, it must be immediately filled, not sufficient time being given to properly cleanse, air and put it in good shape. This same applies to the private rooms. Again in this crowded condition, many patients who would be benefited by treatment are necessarily refused admission, while the tendency is to hurry others out before they are fully recovered.

At present the public wards are all badly ventilated, most of them badly lighted and were never constructed with a view of maintaining that strict cleanliness which modern science shows to be strictly essential. There are vermin in many of the wards and corners so dark that it is impossible to see them. It is even true that patients have been bothered in the public wards and private rooms by rats running around the floor and even over their beds.

There should be connected with each ward a room where dying patients or those very sick, can be placed. It is certainly very dispiriting to the other patients to have someone dying in the room. A room for the head nurse should be next to the ward, for her better supervision, and so that she may be called upon for aid in an emergency. There should be a place in which food, etc., can be heated; it should not be in close proximity to the water closets and these latter should be more completely separated from the wards.

There should also be at the end of each ward a "sun room" where convalescents can sit and get fresh air and light; and there should be some grounds around the hospital where patients could get a little exercise.

There is a great need for improvement in regard to the private rooms. The water closets for these rooms are dark and dirty and men and women have to use the same closet, which is very disagreeable to the latter. The rooms are very badly heated, especially those heated by stoves, which, if they are large enough to keep a fire, are too large for the rooms and the entrance of a man at midnight to put more coal on the fire is extremely unpleasant, especially for women.

The only way the patients can call the nurse is by ringing a large bell, which always distracts the neighboring patients, often at most inopportune times and does not always reach the nurses' ears. There should be a system of electric bells.

The nursing in the hospital is very bad. The nurses are not trained and it is impossible to get good nurses for the price paid unless at the same time they are being taught and earning a diploma. The discipline of the nurses and the care which they take of the patients would be greatly improved by having a training school for nurses in connection with the hospital, and the lady managers of the training school by their visits exercise an excellent influence on the whole housekeeping of the hospital. Albany is very backward in this respect. There is probably no city of its size in the country that has not a training school in connection with its hospital.

A pavilion for obstetrical cases is greatly needed in the city and cannot be furnished and maintained in the present building.

It is most unfortunate that there is no pavilion in the city for the care of those who contract contagious diseases, and in our institutions there is no way of properly caring for those happening to contract such while under our roof.

The facilities for caring for dispensary patients are inadequate in all departments, and especially so in that of the eye and ear.

(signed)
A. Vander Veer, M.D.
Henry Hun, M.D.
C.S. Merrill, M.D.

June 1st, 1896

1896 REPORT IN COMPARATIVE CONTEXT

This report is indeed lengthy but its full reproduction is warranted for it portrays a firsthand, expert, and unvarnished description of Albany Hospital nearing the turn of the century. While the picture is depressing, it could probably be descriptive of many other hospitals throughout the nation. It should not go unremembered that many of the everyday conveniences, that are now taken for granted, were not available or only in the homes of the wealthy. In 1900, most homes were illuminated by gas light and some by kerosene lamps. While running water was available in the City, many homes were still using outhouses —and toilets were toilets—not bathrooms. Hot water was a luxury and central heating far from universal.

On the other hand, farmers carrying their produce to market and streets frequented by horse-drawn carts and carriages would now seem quaint and attractive. Carbon monoxide fumes and automobile horns would in the future replace the odor of horse manure and cart drivers' angry exchanges. The language of frustrated motorists and truck drivers may have even deteriorated from that of draymen.

However, there is no evasion of the horrors that a verbal montage would depict of a hospital stay. Imagine being in a bed with the person next to oneself who is in the final throes of death, someone else banging a large bell to attract a tardy and ill-trained nurse, vermin crawling in the base boards, rats scurrying across the bed, patients subsisting on poorly prepared food, suffering the heat of the day and the cold of night. Add to this the possibility of contracting a contagious disease and removal to some place even worse. Fortunately, the patients were probably unaware that the foundation under one of the additions was threatening imminent collapse. No mention is made of visiting hours, but only a brave and devoted relative or friend would venture into such a place.

REACTION TO THE 1896 REPORT

Upon receipt of the report, the Board of Governors appointed a committee of three to meet with the signators of the report and reply to the Board at the earliest date possible. The joint committee of the three doctors and three Board members submitted a plan to raise the necessary funds via subscription and to obtain a site for the construction of buildings for a hospital and a training school for nurses.

On May 17, 1897, an act of the Legislature authorized the Board of Commissioners of Washington Park to deed to Albany Hospital the tract of land which it and the Medical College now occupy. The first to subscribe was Mr. James B. Jermain who contributed $10,000. The largest contribution was $25,000 given as a memorial to J. Townsend Lansing. Contributions came from the wealthy in thousand dollar

(Fig. 32) The entrance to the new Albany Hospital in 1899.

(Fig. 34) A private room, circa 1925. Note the brass bed and oriental rugs.

(Fig. 33) The Albany Hospital, 1916, showing four of the six pavilions.

amounts, from those less affluent in the hundreds, and from the least fortunate in $25, $10, $5 and even $2 contributions. Assuming that the person could afford no more, there is something genuinely poignant about that lowest gift.

The building committee was composed of James McCredie, Charles R. Knowles, Henry Hun, M.D., John G. Myers, Albert Vander Veer, M.D., and William J. Walker. After much research and consultation with other hospital officials throughout New York State and Pennsylvania, plans drawn by Albert W. Fuller were approved. Mr. Fuller donated his services and continued without payment to oversee the construction work.

NEW HOSPITAL OPENS

On June 23, 1898, the cornerstone of the Hospital was laid and less than one year later on May 1, 1899, the transfer of patients from the old hospital was undertaken *(Figure 32)*. The financial burden of erecting the building was such that the furnishings from the old hospital were transferred to the new hospital. We may assume that the furnishings were cleaned so that the vermin were not also relocated with the patients and medical staff.

The new hospital was 416 feet in length and each of the six pavilions was two stories in height *(Figure 33)*. The structure was functional both in appearance and design. The "pavilion" design provided proper ventilation and the admission of some sunlight to all patient areas. The hospital had the capacity for 100 "free" patients and 85 who were private or "paying" patients. Some of the private rooms were furnished with fireplaces which were intended for ventilation and ornamentation. The entire hospital had a central heating system. Not all of the private rooms had private toilet facilities *(Figure 34)*. Each of the front four pavilions had solaria measuring 9 by 20 feet. Food was prepared in a central basement kitchen and carried to the pavilions via dumb waiters. At that point, the food was placed on steam tables located in the pavilion. A description of the hospital appeared in the *Times Union* in 1899. The last sentence in the piece referring to the rooms containing the steam tables stated: "All kinds of convenient cooking arrangements will be found here, so that any time a patient craves a dainty, it is likely to be found in this room and may be served at short notice." *(Figure 35)* A week's board at the hospital cost the patient $5.00—presumably dainties included.

During the week of December 11, 1899, a group of ladies conducted a bazaar to provide funds for new furnishings. Whether is was a "white elephant" sale or something of a more pretentious nature is not recorded. As the Mayor of the City, the Hon. Thomas J. Van Alstyne, delivered the opening address for the bazaar, we may conclude that it

(Fig. 35) The Diet Kitchen in 1899.

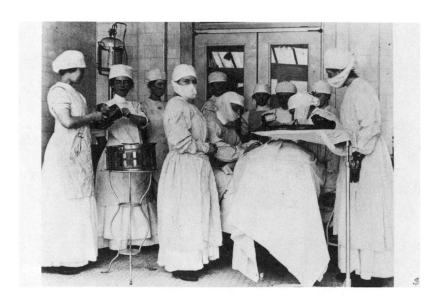

(Fig. 36) A 1910 view of the Operating Room.

was of an imposing and decorous nature. The effort of the ladies prompted others to donate funds for the further furnishing of wards and private rooms. It is significant to note that in contrast to present times the only contribution of local, state or federal government was the site for the buildings. Approximately 86 tablets were inscribed and located throughout the hospital to identify those who donated funds for specific parts of the building and furnishing. As "Big Daddy" government was still many years away, the complete finishing of the hospital and nurses' residences was contributed by private donors. Gifts were made for landscaping the grounds, providing screens for the windows, paving the basement floor, painting hallways and operating amphitheatre, and the care of the indigent patients *(Figure 36)*.

HOSPITAL STATISTICS 1896-1914

The goal of present day building fund drives, whether for a school, hospital, or museum, are normally established in the millions of dollars. It is, therefore, interesting to review a listing of the estimated investments in Albany Hospital in 1914. The following figures are estimated total costs as of October 1 of that year and the accuracy can be judged by the listing of costs to the penny.

Hospital building	$250,493.90
Furniture and furnishings	49,554.28
Improvement of grounds	15,551.95
Ambulance house	12,857.94
Furnishing ambulance house	500.00
Tuberculosis camp	75,000.00
Nurses' home	166,000.00
Total	$569,958.07

Not included is the value of the land which was granted by the City, nor the costs of Pavilions F and G which were built by the City subsequent to the building erected in 1899.

The need for the new hospital is proven by a record of the number of cases treated in the Albany Hospital for the years 1896 through 1907 with the exception of 1898-99.

1896-97	1245
1900-01	2023
1901-02	2279
1902-03	2586
1903-04	2630
1904-05	2903
1905-06	2886
1906-07	4120

The following figures are available for the cost of operating the Hospital for the years 1898-99 through 1913-14 with the exceptions of 1899-1900 through 1903-04. The years 1898-99 through 1909-10 are "about" but for the later period are exact to that intriguing penny.

1898-99	$ 40,000.00
1904-05	114,000.00
1905-06	125,000.00
1906-07	126,000.00
1907-08	143,000.00
1908-09	139,000.00
1909-10	160,432.02
1910-11	181,154.02
1911-12	230,083.90
1912-13	217,425.38
1913-14	231,122.07

The income to meet the expenses came from six sources. They were:

1. The City of Albany, which until 1908 annually contributed $8,000 for the care of the indigent. This figure was based on an estimated cost of $8.00 per week per patient. At times, the deficit to the Hospital amounted to as much as $7,000 per year. In 1908, a more equitable arrangement was made through the City Department of Charities.

2. Albany County appropriated a fund each year for care of patients in Pavilion F and G.

3. The State of New York and various cities and towns contributed for the care of employees and inhabitants of their communities.

4. Payment by patients who could afford to pay for their care.

5. Income from endowment fund.

6. Annual appeal.

The endowment fund grew from $75,000 in 1898 to $452,426.43 in 1914. Paying patients contributed approximately $25,000 in 1898 and $142,311.34 in 1914.

AMBULANCE PROBLEMS

An interesting and, in retrospect, humorous side story to the move from the old to the new hospital concerns the ambulance which served the Hospital. When the Hospital was located on Eagle Street, the ambulance team of horses and the driver were all housed in an adjacent building. On the new location, no immediate provision was made for housing the ambulance, which remained at Eagle Street *(Figure 37)*. This presented a serious problem. When a call for the ambulance came in, the driver and conveyance had first to go from Eagle Street to the Hospital to get a doctor who would accompany it on its errand of mercy. Even at a lively trot, a considerable amount of time was lost. This rather tedious routine existed for some time because of a lack of funds to construct the stable, carriage house and accommodation for the driver. Finally, a Mr. Walter L. Lawrence of New York together with Mr. William H. Weaver, one of the Governors, contributed funds to erect the necessary buildings. It would be interesting to know how Mr.

(Fig. 37)
One of Albany Hospital's "fleet" of horse drawn ambulances.

(Fig. 38)
The Hospital's first motorized ambulances.

Lawrence in New York City learned of this problem in Albany. A record in the archives of the Medical College records the following as a conclusion to the episode. "When Mr. Lawrence's liberal contribution was made, Mr. Weaver exclaimed, 'There is no doubt of our success. I see a way clear to carrying it through to completion.' Before the work was done, however, his fatal illness came on, and just what he had in mind we do not know." One can only wonder in bewilderment of his statement exactly what, indeed, Mr. Weaver did have in mind.

In the first decade of the 20th Century, the horse drawn ambulances were replaced with motor driven vehicles *(Figure 38)*. In 1923, the then ultimate in ambulance accommodations were provided by the Hospital with the acquisition of the most luxurious ambulance of the time. It cost $7,077 and the interior is described as being furnished with black walnut wood. The patient had the choice of sitting upright, reclining or lying prone. A stretcher could be suspended from the ceiling in an emergency to accommodate a second patient. The ambulance provided three seats for nurses and doctors. Included in the equipment was a thermos bottle, an electric fan and two cabinets for emergency equipment.

FEAR OF CONTAGION

It is difficult now to appreciate the great fear which accompanied contagious diseases as recently as the early twentieth century. Those with contagious diseases were feared almost as lepers. In 1901, the "Conditions of Admissions" to the Hospital were, "All diseases are treated but those of a chronic, incurable, contagious or infectious character." This excluded a great number of sick people. So great was the fear of contagion that, in 1906, a special ambulance was purchased by the Hospital for the transportation of persons with a contagious disease. As a further precaution, a separate building was provided to house the vehicle distinct from that used for the other ambulance. That same year, 1906, a special pavilion, now called the Hun Memorial, was funded and built by the City for the treatment of persons with contagious diseases *(Figure 39)*. Prior to that there was no other provision in the City for hospital treatment of those suffering from erysipelas, measles, scarlet fever, chicken pox, and diphtheria. Persons suffering from smallpox or pulmonary tuberculosis were not admitted to the pavilion for contagious diseases. The former cases were taken to a separate building elsewhere in the City. It is impossible to establish the exact year, but sometime between 1900 and 1910 there was an outbreak of tuberculosis in the area. So dread was the disease that those afflicted were not admitted to the Hospital but were cared for in tents erected on the grounds *(Figure 40)*. The difficulty attendant with such a provision motivated the City to underwrite the cost of providing

Left: (Fig. 42) The open air wing of the Tuberculosis Sanitorium.

Middle: (Fig. 39) The Hun Memorial Contagious Disease Pavilion, circa 1925, before the enclosed porches were added.

Bottom: (Figs. 40 & 41) This 1931 montage shows the Red Cross tent colony (est. 1909) for the care of tuberculosis patients (top) and the Albany County Tuberculosis Sanitorium off Western Avenue (bottom).

better facilities for the treatment of tuberculous patients until they could be transferred to a sanatorium. Many patients were cared for at the Western Avenue Tuberculosis Sanatorium established and staffed by the Albany County Health Department and the Albany Hospital and Medical School *(Figures 41 and 42)*. Containment of tuberculosis was understood but the treatment was prolonged often requiring months or years of sanatorium care. Dr. William E. Lawson was the first Director of the Western Avenue Sanatorium, succeeded by Dr. Reuben Erickson.

DEPARTMENT FOR MENTAL ILLNESS, PAVILION F

Demonstrating a sincere sensitivity for the patient, Pavilion F was the identification used for the pavilion added to Albany Hospital in 1902 for the care of patients suffering from mental illness. The stigma associated with mental illness and commitment for treatment frequently marked the individual and even his family for life. Therefore, if a person was committed to Pavilion F, it had a lesser effect on his life than had he or she been committed to an insane asylum.

The State at the time maintained three institutions which, for practical purposes, amounted to incarceration for persons suffering from any of the wide variety of mental afflictions. The trauma of being transported to such institutions completely removed from friends and familiar environment may have thrust the sufferer deeper into the abyss of his affliction. As the institutions were in most cases a day's travel time from the patient, it was common practice to jail the patient pending commitment procedure required by law, it being assumed that the patient could not or would not submit to voluntary commitment. The routine, though humane and necessary, would be unsettling even to one who was completely rational. One gathers that once committed to a mental institution, it required some doing to gain release.

Dr. J. Montgomery Mosher *(Figure 43)* was a specialist in Mental Diseases and he perceived the need for a "half-way house" where mental cases could be cared for, where a cure could be effected for less serious cases and temporary care afforded those serious or incurable cases. He reasoned that if a person suffering appendicitis or pneumonia had to undergo the delays inherent in the commitment procedures, he would probably be dead before treatment was begun. Why not afford those suffering mental disorder the same compassionate care as those suffering physical ills. As a result of his efforts, the Supervisors of Albany County agreed to underwrite the cost of adding to Albany Hospital a pavilion for the treatment of persons suffering from mental disorders. This was one of two pavilions referred to earlier as having been erected by the City, the other being for the care of certain contagious diseases. The pavilion was similar to those which already

(Fig. 43)
Dr. J. Montgomery Mosher

comprised the Hospital, being of brick construction and two stories high. The patient capacity of Pavilion F was thirty-three beds, seventeen on the first floor for women and sixteen on the second for men. Four beds on each floor were located in a dormitory and the remainder in separate rooms. Each room had a window and was comfortably, if simply, furnished. Each floor had a day room which was 16 feet by 36 feet and pleasantly furnished, not unlike a lobby in a small hotel of the time. Four rooms on each floor were reserved for violent patients who had to be separated from others.

In contrast to modern psychiatric hospitals, the foregoing might not be impressive until one realizes that this was the first of its kind in the world. As a result, it created great interest and requests for information concerning it came from all quarters of medical society both in this country and abroad. So unique was the concept that the State Commission on Lunacy requested an exhibit of the interior view of the pavilion and its history for display at the St. Louis Exposition. Albany Hospital had progressed a longer way than the approximate linear mile from its old location in a few years.

A few statistics will afford a better understanding of the new facility. During the first two years, 331 patients were treated; of those, 194 were women and 137 men. One hundred and eight recovered and were discharged. In 96 cases improvement was made and 88 were reported unimproved. Those who remained unimproved after a period of treatment or who had been incurable were then taken to a State institution. During the two years, 14 patients died.

The income for the first two years totalled $6,148.89, of which approximately a third was received for the care of public patients and the balance for private patients. The average income from each patient per week was $10.68. The $10.68 had to cover the expense of board, room and treatment—a figure worthy of repetition and food for thought.

Again, as in the furnishing of the Hospital in 1849, the archives contain a list of gifts from appreciative people of the City. The long list includes such things as chairs, rugs, window curtains, books, magazines, and most poignantly, a soft pillow. A Mrs. McCarthy donated $500 which was the initial contribution to a much needed endowment fund to sustain the new institution.

In the first two years, persons suffering from 28 different forms of disease were treated in Pavilion F. Acute alcoholic delirium was equalled by melancholia as the most common problem, there being 63 cases of each. Drunkeness was well up on the scale, there being 25 cases. Of this affliction, 15 were reported as recovered, 8 improved, 1 unimproved, and no deaths. Therein lies a subtle message. Drug addiction was making its insidious entry with four cases. Persons suffering from epilepsy and ptomaine poisoning were also listed in the forms of disease treated in the Department of Mental Disease. Perhaps an epileptic in the throes of a seizure or one suffering from ptomaine poisioning and the accompanying convulsive vomiting was thought to be temporarily void of his senses.

As witnessed by numerous criminal trials, when a plea of insanity is made in behalf of the accused and affirmed by competent psychiatrists, the State may present equally qualified testimony that the defendant is sane. The final, frequently difficult, decision of the defendant's sanity must be made by the jury. One can only conclude that at times the line between the sane and insane is thin and wavering and demarcation is disputable even with today's advanced learning in the field of psychiatry. To avoid such decisions, the Hospital declined a charter by which it would be an asylum for the insane. This avoided the necessity of the officers of the Hospital making decisions concerning the presence of insanity. The only patients accepted were those committed by the courts, or those who voluntarily sought help. Those who came voluntarily were always free to leave at their own discretion. Examples of the situations avoided by this procedure for admission to Pavilion F is detailed in the "Second Report of Pavilion F, Department of Mental Diseases, for the Year Ending February 29, 1904." It reads as follows: "Husbands with quarrelsome wives, wives with intemperate husbands, children with degenerate parents, parents with disobedient children have applied for relief from their burden." Wise indeed were the heads which guided the Hospital to avoid having to intervene in such disputes.

In the early 1900s, some of the gentle sex were still given to swooning when confronted with a distressing situation. It is, therefore, surprising that female nurses were in attendance in Pavilion F for all cases. Women did provide nursing in mental institutions but were not in charge of all types of cases especially the male section and violent cases. All nurses in training were required, as a part of the instruction, to work several weeks in Pavilion F before receiving their diplomas. Pavilion F afforded students of Albany Medical College an opportunity to observe the variety of mental diseases. On Monday of each week, sections of the senior class attended the Pavilion. After their observation of the patients, classroom discussion took place. The students were thereby afforded an opportunity to observe and discuss the progress of the patients over a period of several weeks.

DR. THOMAS WILLIAM SALMON

Thomas William Salmon was the son of Thomas Henry Salmon, a general practitioner, and his English wife, Annie Frost. He was born in Lansingburgh, New York, on January 6, 1876.

By 1890, when Thomas William Salmon was fourteen years old, the family existed in straitened circumstances, and none enjoyed robust health. Dr. Thomas Henry Salmon was over-worked and worried by debt. He could not devote to his family the time they deserved and he wished to give them. This pattern was one that, in later years, also beset his son.

Thomas William had been undecided about choosing a career, but after teaching school for a short time, he entered Albany Medical College in 1895. At that time, and until 1934, the College required only a high school diploma for admission. In later years, Salmon regretted that he had been unable to afford an academic college degree. Its lack sometimes made his contacts with more formally educated colleagues a bit prickly.

Because of his health, in 1896, Salmon left medical school for a year, and travelled to England. He returned to be graduated in 1899. He had been much influenced by his teachers, Doctors Hun, Mosher, Archambault and Blumer, and because of his skill in drawing, he had helped to illustrate Dr. Hermon Gordinier's *Anatomy of the Central Nervous System.* His special interests lay with bacteriology and psychiatry, departments in which Albany Medical College was ahead of the times.

In 1900, having persuaded Helen Ashly, a schoolmate of his academy days, to marry him, Salmon set up medical practice in Brewster, New York. But the venture was of short duration, for he developed tuberculosis and went for a long time to recuperate in the Adirondacks.

Shortly thereafter, he was asked to investigate an epidemic of diphtheria at the Willard State Hospital for the Insane. His experience there stimulated his previous interest in the condition of the mentally ill. In 1903, Salmon entered the United States Public Health Service and expanded his concern with psychiatry because of his contacts with immigrants at Ellis Island. Then, in 1912, he became the first medical director of the National Committee for Mental Health.

For many years he continued to work for the Committee which was much helped by the Rockefeller Foundation. His service continued after his return from France where, from 1917 to 1919, he held the post of Director and Consultant for Psychiatry in the American Expeditionary Force.

His base hospital at Neufchateau deserved its fame. It always remained under-staffed, though Salmon complained bitterly to powers in Washington. However, he was aware that in 1917, there were only 150 well-trained neurologists in the United States.

An American woman wrote from Paris to a friend that Dr. Salmon,

> the first psychiatrist honored in any army, would hold sessions with soldiers who had retreated out of fear—sit up all night with any one individual soldier, three people being present—himself, the Devil, and the soldier—and win out over the Devil. Dr. Salmon and Dr. Alfred E. Cohen of the Rockefeller Institute for Medical Research, had noticed a nervous heart disease which proved curable, as it was not organic...I did not yet know Dr. Salmon, but his reputation proved him one of our great war leaders. (Elizabeth Shepley Sargent, Willa Cather, a Memoir. N.Y. Lippincott, 1952, p.156)

Dr. Salmon's skill in helping patients apparently was rooted in what Dr. Edward A. Strecker described as his "visualization of the emotional conflict underlying war-conversion hysteria," the instinct for self-preservation versus the requirements of "soldierly ideals" of discipline and patriotism. Dr. Salmon's concept "was so dynamic and stimulating that it served as a beacon light to every psychiatrist in France." Dr. Salmon had something more than formal psychiatry. His practical humanism and ideals of service provided the ways and means to meet complex situations. (Bond, p.111 *Thomas W. Salmon, Psychiatrist.* N.Y. Norton, 1950)

Letters to his wife disclose some of the problems that Dr. Salmon faced in France. In January 1918, he wrote:

> I have to fight to get the mental cases what they need. Invariably, they are overlooked or forgotten in planning new things, unless I bring them to attention. What a pleasure it must be to be a surgeon, a sanitarian or an internist, and not to have to keep making the point that your patients are sick people. (Bond p.126)

In March he complained:

> One thing that depresses me is that no one takes an interest in my work. The surgeons have so much in common that I can't help feeling out of things. What folks do for my patients they do for me personally. I get tired of being grateful for things that are due to soldiers who

> *came in good faith to fight in spite of their neuropathic handicaps. . .*
> *It's lonesome to be working in a field that is so far off in a corner by*
> *itself. If my patients only had leg ulcers, I could get everything for*
> *them.*

Ruefully he wrote in August, 1918:

> *Folks don't like my patients, and sometimes I don't like them myself.*
> *Shell-shockers are pretty unattractive compared to the cheerful,*
> *patient, wounded. (Bond p. 139)*

The day after the Armistice, Dr. Salmon wrote:

> *I met Dr. Lipes of Albany, a Major, going home wounded. He was*
> *happy to go—full of his experiences as a medical officer in the Field*
> *Artillery, and in his contempt of all officers who served behind the*
> *lines and got to be Colonels. I tried to explain that I sometimes at*
> *least went near the back of the front, but he wouldn't listen, and I*
> *don't blame him.*

Dr. Salmon's concern for the individual patient is evident in a letter of
January 17, 1919, which holds no touch of humor:

> *I wonder what there is in organized medical work that dries up*
> *human sympathy and makes doctors deal with sick people as if they*
> *were criminals. I think ours must be a frightfully individualistic*
> *profession and that the relationship of doctor and patient ceases as*
> *soon as the doctor gains offical authority over the patient.* We must
> *teach social medicine in the schools, and we* must *make the military*
> *medical services maintain civil control the same tendency is just as*
> *marked in the State Hospital Service, so it must* depend *upon*
> *something inherent in treating patients as groups. (Bond p. 152)*

When Dr. Salmon returned from France, he continued his concern
for soldiers. A spokesman for the American Legion considered him
"the greatest single factor in getting help for disabled veterans, whether
the need were tuberculosis, mental diseases, or other conditions." In
December, 1929, 5,500 ex-service men were in neuropsychiatric wards,
and only one-third were in government-owned hospitals.

It is no surpise that a man of Dr. Salmon's imaginative quality could
obtain no help from President Harding who would have been incapable
of appreciating these words from Salmon's essay on leisure:

> *Without phantasy the world would be intolerable. The world of*
> *childhood with its terrific limitations could not possibly be supported*
> *unless those limitations could be bridged by this heaven-sent mecha-*
> *nism of phantasy. Old age would be intolerable unless phantasy*
> *persisted. . .In phantasy, the weak are strong, the lonely have friends,*
> *the poor are rich, the mortal, immortal. (Bond pps.188-189)*

Dr. Bernard Glueck said that Dr. Salmon's concern with the
psychopathology of crime laid the foundation for the child guidance
movement. (Bond p.196) In this connection, Dr. Salmon commented:

> *It was in the children's court that the earliest studies of the emotional*
> *states of children began. It was with irrational people that irrational*
> *thinking came under scientific observation. But it is no longer neces-*
> *sary for a child to get arrested, or a mental patient to be committed to*

THOMAS WILLIAM SALMON M D
1876 – 1927

DISTINGUISHED LEADER IN MENTAL HYGIENE
CHIEF OF PSYCHIATRIC DIVISION OF THE U.S. ARMY IN
THE WORLD WAR WISE EDUCATOR AND BELOVED PHYSICIAN
CLASS OF 1899 – ALBANY MEDICAL COLLEGE

(Fig. 44)
A bronze bas-relief honoring
Dr. Thomas William Salmon.

have his emotional difficulties treated. (Bond p.197)

When in 1927, Dr. Salmon accepted the post of Professor of Psychiatry at Columbia University, only thirty of the 4,000 hours devoted to the study of medicine were allotted to psychiatry, and those were crowded into the fourth year. Dr. Salmon was popular with students, and so persuasive that the administrators of the medical school increased the number of hours available to him. His was the first suggestion that New York State's Psychiatric Institute for teaching, treatment and research be established on a site in the Columbia Medical Center. Its cornerstone was laid in 1927, after Dr. Salmon had died, and it was dedicated in 1929.

Speaking in 1934 when a bas-relief of Salmon *(Figure 44)* by Charles Keck was unveiled at the Institute, Dean Darroch paid this tribute:

> *What he accomplished was to make those of us who are working in other fields realize that we could not solve our problems without the help of his group.*
> *Whether we are trying to repair injuries, cure or alleviate diseases, or avoid their appearance or development, we must consider and handle the mental problems of each individual. . .Before his era, we in surgery and medicine thought of psychiatry in terms of the terminal stages requiring segregation. He made us conscious of the necessity of considering and helping the mental aspect of every patient who is entrusted to our care. (Bond p.204)*

Dr. Salmon thought that the year he spent as President of the American Psychiatric Association was one of the happiest in his life.

(Fig. 45)
Dr. D. Ewan Cameron

Under his guidance, the Association's Committee on Standards and Policies presented a set of rules for conducting a good mental hospital. The rules set forth in 1923-24 are still valid. They postulated an experienced psychiatrist at the head of the hospital; one doctor for every 150 resident patients; one nurse for every eight patients; intensive treatment units; no politics.

Dr. Salmon's untimely, accidental death in August, 1927, prevented his participation in the rapid development of psychiatric practice in the third decade of this century. But his memory is kept alive by the annual lectures given in his honor at the New York Academy of Medicine, and by the *Cinderella Story* which, just as he wrote it, describes the condition of psychiatry in his time.

DR. D. EWAN CAMERON

Subsequent to Dr. Mosher's innovations, psychiatry made notable advances through the work of Freud and Jung, and European researchers and sanatoria provided much of what was discovered and developed in that field. However, as recently as 1938, the now individual fields of neurology and psychiatry were coupled and recognized as one specialty. The basis for the coupling was that all mental disturbances originated in the brain.

It was at that time, 1938, that Dr. D. Ewan Cameron, a native of Scotland, was appointed Professor of Neurology and Psychiatry at Albany Medical College. Dr. Cameron had graduated from Glasgow Medical College in 1924 *(Figure 45)*. After graduation, he continued his studies in Zurich, Switzerland, then one of the foremost centers for research in neurology and psychiatry. He then came to the United States where he contined his work and research. His next move was again out of the United States, but this time to Canada where he joined the staff of Provincial Mental Hospital in Brandon, Manitoba. After serving there, he returned to the United States joining the staff of Worcester State Hospital at Worcester, Massachusetts.

In 1938, fourteen years after graduation from Glasgow, he was appointed to his position in Albany Medical College and remained there until 1943. During that period in the United States, he became a citizen of this Nation. Five years after coming to Albany Medical College, Dr. Cameron again moved, this time back to Canada where he joined the staff of McGill University in its School of Medicine. While there, he devoted his work to researching the possibility of restoring memory to the aged. He first worked with ribonucleic acid and later with Cylert. At the time both seemed to offer promise to restore memory to the senile.

Twenty-one years later, Dr. Cameron resigned from his position of Professor of Psychiatry and Head of the Department at McGill. He then came to Albany for a second time. He had not relinquished his United States citizenship during this period and having developed a fondness for the mountainous region of upper New York State, had maintained a home in the vicinity of Lake Placid.

On return to Albany, he was appointed by the United States Veterans' Administration to direct the psychiatric laboratory research of the aging at the Veterans' Hospital in Albany. He was also appointed Professor of Psychiatry at Albany Medical College, where he served until his death.

One of his notable achievement was the establishment of a half-way house or out-patient clinic for the mentally ill. Persons so afflicted could come to the clinic for daily treatment, returning to their homes after treatment. This was a new concept which has since become an accepted routine for the less seriously affected.

While at McGill, in 1961, he was elected first President of the World Psychiatric Association for a six-year term by its 3,000 representatives. During the Nuremburg Trials, he was one of the psychiatrists appointed to examine Rudolf Hess and other Nazi war criminals. The Schaffer Library now contains 43 papers published by Dr. Cameron, some of which were in association with others. This is testimony of his research efforts and willingness to share his findings with others.

On September 7, 1967, while climbing one of the Adirondack Mountains in company with his son, he was suddenly stricken with heart failure and died on the mountain. The years of work had taken their toll. It was impossible to bring his body down the mountain until first light of the next day. Members of his family stood vigil beside him through the night as did the eternal mountains.

FUND RAISING AND COMMUNITY SUPPORT

It is interesting that the Hospital could raise the funds through public donations to build an entirely new structure but then for the next forty years operate on a hand-to-mouth budget. The Albany Hospital Board of Governors, beginning in 1902, annually issue a booklet entitled "Annual Report and Appeal." The purpose, as the title states, was to report on their stewardship of the Hospital and to appeal for financial support. The reports included a listing of donors and the amount contributed by each during the previous year. Taking the report issued in 1916 as a typical example, the largest single contribution, of which there were two, was $500. One of the two was given by Dudley Olcott who had contributed generously on other occasions and would continue to do so until his death. The other $500 contribution was made by the German Hospital Association. This was in 1916, two years after the Germans had started to ravage Europe and at a time when it was not prudent to emphasize one's German ancestry in the United States. That same year, the smallest donation was one of $2.00. The total amount raised by the appeal of 1915 was $6,979.61. The $.61 was part of the $37.61 contributed by the E.L. Patch Company. The odd amount suggests that the contribution resulted from a collection within the Company. Included in the report is an amazingly detailed report of articles donated by individuals and organizations. Included in the listing are a wide variety of articles ranging from a new piano to articles of clothing, flowers, magazines, fruits, blankets, and fancy cakes for children. The gift of fresh fruit and other food stuffs to a hospital seems strange. Yet, at that time and for several years thereafter, the Hospital maintained a farm to supply fresh vegetables and even raised pigs on the grounds of the Tuberculosis Pavilion on Western Avenue. Much of the food for the pigs came from Hospital garbage. Surplus fresh vegetables from the Hospital farm were preserved by the Hospital kitchens for use during the year. In 1901, 600 cans of fresh fruit were "put up" (preserved).

Despite the receipts from the annual appeals and measures toward self-sufficiency, the Hospital in 1916 had a debt totalling $79,163.88. Each year the Hospital expenses substantially exceeded the income received from paying patients. Albany and adjacent communities sent charity cases to the Hospital and paid only $7.00 per week toward the cost of their maintenance and care in the Hospital.

In 1916, the total amount of disbursements was $191,820. Of this, the largest single expense was $60,562 for provisions. Salaries and wages cost the Hospital $30,155. In addition, nurses' salaries were $16,027. Heating and lighting the Hospital cost $17,258 for the year. Approximately $1,000 more than the $16,214 paid for medical and surgical supplies.

On the subject of heating, in 1909, the Hospital used 88 tons of stove coal and 2868 tons of boiler coal. An interesting sidelight on the requirement for burning coal was the sheer logistic problem presented by approximately 3000 tons of coal and the ash residue. Some ten years later, the report of the Hospital Visitors was critical of the procedure for moving the coal and removing the ashes as excessively expensive. One man was employed to move the mountain of coal to the boilers and remove the "clinkers" after burning. He was paid $25 per month in addition to his board. The report of the Visitors recommended that a mechanical system be installed to replace the $25-per-month-and-board employee. He must have had a prodigious appetite to financially justify his replacement with a machine. Not including his board, the man moved the coal for $.10 a ton. The calculation allows no payment for shoveling and carting out the ashes.

The continual insolvency of the Hospital was certainly not the result of wasteful expenditures. The Visiting Committee maintained a vigilant eye on the smallest detail. One report recommended that all garbage be weighed before removal to the pig farm. The weight would determine the amount of wasted food being generated. Very little if anything was wasted. Not only did the pigs dine on the garbage from the Tuberculosis Sanitorium, but the Hospital received $175 in 1909 as payment for the garbage contract. Presumably, this was the garbage removed from the Hospital by the pig farmer. In the Visiting Committee's report of 1919, the Committee visited the piggery and reported that there was "a fine lot of pigs and adult hogs about 400." The use of pork in the Hospital kitchen was considerable— 100 pounds of ham having been served for each breakfast. Ironically, in consideration of the supply of fresh vegetables from the farm, pork from the piggery and preserves from the pantry shelves, the Hospital staff was not provided with sumptuous meals. In 1908, the *Albany Telegram Newspaper* reported a "first" and to date "last" happening in Albany Hospital. The initial incident was the protest lodged by eight interns concerning the quality of meals provided to them by the Hospital. They complained, contending that they were fed "old potatoes" and salmon two and three times a day. "Old potatoes" could have been a typographical error for "cold potatoes." Today, salmon, even in canned form, is a delicacy—at that time, salmon was an inexpensive substitute for meat and pink salmon considered by many only fit for cat food. Whatever the case, old or cold potatoes and salmon two or three times a day does sound unappetizing. After the protest, the meals improved for several months.

However, the improvement was only temporary and the interns planned another expression of dissatisfaction. Before the protest, another incident resulted in the dismissal of eight interns. One of the interns, after a late night on duty, was called in to accompany a patient from the Hospital to the Tuberculosis Sanitorium. As the patient was being placed in the ambulance, the Superintendent happened on the scene. He told the intern to remove the patient from the ambulance and transport him in an "auto truck" which was used to transport refuse—again the spectre of contagion. The intern refused and the Superintendent dismissed him immediately. When the seven remaining interns learned of the dismissal of their associate, they submitted their resignations to be effective at ten days interval. But before the resignations were submitted, the Board of Governors met and dismissed the remaining seven interns. The first "labor problem" was thereby handled with great dispatch—no arbitration, everyone fired.

Dietary habits were quite different at that time from the modern concept of almost antiseptically clean surroundings and the preparation of fresh, refrigerated, or frozen foods. In 1919, a member of the Visiting Committee, while inspecting the kitchen in the Tuberculosis Sanitorium, suspected that the eggs being cooked in a large pan had been in cold storage longer than 6 months. Upon questioning, the chef reported that he "got on with them very well." Earlier, the Visiting Committee had noticed some flies in the kitchen but seemed satisfied that the situation was being controlled by the use of "fly paper" and "watch screens." Again the attitude or degree of sanitary practice is reflected by the suggestion of the Visiting Committee that a metal lined room be used to store flour and cereals in such a way that would prevent mice and rats from getting at the food stuff. How did the Committee know that rodents had access to the flour and cereal? It was reassuring to read that in the next inspection report, a rodent-proof storage room had been constructed.

At the same time, certain amenities and comforts were available that are no longer provided. Ambulatory patients and others who could be moved in wheel chairs were taken out to the lawns of the Hospital in good weather so that they could enjoy fresh air, sunshine, and a pleasant change from hospital atmosphere. Consideration was given to the provision of pleasant and comfortable accommodations for visitors also. With the addition of the new section in 1925, the lobby was furnished with comfortable chairs and earlier the solarium was furnished as a place where ambulatory patients and those in wheel chairs could visit. In 1922, three rooms were furnished with beds, reading lamps and easy chairs so that friends and relatives of those gravely ill might stay nearby during the night. Those rooms were seldom unoccupied.

Reformation
of
Albany
Medical
College — 1915

DR. THOMAS ORDWAY APPOINTED DEAN

In 1915, Dr. Thomas Ordway was appointed Dean and given free rein to reorganize Albany Medical College. One of his first acts was to request the removal of the elephant skeleton from the anatomical museum, reasoning that its continued exhibition served no useful purpose.

If the elephant's skeleton was disposed of directly, it would provide an indication of the decisive action that was required in subsequent years to bring Albany Medical College to the forefront of medical education. But this was not the case. First an elephant's skeleton, because of its size, is not the sort of thing that can be summarily disposed of with the week's accumulation of trash. Secondly elephants' skeletons are not the type to be found in everyone's closet and the Board of Trustees had long ago evidenced a fondness for this huge arrangement of calcium and wire. And, as the disposition of the skeleton was subject to a final decision by the Board, it was not removed immediately. A board, whether of trustees or directors, is really a committee of sorts. Committees are never guilty of reaching a conclusion hastily, preferring, instead, to table the matter for the time or to delegate the subject to a subcommittee for further study and submission of a complete report on the matter. The subcommittee, being an offspring of the full committee, is genetically subject to the same slothlike approach to decision-making as the parent. As a result, the skeleton continued to dominate the anatomical museum until 1916 when by a piece of good fortune, Cornell University learned of its availability and expressed a desire to possess the specimen. It was removed to the cellar of the school and prepared for shipment. On January 10, 1917, Dr. Ordway advised the Board of Trustees that the skeleton was out of Albany Medical College's "closet" and in residence at Cornell, the shipment having been paid for by the new owners. It would be interesting to know if it still stands somewhere or if it has been laid away to peaceful rest.

CALVIN EDISON AND COMPANY

At least one exhibit was removed from the medical museum with less formality than that of the elephant's remains. The story of the rather extraordinary exhibit was told in the September 20, 1926 issue of the *Albany Times Union* by the columnist Edgar S. Van Olinda. A Mr. Calvin Edison, a resident of Albany, though of normal height and stature, weighed but 60 pounds, and in his prime was said to have weighed only 48 pounds. To provide a legacy for his wife after his death, Mr. Edison bequeathed his rather unusual body to the Albany Medical College for an agreed upon sum to be paid to his widow at the time of his death. When in the normal course of events Mr. Edison died, his body was transferred to the Medical College where it was embalmed and placed in a glass case for display in the museum. It is a matter for lengthy conjecture as to what the medical students were to learn by gazing at the mortal remains of Mr. Edison except for the need to recommend a nutritious diet for their future patients. Mr. Van Olinda some years later learned of the existence of the unusual exhibit and arriving at the museum to view it, was told that it was no longer in existence. It was explained that student interest had fallen off and no longer were students studying the exhibit or even glancing at it. One day without ceremony, the remains were taken to the rear of the College and cremated with benefit of the high combustibility of the embalming material used. No dates of any of these events were recorded in the Van Olinda article and one must assume the dates to be early.

A second Van Olinda column, again without dates or specifics, told of a prank worked by two medical students. One night, as the story goes, the students removed a cadaver from the tank in the basement of the Medical College. They clothed the cadaver and proceeded to convey it to a local tavern which, in those days, would have been called a saloon. Supporting the cadaver between them, the students entered, sat at the bar and ordered a round of drinks. After several succeeding rounds, none of which was paid for, the students departed, presumably refreshed, to resume their studies. The cadaver was left slumped over the bar. When, at closing time, the remaining "customer" had not changed his position or offered to pay for the drinks, the bartender poked him with the bung starter, a sizeable wooden mallet. The cadaverous customer fell from the stool to the floor. At that moment a patrolman entered the establishment; he examined the customer and immediately determining that he was deceased, he turned to the mallet bearing bartender for an explanation. The bartender, aghast at the turn of events, quickly explained the situation by stating that he had acted in self defense. Could this have been the origin of the term "to dig up an unusual news story."

DR. THOMAS ORDWAY

Of the six prior deans of Albany Medical College (Doctors March, McNaughton, Armsby, Hun, Vander Veer, and Tucker) none with the exception of Dr. March, the founder, can be reckoned to have had as profound an influence on the Albany Medical College as Dr. Thomas Ordway *(Figure 46)*. At the time that Dr. Ordway was appointed Dean by the Board of Trustees, the College was in serious condition and would undoubtedly have closed had not a sweeping reformation taken place.

Academically, the school had been practically condemned by the Flexner Report. And indeed, the Flexner Report, as later events proved, mistakenly predicted that the College would fail for several reasons, not the least of which was absence of necessity for its continuance. The physical plant was archaic and its associated facilities, such as the Albany Hospital and Bender Laboratory, were inconveniently located in other sections of the City. The annual income of the College was insufficient and reserve funds were non-existent to rectify the adverse conditions. The faculty was factionalized and in almost bitter contention with each other and with the Board of Trustees. It is difficult to imagine a less enviable position than that of Dean of Albany Medical College in 1915. The fact that Dr. Ordway was willing to accept the challenge gives testimony to his courageous and confident personality. That he insisted on having absolute freedom in the reformation of the College and a guarantee from the Board of Trustees for at least adequate funding for a specified period indicates the depth of his practical wisdom.

Dr. Ordway was born in Dorchester, Massachusetts in 1877. His father, Gilbert Francis Ordway, was a successful businessman and took his family from Dorchester to Lowell and finally to Boston in pursuit of his business interests. Coincidentally, Dr. Ordway's mother, Julia Maria Gilbert, had the same family name as her husband's first name— Gilbert. Thomas was one of five children born to Julia and Gilbert, two of whom, Thomas and Gilbert were boys, and three were girls; Julia,

(Fig. 46) Dr. Thomas Ordway

Mabel and Jessie. Julia and Mabel attended Tufts, the former becoming a teacher and the latter a doctor. Gilbert, Thomas and Jessie
attended Harvard University. Gilbert continued his studies, becoming
a lawyer and Jessie became a business woman in the insurance field.
One can only surmise but it seems likely that the patriarch must have
been financially successful because of the choice of his children's
colleges. However, in keeping with the puritan ethic all five young
Ordways were required to earn money to help with the expense of their
education. A sense for the frugal use of money was demonstrated by
Dr. Ordway during his administration at Albany Medical College when
he was able to save sufficient of the school's funds to equip the College
when it moved from Eagle Street in 1928 to its present site.

Thomas Ordway graduated from Harvard University in 1901 and
continued his education at Harvard Medical School from which he
graduated in 1905. While in medical school, he studied Pathology
under Dr. B. Mallory and may have thus developed his preference for
this field of medicine. Four years after graduation, having completed
his residency training under Dr. Henry Jackson and Dr. George Sears
of the first medical service at Harvard, Dr. Ordway came to Albany,
having the position of Director of the Bender Hygienic Laboratory. In

addition, Dr. Ordway was appointed Professor of Pathology and Bacteriology at Albany Medical College. At the time of his appointment to these important positions, the faculty of the College was not receptive to granting high posts to "outsiders." Dr. Ordway's credentials must have been impressive. He remained in Albany for just two years, leaving in 1911. As his accomplishments indicate, Dr. Ordway was primarily a scholarly person with strong opinions and a desire for academic excellence. His departure may have been due to these traits and an unwillingness to enter into the political maneuvering within the faculty at that time, and the lack of high academic standards of the College. Another reason may have been the challenge offered by his next position in which he became Physician-in-Charge at the Collis Huntington Memorial Hospital of the Cancer Commission of Harvard University. As if one assignment was insufficient to contain his energy, he also served as Lecturer in Pathology and Instructor in Medicine at Harvard Medical School from 1911 to 1915.

In 1915, a representative of the Board of Trustees approached Dr. Ordway with the offer of becoming Dean of Albany Medical College. There is no mention of other candidates having been considered for the position and it may be concluded that Dr. Ordway was the prime and only candidate considered and the search would have been extended only after his refusal. The desire of the Board of Trustees to appoint him is shown by their willingness to accede to his every condition. The selection committee figuratively pointed a finger to Dr. Ordway as their choice when the Board of Trustees stipulated that the next dean must not be an Albanian. Dr. Ordway was then a Bostonian. This stipulation automatically removed all the present members of the faculty from consideration.

Dr. Ordway remained an Albanian until his death in 1952 at the age of 75. During those 37 years, he served as Dean of the College until his retirement from that position in 1937. He was also Physician-in-Charge of Albany Hospital for the same period and served as Associate Professor of Medicine from 1915 to 1931, and Professor of Medicine from 1931 until his retirement as Dean in 1937. After retirement, he was appointed Professor Emeritus of Medicine and developed his practice in Albany until his death.

Prior to 1937, Dr. Ordway published prodigiously on a wide range of research and medical observation. His work covered cancer, leukemia, typhoid, radium therapy, x-ray therapy, cholesterol, diseases of the heart, diabetes, pernicious anemia, pneumonia and diphtheria. He wrote and lectured extensively on the subjects of the rural doctor and the administration of medical schools. He was investigating the subject of "fireproof wood," and intended to publish on that far afield subject. The wide range of subject matter on which he published is indicative of the scope of his mental capacity. It is also indicative of his attitude toward what he considered excessive specialization in the medical profession. There is a question as to whether this position was the father or offspring of his strong encouragement of rural medical practitioners. He believed that the rural doctor could successfully treat most of his patients' ailments. As abruptly as if a light switch was thrown, Dr. Ordway ceased publishing in 1937 when he resigned as Dean. His resignation was tendered to the Board of Trustees without any expressed rancor but the effect of the situation may have been an internal scar. After all, the man was human but the willingness to accept the unavoidable placed him above others who in similar situations spoke openly to the press regardless of the effect on the institution.

In retrospect, Dr. Ordway's life was filled with success. He had rescued a medical school then in dire straits, he was recognized as a medical authority on a wide range of subject matter, and he had a multitude to whom he had restored health and comfort. It is almost a prerequisite that the leader of an organization have a personality that enables mixing with his associates in professional and social situations. Dr. Ordway was not a social person and preferred a life of social privacy free of contention. One of his enjoyments was to ride his rather small black horse on the grounds of his summer home in Rensselaerville attired in a black derby, black habit, and black boots. The color selected was probably more in keeping with his personal taste than to match his horse. The horse, being small, tended to detract from Dr. Ordway's slight figure and the horse felt bigger carrying his diminutive rider: a fortuitous combination for rider and horse.

While Dr. Ordway avoided unnecessary conflicts and gave the impression of being passive and easily manipulated he could, when the occasion warranted, display fierce spirit and determination. One associate tells of traveling in a car with Dr. Ordway to a speaking engagement. The car was unexpectedly flagged down by two policemen, one of whom opened the car door and smilingly asked if the good doctor would buy four tickets to the Policeman's Ball. Dr. Ordway responded with unexpected fury both in his verbal and facial expression, "This is coercion, blackmail, remove your foot from the runningboard—drive on," he shouted to the chaffeur. The return trip was viewed by the associate with trepidation, but Dr. Ordway's reaction was effective—solicitations had ended for that day at least.

In contradiction of this side of his personality, another associate recalled that Dr. Ordway would listen passively to an opinion contrary to that which he held and then proceed as if he had never heard. Such an attitude is often more frustrating to others than an outright heated exchange and may have been the source of resentment toward him which grew and culminated in the unfortunate events in 1937 which closed out the academic portion of his life in controversy instead of the accolades that he richly deserved.

After his resignation, Dr. Ordway directed his attention to private practice and had his office and home at 160 South Lake Avenue in Albany. On his death, he was survived by his wife and son.

At the time that Dr. Ordway was quietly directing Albany Medical College and making every attempt to avoid contention and the limelight there was another prominent member of the faculty who was almost a direct opposite of the shy, retiring Dean—Dr. Arthur Wells Elting.

DR. ARTHUR WELLS ELTING

The dynamic energy that made Dr. Arthur Wells Elting a formidable figure among surgeons, teachers of medicine and amateur big game hunters carried him through seventy-six years of tempestuous existence from his birth on October 6, 1872, at South Cairo, New York, where his parents lived on a farm, to his death on January 2, 1948 *(Figure 47)*.

By rigid economy, his family provided for a year's study at Phillips Exeter Academy where Arthur's record was so outstanding that he won enough scholarships to complete the course. From Exeter, at the age of eighteen, he proceeded to Yale University from which he was graduated cum laude, in 1894. Choosing then to enter the Johns Hopkins Medical School, he was graduated with a medical degree as a member of its second class in 1898.

Two years later, he came to Albany to accept a position at the Bender Laboratory where he remained for a year before entering the field of surgery. He thought of pathology as the cornerstone of surgery, and believed that all surgeons should receive training in basic pathology.

Dr. Elting's choice of surgery as his life work probably grew from his association at Johns Hopkins with Dr. William Halstead, who had been brought there by Dr. William Henry Welch to establish a department of surgery and to institute practices which prevented infection and bleeding at operations.

Dr. Elting was as fearless in the operating room as he had been on the football field at Yale. He expected perfection and compliance with his standards, both as Chief Surgeon and as President of the Albany Hospital Staff, offices which he retained for years, in part because colleagues feared to vote against him in annual elections. Woe be to any members of the surgical department who inadvertently removed a normal appendix or uterus! Each day, with Dr. Victor Jacobsen, Pathologist-in-Chief, Dr. Elting reviewed all material received in the department of pathology. He scorned the idea of having a tissue committee: he was it.

Such complete dominance of the staff produced a feeling of insecur-

(Fig. 47) Dr. Arthur Wells Elting

ity among younger members, especially because Dr. Elting seemed unable to develop confidence in their judgment. With the aid of his constant companion, Dr. Henry Hand Hun, he performed most of the general surgery, thus augmenting unrest in the department.

But as his reputation grew, he was called to various cities in the Albany area to handle unusual surgical problems. Gratitude of patients made is possible for him to raise funds for the Albany Hospital, to which he was devoted.

One such contribution from George Hawley, a wealthy industrialist, produced the operating suite on the seventh floor of the Hospital. There, in an overhanging balcony, students would sit spellbound while Dr. Elting explained what he was removing from an abdomen which was well out of their view. Only those assisting at the operation benefitted. Such a method of teaching surgery has been long abolished *(Figure 48)*.

Dr. Elting was opposed to specialization in surgery. He taught that a general surgeon should be capable of removing any diseased organ, be it a tonsil, a uterus or a prostate. He averred also that surgical research should not be considered an end in itself.

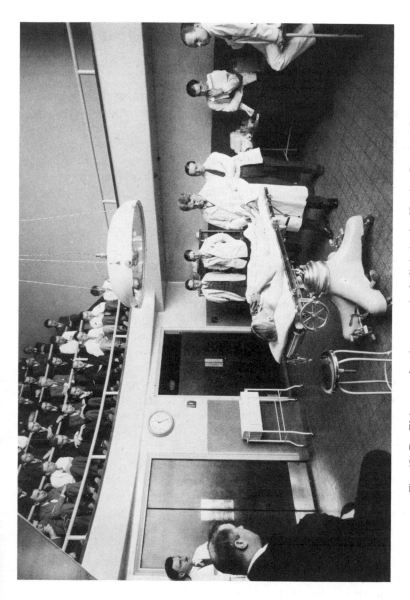

(Fig. 48) Dr. Elting conducting a surgical clinic in the Hawley Surgical Suite.

Therefore, he found it difficult to adjust to the presence of Dr. John A. Sampson who came from the Department of Gynecology at Johns Hopkins to establish a similar unit at Albany Hospital. After Dr. Sampson's arrival, Dr. Elting accepted with better equanimity the need for subdivisions of obstetrics and urology. The Hospital and the Medical College were fortunate in securing as the head of the sub-department of obstetrics Dr. Thomas Gamble, another product of Johns Hopkins, trained by Dr. John Whitridge Williams.

Dr. Gamble soon became a leader in the continuous development of the Hospital and the Medical College. He was a talented physician and obstetrical surgeon, highly respected by the staff. Being much interested in medical politics, he sometimes served as mediator when problems arose among the Medical College and Hospital and the County and State Medical Societies, or the American Medical Association.

When Dr. Elting realized that urology must inevitably become a sub-department of surgery, Dr. John Heslin was engaged to develop that unit *(Figures 49 and 50)*. .With Dr. William Milner, he soon established an active service which increased when transurethral resections were introduced, eliminating the trauma of superpubic and perineal resections of the prostrate.

As medical knowledge increased, orthopedic surgery manifested areas with which the general surgeon could not cope. To manage these at the Albany Hospital, Dr. John Ghormley, another well-trained Johns Hopkins graduate, created the sub-department of orthopedic surgery and remained at its head until his death. He was succeeded by Dr. Crawford Campbell.

Fortunately, Dr. Elting's wish to increase the scope and quality of service at Albany Hospital led him to realize the need to make neurosurgery available in the Albany region. He consulted Dr. Walter Dandy, Head of Neurosurgery at Johns Hopkins, who recommended his Chief Resident, Dr. Eldridge Campbell.

With his surgical skill, Dr. Campbell also brought the academic knowledge which had made him a Rhodes Scholar. Not incidentally, Dr. Campbell had deep interests in hunting, fishing, and tennis — these interests had helped draw Dr. Elting to him. Dr. Campbell soon was recognized at home and abroad as a leader in the field of neurosurgery.

Throughout his life Dr. Elting jealously guarded his professional and social status. Though he contributed much to the progress of surgery at Albany Hospital and to teaching in the Medical College, even there, he demanded, if he were to remain on the faculty, precedence over a colleague who held right of seniority, and he obtained from the Trustees the concession that his name should stand first when a choice was made for Chairman of the Department of Surgery. Other members of the faculty concurred in order to promote harmony. Thus, in 1915,

(Fig. 49)
Dr. John Heslin

(Fig. 50)
Dr. William A. Milner

when the faculty of the Medical College was reorganized by Dr. Ordway, Dr. Elting was appointed Chairman of the Department of Surgery.

Dr. Elting's first marriage ended in the death of his wife, Mary Lord Elting. He remained a lonely man for several years after her death. In 1917, Dr. Elting married Harriet Corning Rawle, whose place in Albany stemmed from birth. She was the daughter of Erastus and Mary Parker Corning, a sister of Edwin Corning. The marriage reinforced Dr. Elting's social standing in the community.

Like Dr. Elting, Harriet Elting was a determined and outspoken person. Their similar temperaments created difficult moments augmented considerably because of Mrs. Elting's complete deafness. One bone of contention was the use of their cars. Neither had learned to drive, and neither would share chauffeurs.

Dr. Elting's choice of Dr. Henry Hand Hun as his chief assistant in surgical operations added much to the prestige of the team and to the status of the Department of Surgery. Dr. Hun had been trained by Dr. William Halstead, and in neurosurgery by Dr. Walter Dandy at Johns Hopkins. Dr. Elting was aware that Dr. Hun had been made famous at Hopkins because he was reputed to be the only Resident who won Dr. Dandy's respect not only in the operating room but also on the tennis court.

Teaching in the Department of Surgery was excellent in quality. Its staff maintained high standards, and Dr. Elting made daily ward rounds a part of training. Students who were privileged to attend his sugical clinics seldom forgot the inspiration of his delivery and his approach to his subject.

He hoped to stimulate his hearers to think for themselves and not to accept blindly the didactic concepts of the previous generation. He wanted to awaken in his students an interest in the field of surgery rather than to instill in their minds a collection of facts.

Among some of the topics he presented and discussed were improved methods of applying plaster of paris dressings to deformities, and the importance of microscopic examinations of the urine. He demonstrated the diagnostic value of blood examinations for anemia, leukemia, and infectious processes. He discussed treatments for deformities of the feet, and illustrated tendon transplantation.

He encouraged his students to read, and set an example by reviewing in the *Albany Medical Annals* many books related to surgery. Some he damned outright, and some with faint praise, but he could be generous with deserved commendation.

When at a meeting of the Albany County Medical Society, on February 18, 1903, Dr. George E. Gorham described an improved extension apparatus which he had invented, Dr. Elting commented that he had found the device very useful, and no bed to which it could not be attached. But he held a low opinion of costly whims and gadgets that burdened surgical departments and had little practical value.

He opposed increasing participation of government in hospital administration. He set forth his ideas for conducting hospitals before the American Surgical Association meeting in Atlantic City in 1938. He wanted:

> . . .establishment of harmonious relationships between the professional and the lay groups in directing hospital activities; efficiency and economy in these activities; development of a teaching atmosphere in hospitals, based on more active, unselfish interest on the part of surgeons in directing the professional affairs of the hospital with which they were connected; careful supervision and direction of medical education by the medical profession; and more careful inspection and accurate grading of hospitals.

In that same year, he lashed out against current nursing education, saying the assumption that "so-called" degrees in nursing improve the quality of service rendered is erroneous. "Thoughts of possessors of such degrees are too much occupied with eductional themes and too little with the needs and care of the sick." He continued:

> The direction and control of nursing education is largely in the hands of women of great crusading zeal whose minds are filled with fine theories, but who often do not possess the practical knowledge and skill required for the training of efficient nurses.

All who knew Dr. Elting recognized his ability to pierce to the heart of a problem, his refusal to compromise principle, and his loyalty to friends. Being a stickler for principle sometimes lost him adherents, but it earned the respect of even those who strongly opposed him.

Dr. Elting was one of the prime organizers of Base Hospital Unit No. 33 during World War I. He contributed generously to the funds needed to equip the Unit and from his friends raised $100,000. He organized the officer and nursing compliment and personally interviewed and evaluated each enlisted man. On arrival in Portsmouth, England with the Unit, Dr. Elting was entertained by the Southern Branch of the British Medical Association. Almost immediately, he was detached from the Unit, promoted in rank to Colonel and assigned to active duty in France. He did not rejoin the group.

At the close of the war, Dr. Elting resumed his crowded and hectic schedule at the Medical College and Albany Hospital. He reported having performed a diversity of surgical operations, demonstrating his belief that a general surgeon should be able to do anything: hysterectomy, umbilical hernia, exploration of abdominal tumor, removal of gall bladder and appendix, gastroenterostomy, excision of angiomatous veins of the thigh and penis, amputation of the cervix, and the Whitehead operation for hemorrhoids and fissures.

But life was not all work. Members of the Interurban Surgical Society met at Dr. Elting's home before partaking of dinner at the Fort Orange Club. He also became an active member of the Esculapian Club.

As a host, Dr. Elting displayed kindly and humorous qualities. He had many friends whom he inspired and who enjoyed hearing stories of his adventures while fishing or big game hunting. The walls of his large living room were decorated with trophies from Africa, Alaska and the Rocky Mountains. It was a lucky guest who, upon rising quickly from a chair, avoided having his head struck by a walrus tusk or a tiger's tooth.

Dr. Elting was a proponent of strenuous exercise. When in Albany, until the age of sixty, he played tennis regularly. When that recreation became indiscreet, he substituted walking and he could encompass six miles in an hour and a half. He also delighted in quail shooting on his plantation on St. Helena Island, South Carolina. There he became concerned about the social problems of Negroes and contributed liberally to schools and churches to improve the economic situation of the permanent inhabitants.

Dr. Elting's activities included office holding in the Albany County Medical Society, the American Surgical Association and the American Board of Surgery which had been established largely through his efforts. He was passive in no organization to which he belonged.

He could not avoid nor always ignore animosities incurred through his choleric temper. Yet slings and arrows never deterred him from speaking his mind. When declining appointment as Chief Surgeon at St. Peter's Hospital in Albany, he wrote:

The notification of my appointment as Chief Surgeon at Saint Peter's Hospital has just been received. In all other hospitals with which I am acquainted, this is a purely honorary position, and in as much as four attending surgeons have been appointed, I am left without any power to insure what I regard as the proper treatment of the patients, which is the chief and essential function of the hospital. I am unwilling to assume this responsibility and must decline the appointment.

I should also like the public of Albany to know that I am in no way connected with the hospital, and not responsible for the future conduct of the surgical department.

It is with deep regret that I sever my connection with the institution to which over a period of many years I have devoted my best endeavors.

The acerbity exhibited in this letter is mild compared to the wrath Dr. Elting displayed when he was compelled to relinquish the Chairmanship of the Department of Surgery and the Presidency of Albany Hospital staff after the Trustees had established an age for mandatory retirement. At that time, he was President of the American Surgical Association and a wealthy man.

He had planned to leave a considerable sum to the Medical College and to the Hospital, but immediately changed his will. Rumors flew that the two institutions had forfeited approximately two million dollars. Life use accrued to Mrs. Elting, and the residue was bequeathed to Phillips Exeter Academy with the suggestion that it be used to establish a pension fund for the faculty.

Since Dr. Elting made no effort to conceal his sense of outrage over his forced retirement, his influential confreres throughout the United States acquired an unfortunate picture of the Albany Medical College and the Albany Hospital. Many years would elapse before the two institutions could overcome their loss of prestige in the medical world.

With a feeling of compassion, one looks upon Dr. Elting's creative life and wishes that he could have approached more philosophically the diversities of existence. He thus might have evaluated more accurately the place for research in medicine, and he need not have been cut off so abruptly from colleagues in 1937, when many accepted his departure with sighs of relief rather than with feelings of regret.

DR. HERMON CAMP GORDINIER

In 1888, the following letter was sent to Professor Samuel B. Ward, M.D., then Professor of Pathology, Practice, Clinical Medicine and Hygiene of Albany Medical College:

Dear Doctor

I wish to write you in behalf of Dr. Hermon Gordinier who desires with the sanction of the Albany Medical College faculty to give instruction in Physical Diagnosis in the absence of the gentleman who has heretofore done so.

I know him to be a most estimable man and I believe well qualified to instruct. He has been the hardest student I ever knew and retains and has at his finger ends all he has learned. You will not regret helping him. Dr. Hun thinks well of him and all do who know of him. He is destined to be a shining light in the profession.

> Very respectfully
> Sincerely yours
> W.B. Boutecon

This letter might have initiated the beginning of Dr. Gordinier's teaching career at Albany Medical College if Dr. Russell, whom he was to replace, had not returned to fill the position.

Dr. Gordinier was born in Troy, New York, in 1864, and was to remain a resident of that city for the 66 years of his life *(Figure 51)*. Perhaps as a consequence of the proximity of Albany and Troy, he studied medicine at Albany Medical College, graduating in 1886. After graduation, he pursued post-graduate studies at the New York Polytechnic School for the academic year 1887-88. When his offered service to Albany Medical College was nullified by Dr. Russell's return to the post which he sought, Dr. Gordinier spent the following year studying at the universities of Prague, Vienna, and Berlin. It may be assumed that his interest while attending these universities was in the field of neurology for which they were famous.

Much of the foregoing information about Dr. Gordinier was taken from the publication "New York State Men" of which Frederick S. Hills is the Editor and Publisher. A review of the catalogs of Albany Medical College lists Dr. Gordinier as Professor of Physiology from 1896 through 1913. The aforementioned publication does not place Dr. Gordinier in that position until two years after his return from Europe. It is likely that the catalog is in error and may have gone to press in 1887 under the assumption that Dr. Gordinier would replace Dr. Russell. The same error was probably repeated in the catalog of 1888-89.

When Dr. Gordinier returned from his European studies in 1890, he was appointed Physcan and Neurologist to the Samaritan Hospital and Marshall Sanitorium in his native Troy, New York. That year, he joined the faculty of Albany Medical College as Professor of Physiology as shown in the catalog of that year. He held that position in the faculty until 1913. The "New York State Men" publication describes Dr. Gordinier's position on the faculty as Professor of Physiology and Anatomy of the Nervous System. It is likely that the latter title is correct. Dr. Gordinier's special interest was in the field of neurology. A review of the catalogs of that period demonstrates the evolution of faculty titles and, perhaps, a somewhat casual approach to the wording of the titles. The title, Professor of Medicine, does not appear until 1915 when Dr. Gordinier was appointed to that post. One is somewhat free to choose the specific title which Dr. Gordinier held during this

(Fig. 51)
Dr. Hermon C. Gordinier

period as a result of these contradictory accounts.

It may be recalled that the two years preceding 1915 were a period of tumult in Albany Medical College which almost resulted in the closing of the College. The entire faculty was asked to resign in 1914 so that Dr. Ordway would have a free hand in his reorganization. Dr. Gordinier may have anticipated the condition and resigned prior to the academic year 1913-14 as his name is not shown as a member of the faculty for that year. No catalog was published for 1914-15 and it is uncertain if he had rejoined the faculty. However, it is certain that he joined the faculty once again in 1915 and had the title of Professor of Medicine, which he held until his death in 1930.

Prior to 1889, that position was titled Professor of Pathology and Practice of Clinical Medicine and Hygiene. In 1889, the title became Professor of Theory and Practice of Medicine. In 1899, the title was again changed to Professor of Theory and Practice of Medicine and Hygiene and remained so until 1905. That year it was again changed to Professor of Theory and Practice of Medicine. In 1915, it was simplified to the present title, Professor of Medicine, with no distinction made between the theory of medicine and the practice of it.

Dr. Gordinier did not accept the position when it was offered in 1914 without deliberate consideration. He stated in his reply to Dr. Willis G. Tucker, then Dean of Albany Medical College, concerning the offer that he would gladly accept the position if two conditions were met. The first condition was that there be a reorganization of the faculty on the basis of a selective or visiting faculty, to consist of the head of each department. The second condition was that Albany Medical College become an integral part of Union University. He further set forth in his letter of reply, that unless Dr. Elting be appointed to the chair of Surgery, and Dr. Sampson to the chair of Obstetrics and Gynecology, that he doubted whether he "would care to be associated with the enterprise." Dr. Henry Hun had written to him strongly recommending that he not rejoin the faculty. With the appointment of Dr. Ordway as Dean and the resulting organization, these conditions were met. Dr. Gordinier became Professor of Medicine in 1915 and served Albany Medical College in that post until 1930.

Frederick S. Hills in his "New York State Men" wrote of Dr. Gordinier as follows:

> With untiring zeal and devotion he served the school and brought to it the fertile influence of his scholarly equipment and exemplary courage. His share, in shaping the future destinies of the institution, in perfecting its humble size and inadequate endowment, to attain and maintain the highest degree of efficiency, is incalculable. If Dr. Gordinier gained wide recognition as a scientist and a clinician, it was in his capacity as a teacher that he gave the full measure of his talent and ability and achieved his greatest triumph. Few men have brought to the clinical amphitheatre a more conscientious preparation, a more unassailable document or a more dynamic and convincing presentation. With a magnetic personality, a countenance glowing with energy and intelligence, a melodious and resonant voice and an exquisite diction, Dr. Gordinier was the embodiment of professorial prestige and distinction. An educator of the first magnitude, he was eminently qualified to fill the chair of medicine in any medical school. No one held a warmer place in the hearts of his pupils and associates. He worked for them and with them, kindling their enthusiasm, encouraging their original trends, guiding their researches with the utmost patience and solicitude and giving them the invaluable aid of his vast erudition and experience.
>
> As an author, Dr. Gordinier has left an imperishable record in the annals of American Medicine. The impressive list of his publications, comprising more than seventy titles, is an eloquent index of his unusual voltage. A critical survey of the content of Dr. Gordinier's bibliography reveals not only the wide range of his scientific pursuits but the highly significant fact that purely clinical studies are few while clinico-pathologic contributions, many of them of the highest merit and originality, constitute the overwhelming majority. A fitting appraisal of his accomplishment is practically impossible for he delved into almost every major problem in medicine. Although necessarily obsolete in some of its chapters, Dr. Gordinier's text-book on the Anatomy of the Nervous System nevertheless stands as a monument to the part he unquestionably played in the emancipation and assertion of American authorship. An ardent supporter of the classic doctrine of cerebral localization and a firm believer in the rigid delimitation of functional centers in the cerebral cortex, Dr. Gordinier valiantly fought for the existence of a separate cortical centre for writing at the base of the second frontal convolution of the

left hemisphere in right-handed individuals. One of the first in this country adequately to describe the clinical features and underlying pathology of acute ascending paralysis of the Landry type, reports of cases of which he published on several occasions, Dr. Gordinier apparently continued to envisage this syndrome as a well defined disease entity. He reported a number of unusual and instructive cases of brain tumor and contributed valuable articles on multiple neuritis, syringomyelia, and occlusion of the posterior inferior cerebellar artery. Outside the realm of neurology, Dr. Gordinier's chief interests were centered on diseases of the cardio-vascular system, the blood and blood-forming organs and the endocrine glands, and accordingly one finds in his collected papers a large number of illuminating articles on aneurism of the thoracic aorta, pernicious endocarditis, lymphatic and myelogenous leukaemia, onyxedema and sporadic cretinism, acromegaly and other closely related disorders. In 1889, he published a "Case of Sclerodactyle with Diffuse Scleroderma" which was the first recorded case in America.

Throughout his writings, Dr. Gordinier betrays the predominating influence of his pedagogic instincts and, without neglecting correctness of form or choice of expression, he is more concerned with descriptive accuracy and clarity or exposition than with elegance of style. Invariably prefaced by a loyal account of the legacies of earlier investigators, Dr. Gordinier's subject is presented with methodical order and precision, clinical and pathological data are exhaustively detailed, functional deficits are judiciously co-related with anatomic localization, differential diagnosis is ably discussed and, when indicated, prognositic and therapeutic considerations are scrupulously evaluated. In fine, Dr. Gordinier's articles bear the stamp of scientific thoroughness and practical utility.

Honored on innumerable occasions by medical societies and organizations throughout the State, Dr. Gordinier received in 1896 the degree of Master of Arts from Williams College and, in June, 1930, Union University conferred on him the degree of Doctor of Science in recognition of his notable contributions to medical science. Dr. Gordinier was admitted to the American Neurological Association in 1898. He was Vice-President in 1921 and served as Councillor. He was also a member of the Rensselaer County Medical and New York State Medical Societies, American Medical Association, Association of American Physicians, American Therapeutic Society, Aesculapian Club of Albany and New York Academy of Medicine.

Viewed in the more intimate atmosphere of private, Dr. Gordinier was a man of rare charm, unfailing courtesy and sympathetic nature. Modest to a fault, generous in his judgment of others, cautious in his deliberations and proverbially just in his decisions, his reputation of professional and civic integrity was a byword. Profoundly devoted to the welfare and happiness of his family and knowing no greater delight than the companionship of his children, Dr. Gordinier never allowed personal cares or concerns to submerge his responsibilities as a citizen and took a keen interest in all matters that pertained to the industrial and educational growth of his native city. A standard-

bearer of the highest moral and ethical principles, he enjoyed the unalienable respect, confidence and esteem of his patients, colleagues and fellow citizens. A great lover of outdoor life, Dr. Gordinier eagerly seized every opportunity to take long cross-country jaunts or to pursue his well known hobby of studying the flora of whatever territory he happened to traverse. A botanist of no mean merit, he accumulated an extensive collection of dried plants and flowers and incorporated his observations in at least two noteworthy monographs. Practically every fall, he managed to slip away and indulge in his favorite sport of hunting. His game was mainly woodcock and partridge and he was considered an excellent shot. Very fond of good music and the legitimate stage but again and above all an omnivorous reader, it may be said of Dr. Gordinier that, to the very last, he remained a tireless, enthusiastic and insatiable student.

In 1894, Dr. Gordinier married Miss Alice Beattie and had five children. He is survived by two daughters, Miss Hermione Gordinier and Mrs. George P. Ide, 2nd, both of Troy, and a son, Hermon C. Gordinier, Jr., a medical student at Johns Hopkins University, Baltimore.

DR. JOHN ALBERTSON SAMPSON

Personal association with an event or person provides a richer basis for portrayal than any amount of research into the past. Dr. Arthur Hengerer was a close associate of Dr. Sampson for many years. Dr. Hengerer delivered an address at the First Department of Obstetric and Gynecology Alumni Teaching Day Dinner in 1973 and the preface of his address was devoted to a biography of Dr. Sampson. An abstract of that biography follows.

Dr. John Albertson Sampson was born in the town of Brunswick, Rensselaer County in 1873—the son of John and Sarah Albertson Sampson *(Figure 52)*. He attended Troy Academy and was graduated from Williams College in 1895. He received his M.D. degree from Johns Hopkins University School of Medicine in 1899, and trained in Gynecology under Dr. Howard Kelly.

His interest in research and clinical investigation of cancer of the uterus began during his residency at Hopkins between 1900 and 1905. His first articles dealt with the blood supply of the ureter and the more radical operations for carcinoma of the cervix uteri. He pointed out in 1902 that this operation was more prognostic than therapeutic. In 1903, he presented a paper on the "control of hemorrhage following pelvic operations by packing the pelvis with gauze through a proctoscope and maintaining counter pressure by packing the vagina." He stressed that many women will not stand a severe operation and that the first consideration must be the wide excision of the primary growth and that lymphadenectomy should be reserved for last—and performed only if the condition of the patient would seem to permit it.

He came to Albany to establish his practice in 1905, having his office at 180 Washington Avenue and became Professor of Gynecology until 1937 when he became Professor Emeritus.

Dr. Sampson was a member of Theta Delta Chi while at Williams College. At Johns Hopkins he was a member of A.O.A. and honored into the Sigma Xi, R.P.I. chapter. He received a Master's degree from Williams College in 1915, Doctor of Science degrees from Union University in 1940 and from Rensselaer Polytechnic Institute in 1942.

Dr. Sampson's insatiable curiosity continued and his observations led to his monumental work on endometriosis. Prior to 1896, the presence of endometrium-like tissue in pelvic tumors was attributed to inclusion of Mullerian rests. Cullen in 1896 suggested a Mullerian origin for adenomyoma of the right round ligament. In 1899, Russell reported the first case in which endometrium had been found in an ovary, and attributed its origin to an aberrant portion of the Mullerian duct. Iwanoff in 1898 was the first to suggest that these peculiar endometrium-like tumors in and on the pelvic organs might be due to a metaplasia of the mesothelium covering the serosa. Robert Meyer became the leading exponent of this theory. He claimed to have demonstrated all transitions from the flat coelomic epithelium to structures resembling endometrium.

Ludwig Pick (1905) reported 4 cases of endometriosis in the ovary and was the first to describe the typical "chocolate" cysts of the ovary and to demonstrate the endometrial nature of the lining membrane,

(Fig. 52)
Dr. John A. Sampson

calling them "cystoma ovarii endometrioides." Novak became the chief advocate of the celomic origin of aberrant endometrium.

For many years, the chocolate cysts and the extensive adhesions and pelvic changes were recognized as a definite clinical finding and in 1921, Dr. Sampson presented his first paper on "Perforating Hemorrhagic (Chocolate) Cysts of the Ovary" and drew attention to the endometrial character of these cysts. At that time, the full significance of his findings was unknown. His observations stimulated a search for possible sources of the other pelvic lesions. A series of papers reporting his further studies resulted in the evolution of the Sampson "Implantation Theory of Peritoneal Endometriosis" and established certain fundamental facts regarding the life history of this condition. His theory was a radical departure from theories of celomic metaplasia. His theory was based primarily on transtubal migration of fluid containing bits of tissue to become implanted and grow on pelvic structures. This regurgitation is favored by anything which hinders the outflow of menstrual blood through the cervical canal.

In 1925, Dr. Sampson's paper was read before the American Gynecological Society, in which he presented his classic arguments as we know them, including the experiments on the viability of cast off tissue.

Dr. Sampson did not contend that all forms of endometriosis are the result of implantation. He did not deny the possibility of metaplasia or embryonic rest. He believed certain of the extraperitoneal forms were metastatic or embolic. He was a chief exponent of the theory that endometriosis where found originated in adult Mullerian tissue, and he demonstrated that it may be disseminated by various routes.

One of these routes is via the lymphatics and in 1922, Dr. Sampson demonstrated the invasion of lymph vessels by endometrial tissue. Many forget that this theory was in his original papers, but it does not account for all forms of this disease.

He published about 15 articles over an 11 year period on this subject. Few clinicians have made such an important contribution to medicine by original, careful, thorough, honest observation and have it stand the test of time. The general term "endometriosis" was suggested by de Josselin de Jong and by de Snoo as well as by Dr. Sampson in 1925. This descriptive form is functional, does not characterize the lesion as a true tumor, nor necessarily imply Dr. Sampson's theory or any other theory. No one has improved on naming this disease.

Dr. Sampson wrote many other papers regarding the blood supply of myomata, the dangers of packing the uterus with radium capsules, and others, numbering over 60 articles. But his prime interest was in endometriosis, encouraging the study of direct endometriosis in Caesarean scars, and its etiologic basis for ectopic pregnancy.

The beautiful drawings used to illustrate his papers were done by Miss Ruth Oliver, who married Dr. Harold Marden and is the mother of Dr. Harold E. Marden, Jr. She studied under Max Broedel at Hopkins. These classic illustrations have been reproduced in all Gynecological literature.

Although a few of us remain who had the privilege of working with him or of having been trained by him, we remember many of his idiosyncracies and what he was like as an individual. Perhaps he was best known for his Franklin automobile. It was a familiar sight to see him driving through Washington Park with his dog beside him. In the late 1920's, a salesman tried to get him to change to a new Franklin, but he preferred the old one, because his dog would not ride in the new one. In later years, his chauffeur and dog brought him to the hospital in a Pontiac. The Franklin was given to the Government for its aluminum during World War II.

Dr. Sampson had a great love for trees, animals and birds and so bought a large tract of land in Grafton which was his second most consuming interest.

Each day he would leave his office at 4 p.m., make rounds on his patients, and then sit down with us to review those patients and the new admissions. It was at these moments we would learn the most from him *(Figure 53)*. In his last few years, much time was spent filling greasy paper bags with scraps of food from the patient's trays in order to feed the raccoons and birds at home. He was not reluctant to take good things that a patient was about to eat. There were complaints and cries, but no one ever rapped his knuckles.

He was a severe task master and required us to work with little time off, the assistant resident getting Saturday p.m. off, and the resident Sundays after morning rounds. We would not go to Keeler's on a Friday night with the Wallingfords without first getting permission from him. He would telephone from his home in Troy by 6:30 a.m., so one had to have seen all his patients by then. One had just time to get breakfast, meet him at the front door of the hospital, and be in the O.R. by 7 a.m. He always called again in the evening, and not infrequently would call during the night if he had a particularly ill lady. On a rare occasion I had to get up at night, go into the hospital, check a patient, and call him back.

The operating room was also an experience. Dr. Sampson was an extremely gifted surgeon, both technically and judgmentally. Dr. C. Stuart Welch, who trained at Mayo's, considered him one of the finest and most natural surgeons he had ever seen. He could be a tyrant in the O.R. and Lord help you if he were in a bad mood. We were always especially careful when he got very polite, or if he got off his box and walked to the window to look out, meanwhile giving his "God help me."

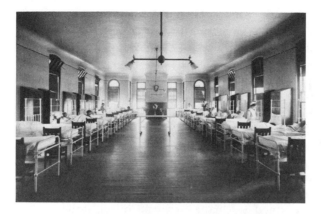

(Fig. 53) The surgical ward for women in 1929.

Albeit he had a fine sense of humor and a great twinkle in his eye as he would tell tales of Dr. Howard Kelly as an evangelist, or tales of other colleagues such as Dr. Elting, or Dr. Beilby or others. In spite of being a bachelor, he was most perceptive of family and married life. Whenever he had a patient who was a witch with a capital "B," or saw the poor hen-pecked husband, his remark was "He's really married." On telling him of my engagement, he did not congratulate me, but quickly asked, "Do you know the mother?" I've rethought that one many, many times.

Well, I've rambled on and had better quit while I'm behind. I am sure that some of you here could add to these tales.

In January, 1946, Dr. Sampson received a fracture of the patella in Washington Park while being driven by the late Dr. Lyle Sutton to his office. This healed poorly and gave rise to complications. Dr. Sampson died suddenly of a heart attack on December 23, 1946, at the age of 73. He died a wealthy man, leaving about one million dollars to the Albany Medical College, and his home and Grafton property to Rensselaer Polytechnic Institute.

It seemed appropriate to talk about Dr. Sampson, the Father of Endometriosis and the First Chairman of this Department, at this First Annual Alumni Dinner. An eminent Gynecologist of international fame, a scientist, teacher, educator, investigator, and researcher, but above all a humanitarian who was deeply respected and loved by his patients and those who worked with him. I have always considered him one of the two great men of medicine with whom it was my privilege to have been associated. He has set a tough example for those who have followed him, but times have changed. We welcome Dr. Swartz, our new Chairman, and wish him well in his task, but tonight we honor the person and the memory of John A. Sampson.

DR. ELDRIDGE CAMPBELL

During Dr. Ordway's administration, a brilliant young surgeon joined the faculty of Albany Medical College. He was Dr. Eldridge Campbell *(Figure 54)*. Dr. Campbell was born in 1901 in West Virginia. After graduating with a B.S. degree from West Virginia University, he was appointed a Rhodes Scholar, awarded for academic and athletic achievement. He graduated from Oxford University being awarded a B.A. degree. Two years later, in 1927, he received his M.D. degree from Johns Hopkins Medical College. His credentials were impeccable. In 1934, he joined the faculty of Albany Medical College. While serving at the Medical College in 1942, he was appointed Unit Director and Surgeon-in-Chief of the 33rd General Hospital during World War II. When he returned to Albany Medical College at the conclusion of the War, he was appointed Professor of Surgery and Chairman of the Department. His death in 1956 was a great loss to Albany Medical College and the world of medicine.

FACULTY RESTRUCTURED

Dr. Ordway, as the new Dean, on May 24, 1915 announced to the Board his proposed structure of the faculty and those men who he was nominating for the position in the proposed organization. The organization and nominees were:

Department of Neurology—Professor, Dr. LaSalle Archambault *(Figure 55)*
Department of Surgery—Professor, Dr. Arthur Wells Elting
Department of Medicine—Professor, Dr. Hermon Camp Gordinier
Department of Physiology—Professor, Dr. Charles M. Gruber
Department of Pathology—Assistant Professor, Dr. Ellis Kellert
Department of Gynecology—Professor, Dr. John Albertson Sampson
Department of Anatomy—Professor, Dr. Wesley Manning Baldwin

(Fig. 54)
Dr. Eldridge Campbell

(Fig. 55)
Dr. LaSalle Archambault (left) conducting a teaching clinic in neurology.

Three years earlier in 1912, the Board of Trustees had amended the by-laws to establish nine departments in the College. However, Dr. Ordway's organization included only seven departments. Dr. Ordway combined the Departments of Chemistry and Toxicology with the Department of Therapeutics (which included Pharmacology and Materia Medica) and placed the combination in the Department of Physiology. The Board accepted Dr. Ordway's recommendations. For the first time, the College faculty was divided into specific departments with a professor responsible for the performance of the department and the subdepartments which constituted it. Of the nominees, three had been members of the faculty prior to the reorganization. The Board approved both the organization and the nominees without discussion or delay.

Dr. Ordway realized the necessity for a firm foundation in the basic sciences in his reorganization of the College in 1915. Dr. Arthur Knudson was chosen to teach Biochemistry; Dr. Victor Jacobsen, head of the Department of Pathology *(Figure 56)* (Dr. Jacobsen was succeeded in 1932 by Arthur Wright) *(Figure 57);* Drs. Stanley Randles and Melvin Dresbach were in charge of the Electrocardiograph and Basal Metabolism laboratories *(Figures 58 and 59);* Dr. Wesley Manning Baldwin was head of the Department of Anatomy.

John Maguire, an author widely recognized and enjoyed for his wit and perception, in addition to writing a daily column in the *Albany Times Union,* contributed to *Albany Hospital News* under the title *Critical But Fair.* In 1968, he related a practical joke worked by 12 medical students on Dr. Wright. Following is the excerpt from *Critical But Fair.*

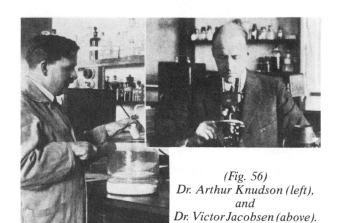

(Fig. 56)
Dr. Arthur Knudson (left),
and
Dr. Victor Jacobsen (above).

(Fig. 57)
Dr. Arthur Wright

(Fig. 58)
Dr. Stanley Randles

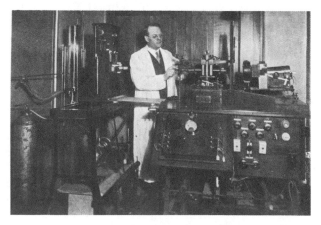

(Fig. 59)
Dr. Melvin Dresbach with early electrocardiograph equipment.

The clinical pathological conference has always seemed to me, as a layman some of whose best friends are doctors, to be a kind of intellectual Russian Roulette, in that participants don't stand to win anything but are in great danger of being shot down. The shooting, of course, is done by the pathologist, who is the only participant who has looked in the back of the book, in a sense, and knows whodunit. A pathologist at a CPC can readily be identified by the knowing observer; he is the guy sitting there looking smug, and every once in a while partly hiding a snicker. Pathologists are rarely elected to anything by their colleagues.

It has been said that there was once a kindly pathologist, but the literature fails to provide evidential support and the statement must be considered unverified. Veteran participants in such conferences say that some pathologists are meaner than others, which in its converse suggests that some are less mean, and perhaps we should leave it at that.

Rarely do CPC participants have a chance to score off the pathologist, or hanging judge. So it is worth recalling here one instance in which a pathologist considered by many to be particularly curt in his dismissal or diagnoses proposed by participants was taken aback at one CPC at this very medical center.

By prearrangement, 12 medical students submitted the same diagnosis, and it was a condition he didn't recognize and, in fact, had never heard of: Meyer-Sniffen-Vortex syndrome. They say he looked blank, startled and bewildered in turn. It is reported to have been several days later that he discovered that Meyer-Sniffen-Vortex was the trademark imprinted on the familiar vitreous china fixtures in the medical center's lavoratories.

The executive faculty was to consist of the Chancellor of Union University, the Dean of the Medical College and the seven department heads. As Dean, Dr. Ordway extended the invitation to other faculty members to attend executive faculty meetings but did not extend the right to vote beyond the nine members of the executive faculty.

Dr. Richmond, Chancellor of Union University, expressed satisfaction with the new organization and also his confidence that genuine University control of the College was assured.

The finances of the College were at best precarious. The Building Fund contained only $10,000 and there was still the outstanding mortgage of $12,000 held in varying amounts by those mentioned earlier. As a final action to break the ties with the past, the Board arranged to have the mortgage assumed by Albany Savings Bank, reimbursing the previous mortgage holders with the funds. An economy was gained by the reduction of interest to 5 percent from the previous 7 percent.

In order to comply with the new regulation imposed by the Regents of New York State, the College was required to have at least six full-time members of the faculty. To offset this newly imposed financial burden, the Board had agreed to guarantee that for each of the next five years, $10,000 would be made available in addition to the regular income from tuition fees. This was one of the conditions that Dr. Ordway had specified before accepting the Deanship.

To put in perspective the amounts involved, following is a condensation of the Treasurer's report of expenditures at the end of the first year of the Ordway administration submitted to the Board on June 7, 1916:

Administration	$ 6,874.60
General	1,275.81
Housekeeping	1,332.69
Anatomy	17,075.35
Physiology	4,291.37
Biological Chemistry	3,711.00
Pharmacology	572.03
Pathology	4,116.75
Medicine	1,867.00
Surgery	56.50
Gynecology	765.00
Neurology	650.00
Miscellaneous	1,720.00
Alcohol	134.00
Total	$44,442.10

It may be noticed that in contrast to recordings of earlier expenditures in this report, the amount expended for alcohol is substantially reduced and confined, we may assume, to the denatured variety—lethal if drunk. Of the set aside $50,000 guarantee, $40,000 remained available for the succeeding four years. The following academic year, 1916-17, students fees amounted to $19,215 or only 52 percent of the cost of maintaining the school.

MOVE TO DELAWARE AVE.
CHANGED TO NEW SCOTLAND AVE.

It was recognized that the Lancaster School had outlived its usefulness for the College and that a new building was needed more suitably located for access to Albany Hospital and the facilities of the Bender Laboratory. Earlier planning had selected the site of the Albany County penitentiary as a desirable location. It appeared that the land and buildings would be deeded to the College but because the land was still required by the County for use as a jail, land on Delaware Avenue was granted to the College. In the spring of 1916, New York State passed a law which would enable the Board of Supervisors of Albany to convey the now available site of the former penitentiary to the College in exchange for the Delaware Avenue site. This was a definite improvement because the proposed land was immediately adjacent to Albany Hospital and not as far removed from the Bender Laboratory. Simon W. Rosendale, then President of the Board of Trustees, immediately requested the exchange of properties. As if to maintain a bargaining position, he stated in the request for the change that the Delaware Avenue property had a higher monetary value than the New Scotland Avenue offer, but the location for the purposes of the College was better. On June 7, the Supervisors transfer was acknowledged by the Board of Trustees and the condition accepted that the College must build on the location within five years.

UPGRADING ACADEMIC STANDARDS

The faculty then set itself to work at its duty of educating medical students. The primary recorded subject of Executive Faculty meetings for the next several years was concerned with discussion of qualification or rejection of students for continuation of studies. Each exceptional case was individually considered. The decision to make an exception for specified reasons or to recommend dismissal was made only after the situation was thoroughly explored. It is interesting to note that many times tuition fees were refunded to students who could not complete their courses for sufficient reason.

With the recommendation of a new faculty organization and approval of it by the Board of Trustees, Dr. Ordway had removed the first obstacle in the path of improved academic standards for the College. Instead of the impeding friction caused by the contending factions prior to the reorganization, all efforts seemed to be directed to increasing the momentum to achieve academic improvement. Dean Ordway may have been influenced by the Flexner Report in its contention that there was in effect an overproduction of doctors for the needs of the nation and insufficiently high standards for those graduated. As a result, the number of graduates during his administration shows a marked reduction in contrast to earlier years. Following is a listing of the number of graduates during the years of his administration.

1915 - 15	1921 -17	1927 - 17	1933 - 30
1916 - 48	1922 - 12	1928 - 26	1934 - 20
1917 - 42	1923 - 14	1929 - 23	1935 - 28
1918 - 11	1924 - 18	1930 - 20	1936 - 25
1919 - 12	1925 - 16	1931 - 29	1937 - 21
1920 - 21	1926 - 16	1932 -27	

The comparatively large graduating classes during the first three years (1915-17) can be attributed to students accepted during the previous administration. A sharp decline from 42 graduates in 1917 to 11 graduates in 1918 is evidence of Dr. Ordway's adherence to the Flexner recommendation in this regard. Of course, it is not possible to assume with any certainty that the quality of the graduates was improved. However, it would seem likely that a student would have the opportunity to learn more if he had closer access to the teacher through the reduction in fellow class members. During the years 1918 through 1937, graduating classes averaged just a fraction over 20 students per year. This relatively small class number was to result in disagreement between Dr. Ordway and Dr. Arthur Bedell in the years prior to Dr. Ordway' resignation as Dean of the College. (A complete list of all graduates from 1839 through 1982 is contained in Appendix F.)

In 1935, the desire of the Board to increase student enrollment resulted in the budgeting of $7,000 to initiate an advertising campaign to attract students. Of this amount, $3,500 was paid to a Mr. Davis as salary to visit colleges for the purpose of making contact with students of high academic ranking. Prior to this effort, 285 students had applied for admission that year, but only 12 or 13 were accepted. In addition to Dr. Ordway's pursuit of academic excellence, there were other factors which may have had an influence on the reduction of class enrollment and graduates.

At the time Dr. Ordway was appointed Dean of the College, the school itself may not have presented an attractive image to the prospective student. Contention within the faculty and between the faculty and Board had become public knowledge. Rumors that the College would be closed abounded and the Flexner Report cast a dark shadow on the school's reputation. Understandably, students were not likely to seek admission to a college which was in the throes of internal strife and on the brink of becoming defunct, if other medical schools would accept them. In 1917, the United States entered World War I and many young men who may have been applicants for medical school were no doubt drawn either by military draft or personal choice to the Armed Services. In 1929, the stock market crash and the ensuing depression placed medical education financially beyond the realm of other potential candidates.

In 1918, it was recommended by the faculty and agreed to by the Board of Trustees that two years of pre-medical education would be required for admission to the College. This placed many potential applicants two years removed from admission. In 1934, this requirement was increased to four years of pre-medical education and delayed another group of candidates two more years. It may be recalled that at the turn of the century, Albany Medical College had increased the term of study from two years to three and then to four.

ENROLLMENT OF FEMALE STUDENTS

Still another factor, of which Albany Medical Center was not the only practitioner, had a dampening effect on enrollment. That practice was the attitude at the time toward women and minority groups. As recently as 1915, the first recorded discussion concerning the advisability of admitting women as students took place. Dr. Ordway said that one woman had already been admitted. Apparently she had been admitted without great fanfare or the person or persons initiating the discussion were not attentive. The discussion was concluded by the statement recorded in the minutes as follows; "It is the sense of the faculty that the experiment was well worth trying and there was no objection to it." This was hardly the expression of a warm and hearty welcome.

Drs. Lucy Elizabeth Bourn and Ruth Gilbert were the first females to graduate from Albany Medical College. They graduated in 1923. Therefore, it may be concluded that the female student admitted in 1915 did not graduate from Albany Medical College. In 1918, two years prior to women being given the right to vote, Dr. Betsy H. Lane (not a graduate of Albany Medical College) was the first female doctor admitted to practice in Albany Hospital. In 1975, 7.4 percent of the graduating class was female. Six years later, in 1981, approximately 20 percent of the graduating class was female; evidence of the success of the lukewarm endorsement of 1915.

TREATMENT OF MINORITY STUDENTS

A second group which did not receive equal treatment were black students. Black students were admitted but were excluded from clinical classes. At that time, prejudice was open and rampant. The exclusion of blacks may have resulted from the objection of white patients and, therefore, not a direct result of College policy. In 1924, the Deans of Maharry and Howard Medical Colleges assured Albany Medical College that they would accept black students for their clinical years.

As recently as March 28, 1935, another group of students received special recognition from the Admissions Committee. The Committee reported that 313 applications had been received and, of that number, 69 percent were Jewish. While this identification has no significance of bias treatment, it does imply de facto segregation of Jewish applicants from those of other religious persuasions or racial background.

What may have been an early sign of the awakening of social conscience to discriminatory practice was indicated by a letter from the U.S. Department of Interior. The letter from the Department of the Interior questioned the policy of the College on the admission of Negroes. Dr. Dixon Ryan Fox, then a member of the Executive Faculty and Chancellor of Union University, suggested a reply stating that they (Negroes) were admitted if clinical materials were available for their teaching. These attitudes toward women, blacks and Jews were not unique at the time that they are recorded. They were a reflection of society's attitude at the time. Women suffrage did not become effective in the United States until 1920; Jews were discriminated against by "gentlemen's agreement," until the 1940's; and blacks were not allowed to sit at lunch room counters in some parts of the Nation until the legislation of the 1960's. Institutions, and particularly those dependent on gifts for financial support, traditionally feel almost compelled to reflect society's attitudes.

RURAL CONCERNS

A further restriction on the number of students enrolled was Dr. Ordway's desire to educate doctors for rural service. In 1935, there were openings in the College for 30 students. Dr. Ordway requested that special consideration be given to those applicants who came from rural areas. His reason was that they were most likely to return to those areas to establish their practice. He further stated that a limited number of applicants should be accepted from Albany and other Capital District cities. It may be recalled that a specific criticism contained in the Flexner Report was to the effect that the Northeast medical colleges were producing far more doctors than the population of the United States required. In the ensuing years, either Dr. Flexner was wrong or the situation changed rapidly because in 1922, Dr. Ordway was recommending that preference be given to students applying from within a 150 miles radius of the College because of the acute shortage of doctors for that area. When considering this apparent conflict between the Flexner Report and Albany Medical College toward student body size and selection of applicants, it should be recognized that the Flexner Report was a survey of the national scene and Albany Medical College's decision was based on the needs of the area of its own location. The accuracy of determining the needs of the specific area must be granted to the College above that of the Flexner Report on the basis of on-site familiarity.

INCREASED APPLICATIONS

Application for admission to the College continued to increase during the years of Dr. Ordway's administration. In 1922, 143 students applied and 34 were accepted; in 1926, again 143 applied and 35 were accepted; in 1936, as of January, 184 had applied to date and it may be assumed that the number of applications soon passed 300. The diminution of applicants at the outset of Dr. Ordway's administration cannot be attributed to competition from other medical colleges. In 1906, there were 162 medical colleges in the nation and by 1927, the number had been halved having been reduced to but 80. The reduction in number of medical colleges was probably due to the higher and more universal requirement to obtain a license to practice medicine and, therfore, the necessity of medical colleges to provide better educational opportunities for the students.

Dr. Ordway's desire to restrict the student enrollment was not without

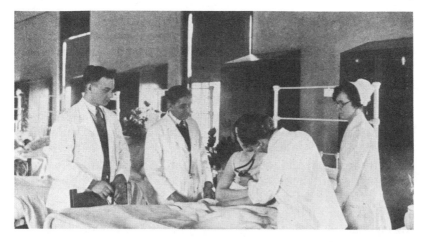

(Fig. 60)
Dr. Thomas Ordway (second from left) during bedside teaching rounds.

substantive reasons. First, he believed that a medical student learned more if he had the opportunity to work closely with the faculty and to observe patients and make bedside examinations *(Figure 60)*. The opportunity for clinical training was limited to the amount of clinical material (patients) available. During the years of Dr. Ordway's Deanship, Albany Hospital had grown to a 600-bed hospital and the College had working arrangements with several other hospitals and clinics in the Capital District. However, access to patients by the students was of no practical value if a member of the teaching faculty was not present with the students. And this presents his second reason to restrict enrollment. While the finances of the College were improving through grants and endowments, the College never attained financial security to the point that it could attract a faculty of the calibre that Dr. Ordway sought and in quantity sufficient to maintain the low ratio of student to teacher in which he believed. This steadfast adherence not to sacrifice the quality of education offered, may have been a factor in the decision of the Board to request his resignation as Dean in 1937.

During these years, Dean Ordway was not oblivious to the growing need for the education of more doctors and he expressed the need numerous times in speaking engagements and papers which he presented. However, he saw the need existing in the shortage of general practitioners who would, because of their background, be willing to practice in rural areas. In 1928, there were 1,329 doctors practicing in Northeastern New York State. His projection was that in 10 years, 544 doctors would be needed to replace those who had fallen by reason of death or retirement, and within 20 years (1948), 833 replacements would be required. Subsequent population shifts from city dwellers to suburban homes would place Dr. Ordway's projection on the low side of the requirement. Today, many suburban and rural areas are served by doctors who have formed group practices.

VISION OF A MEDICAL CENTER

During the period of the late 20's and early 30's, Albany Medical College and Albany Hospital had their vision of becoming a Medical Center in the true sense of the term. While Dr. Ordway perceived the need for more general practitioners who would be willing to locate in rural areas where there was a need for them and sufficient base that they could make a living, he recognized that it would be wrong to therby cut them off from further professional growth. This objective of Albany Medical College was presented by Dr. Ordway in 1929 to the Congress on Medical Education, Medical Licensure and Hospitals in Chicago. Point 4 of his 5-point program to provide physicians for rural communities was, "by cooperating with graduates and other physicians in the large district served by the Medical College, giving them an opportunity to take graduate work, review and advanced courses, either formally or informally, as well as special work in all departments of the medical school." Thereby, he laid the groundwork for the College and Hospital to be the source for area doctors from which they could continue to advance their knowledge.

While preeminently an academician and educator, Dr. Ordway was also a solidly practical man and recognized that a rural doctor could not leave his practice for an extended period to further his education. Therefore, his plan included bringing the teaching of the College from the Center, in the person of lecture teams, to rural physicians who would gather at a local hospital or meeting place. One of Dr. Ordway's concepts of a medical center was that the College together with the Hospital would provide a center for the continuing education of practicing physicians. Here, then, was another reason for the restriction on student body growth. To maintain the ambitious program of postgraduate education both in the College itself and by traveling to meet with groups, was straining the physical limitation of the faculty.

FINANCIAL PRESSURES

As mentioned earlier, Albany Medical College had never attained financial security to the point that the building which it had occupied since its origin in 1839 could be replaced. However, it may be recalled that the Trustees promised Dr. Ordway that $50,000 would be available to the College over the next five years in the amount of $10,000 each year. This money was to be used to offset the cost of maintaining a full-time basic science faculty of five members. It was recognized that with the reduced class enrollment, tuition fees could not be depended on to support the College. In fact, tuition fees, at most, contributed only slightly more than 50 percent of the total expenses of the College. Tuition fees declined during the years immediately following Dr. Ordway's administration. This was, of course, directly attributable to the decline in student enrollment.

In 1918, the total tuition received amounted to only $11,000, a drop from the 18 to 20 thousand dollar tuition received in 1915. In 1918, only 61 students comprised the total student body of the College. Deficits for the 1917-18 and 1918-19 academic years were $15,000 and $10,000, respectively. These deficits exceeded by 25 percent that which was anticipated by the Board of Trustees in 1915 when they agreed to supplement the College's funds with $10,000 for each of the next five years. It is interesting to note that in 1918 the Board suggested that the graduation exercises be held in conjunction with graduation from Union College which took place on that campus in Schenectady. As the students graduated from the Medical College that year totalled only twelve, even with all the proud parents, aunts, uncles, and relatives three times removed, the audience would have been scant for the occasion. With this in mind, the graduation exercise was transferred to Schenectady where an audience of more appropriate numbers could be obtained. While tuition fees increased in 1920-21 to $19,972, they still only accounted for 33 percent of the total operating expense of the College which was $62,996. Of the latter amount, $972 was accounted for by the expense of the research work performed by the College. During these years, the faculty could not be accused of reaping a financial windfall from the College. The salaries of full time professors was $5,000 a year and the Dean received the same amount. In fact, Dr. Ordway traveled to meetings at his own expense. However, there was one small assistance granted to the College by the Federal government. In 1920, the College was given free alcohol and the gift was accompanied by the stipulation that the alcohol be used only in the preservation of anatomical specimens and burning in spirit lamps. This eliminated the possbility of it being the cause of blindness, death, or at the least, horrendous hangovers.

FINANCIAL DONATIONS FROM THE PRIVATE SECTOR

The national government recognized the need for medical education and supported health research in its various departments but it did not contribute to the support of medical colleges or research performed in those institutions. Outside financial support came to the Medical College principally from private donations as memorials to the deceased or gifts from alumni and friends. These gifts in the instance of Albany Medical College were, for the most part, awards to students or establishment of small scholarship funds. The gifts were restricted to the use specified by the donor and were most frequently not the use to which the College would have put the funds had they a free hand in the matter.

Typical of these donations was the establishment, in 1920, of an annual scholarship of $200 by the Albany Colony of New England Women to be known as the Dr. Julia G. McNutt Scholarship. The donors specified that the scholarship be granted to a woman medical student preferably of New England ancestry. Dr. Robert Fuller bequeated $30,000 to the College to be used as a scholarship fund for one or more students who had spent one or more years at Union College. An example of what happened to grants of specific amounts was reported in 1925. On the death of Dr. S. Oakley VanderPoel, a memorial fund was established for the purpose of awarding a microscope to a graduating student each year who had the best clinical examination in general medicine. At the inception of the memorial, $50 would cover the cost of a suitable microscope. By 1925, the amount was insufficient and the award then became a check for $50. Not a mean sum, but substantially less than what the donor had in mind.

If the mortgage on the school for the 76 years averaged $8,000 per year, the 7 percent interest amounted to something in excess of $42,000. Had some wealthy patron stepped forward with a check for the principal, the school would have had a substantial amount to apply to its continuing needs. However, the reluctance of an individual or group to contribute is understandable when it is recalled that the school was a proprietary institution with any profit at year end being apportioned among the faculty who were all practicing physicians.

During the late 19th century and early 20th century, huge fortunes were amassed by individuals who profitted from the growth of the Nation beginning at the conclusion of the Civil War. Railroads were thrust from east to west and from north to south. Oil became the black gold found by successful prospectors, and steel plants could hardly meet the demand for their output. Those in the right place at the right time and willing to take a risk garnered tremendous wealth. The happening was such a phenomenon that the government had not yet enacted legislation to control what is now viewed as unethical practices in some instances. As a result of these circumstances, the wealth amassed was almost incalculable and surpassed the need of the most prodigal spenders of that and succeeding generations. With no income tax or inheritance tax to reduce these fortunes, they grew from snowballs to avalanches of funds. Taking a charitable view of events, one could conclude that the owners of the fortunes looked at mankind and decided that some of the surplus could be used to improve their fellow man's lot in life. A less charitable view might be that some of the

funds were established to amerliorate the pangs of suffering conscien-
ces. Whatever the reason, foundations were established to support
worthy causes of which educational institutions stood foremost in the
ranks.

By 1920, the $50,000 pledge of the Board of Trustees had been
exhausted. The building fund and endowments provided an annual
income of only $18,400. General Electric was one of the earliest donors
to the College, having given $5,000 in 1919 for the maintenance of the
College. General Electric continued to make unrestricted grants to the
College for the next ten years. In 1921, General Electric increased its
contribution to $20,000 for the succeeding three years on the condition
that the College raise $40,000 each of those years in addition to the
income from tuition.

The minutes of the Board of Trustees of January 27, 1920, reflect the
serious financial position of the College. As the first order of business,
the Board moved to request the City to grant a five-year extension of
the building requirement contained in the land grant. The Finance
Committee then reported that a $500,000 endowment fund must be
raised or they would of necessity recommend that the College be
closed to incoming classes at the end of the school year. On the bright
side, they reported that $115,000 had been pledged on the condition
that the $500,000 was raised. If these conditions were not met, the
school could be maintained only until such time as enrolled students
were graduated.

SERIES OF GRANTS SUSTAIN THE COLLEGE

At the June meeting of the Board of Trustees, eleven benefactors
pledged $150,000 if the College could establish an assured annual
income of $25,000. The contributors and the pledged amounts were:

Emily N. Huyck	$25,000
Edmund N. Huyck	25,000
Dr. Arthur W. Elting	25,000
Charles Gibson	20,000
Dr. John A. Sampson	10,000
Benjamin W. Arnold	10,000
Robert C. Pruyn	10,000
J. Townsend Lansing	10,000
Oscar L. Hascy	5,000
William Sage	5,000
Frank C. Huyck	5,000

General Electric's Directors voted a $5,000 annual contribution and
together with $7,500 income from other donations, the College realized
50 percent of the goal stipulated as a condition for the pledge.

At last a small dim light appeared at the end of the long dark
financial tunnel when it was learned that the Rockefeller Foundation
would give $10,000 to the College during the next year. The light was

augmented by a few more candlepower by the announcement that additional endowments had been received which when added to previous endowments would yield an annual income of $18,400. In 1921, the financial picture brightened considerably. It was learned that the Carnegie Foundation was considering a capital contribution, and $20,000 was received from the General Education Board of the Rockefeller Foundation. In addition, of some $45,000 pledged to the school by various benefactors, $31,500 had been received to date with $40,000 more pledged for the future.

The improving finances did not result in a profligacy on the part of the faculty. In 1922, Dr. Sampson contributed $665 to the Department of Pathology for the purchase of new equipment and paid two-thirds of the salary of his assistant in that Department. Even with such examples of generosity, the Board recognized the need to increase tuition and granted permission for the faculty to do so in 1922. Tuition which had been $200 per year was increased to $250. At the time, Union College tuition for pre-medical students was $250—the same amount as tuition at Yale and other private colleges. Tuition at State-operated pre-medical colleges was $150 per year.

Despite the increasing endowments and receipt of grants, the financial pressure did not cease. In the academic year 1921-22, operating expenses increased to $107,600. At that time, a movement was started that would emerge fully in 1924. A desire was expressed by the Board of Trustees to promote a closer working relationship with Albany Hospital and to thereby demonstrate that medical education could be inexpensive when a hospital and medical college worked in unison. In 1923, the Board of Governors announced their decision to enlarge the Hospital. As a result of the close working relationship between the Governors of the Hospital and the Trustees of the College, the consideration of the enlargement of the Hospital was probably known to the Trustees in 1922 at the time of their earlier discussion concerning a closer relationship with the Hospital. As a result, the Trustees in 1923 asked the Governors to consider taking the College as an integral part of the Hospital. As history testifies, somewhere along the line the majority decision of the Governors was "No." The Hospital had no need to add a financially beleaguered medical college to its own problems.

Annual tuition was again increased in 1924 from $250 per year to $300 per year. With only 84 students enrolled for academic year 1924-25, the tuition increase resulted in minimal additional income of $4,200, not a windfall but then, every little bit helped. Good news of a substantial proportion was the notification by the Carnegie Corporation that $52,500 would be given to the College during the next four years. The amounts were $10,000 in 1925, $12,500 in 1926, $15,000 in

1927, and another $15,000 in 1928.

THE MERRILL GIFT AND EFFORTS TO INCREASE THE ENDOWMENT FUND

In 1927, Mrs. Grace Merrill Town, the daughter of Dr. Cyrus S. Merrill who had formerly been the Professor of Ophthalmology and Otology, gave $100,000 to the College *(Figure 61)*. This was the largest gift made to the College to date. It was to be for the establishment of the Dr. Cyrus Merrill Professorship of Pathology of the Merrill Foundation of Pathology. In 1929, Dr. Victor C. Jacobsen was the first to be appointed to that Professorship.

In an effort to broaden the financial base of the College, a letter was sent to Dr. Keppel of the Carnegie Foundation requesting a grant of $200,000. In the letter, it was proposed that the grant be given as part of the effort to raise an endowment fund of $1,000,000. A letter of similar content was directed to the General Education Fund of the Rockefeller Foundation requesting $200,000. Unfortunately for the historian, subsequent minutes of the Board of Trustees do not record the reply. However, as the Board reported the endowment fund to be $370,000 in 1928, it may be concluded that the reply to both letters of solicitation was not affirmative or immediate.

For the first time in many years, Dr. Ordway was able to report in 1927 that the College had generated a surplus of $9,278.84. Expenses for the academic year 1926-27 totalled $87,652 against an income of $96,931, of which $27,593 was received from tuition fees. The Board of Trustees record no celebration of Dr. Ordway's report but there was undoubtedly a collective sigh of relief. Incidentally, this information was conveyed to the Board by the instrument of an annual report which Dr. Ordway prepared each year. The report was very inclusive and consisted of as many as twenty-two pages of typewritten information. He was the first Dean to report in this formal and complete fashion. One incongruous note appears at the outset of each report. Dr. Ordway details the explanation of an insignificant portion of the total funds of the College as they are received from the sale of texts in the College bookstore. In each of these reports, this information is reported in the opening portion of his report with the regularity and formality of the salutation.

As part of Dr. Ordway's annual report to the Board, he cited the various research projects being conducted by the faculty and the papers which they wrote publishing the results. In 1930, Dr. Ordway reported that Drs. Gorham and Hunt were doing research work on infectious mononucleosis and that he and Dr. Gorham had completed a book on diseases of the blood. Research work was reported on the effects of ultra high frequency. As early as 1925, Dr. Wesley M. Baldwin,

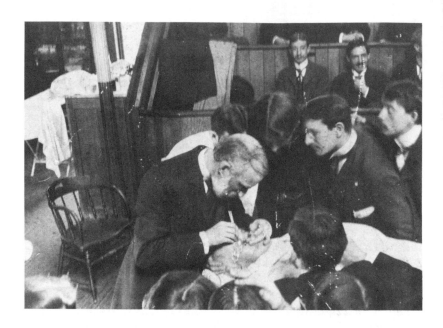

(Fig. 61)
Dr. Cyrus S. Merrill

(Fig. 62)
Dr. Wesley Manning Baldwin

Professor of Anatomy, had conducted a research project on the effects of electricity, magnetism, ultra-violet ray energy and x-rays on developing embryos and adult tissue *(Figure 62)*. This demonstrated the awakening by medical science to the effects of environmental conditions on man. By present day standards, a review of these research projects may seem basic or insignificant. They should be assessed in light of the fact that they were conducted without the finanical support granted to research today. Research funds were measured in hundreds, not the millions to which we have become accustomed.

DECISION TO BUILD

If the College was to retain the land granted by the City of Albany, it would soon have to start building or forfeit the grant. The City had already granted one extension of time over the original agreement and the patience of the City Fathers might not have endured a second request for extension. As a result, the Board of Trustees decided in 1925 to sell the building on the corner of Eagle and Lancaster Streets which the College had occupied since its inception in 1839. The property was purchased by Ten Eyck Mosher and Company for $70,000. From this sum, the $12,000 mortgage was satisfied. Together with the remaining $58,000, ($29,000 from the McDonald fund, and $37,00 in the Building Fund), the College now had $123,247 with which to erect a new building. However, before the sale of the property was completed, the purchase price was increased to $75,000 and it was agreed that the College could occupy the building until July 15, 1926, paying $5,000 for the year's occupancy. As a result of the sale, the Board of Trustees were irrevocably committed to the erection of a new building. The situation is not unlike the home owner who sells his present abode before locating a new one.

COOPERATION BETWEEN HOSPITAL AND COLLEGE

During the June meeting of the Board in 1924, a committee of five members was appointed to sell the old school and begin the erection of the new building. The City had granted land bounded by New Scotland and Lake Avenue to the College for building purposes. However, having been inconvenienced by the physical separation from Albany Hospital since its move in 1898, the Board desired an actual physical connection of the College and Hospital. As the Hospital did not occupy all of the land to which it held title, it was agreed by both interests that the College would exchange its land with the Hospital for vacant land immediately adjacent to the Hospital building. As a result, the College building became an attached part of the growing Hospital complex of buildings. The same year that the exchange was consummated, Dr. Ordway had pressed for a closer affiliation of the College and the Hospital. He requested a working agreement similar to that which existed between Columbia University Medical College and Presbyterian Hospital in New York City. This was agreed to in 1927 while the College building was being built, construction having been begun in 1926. The agreement specified that a joint administration board be appointed. The Board was made up of three members of the Board of Trustees to represent the College, and three members of the Board of Governors to represent the Hospital. The Chancellor of Union University was a seventh member but was without the privilege of voting with the Board. The first Administrative Board consisted of Charles Gibson, Frederick W. Kelley, and A. Page Smith from the Board of Governors; and Alden Chester, Edmund W. Huyck, and Charles Alexander Richmond from the Board of Trustees. The agreement, among other things, specified that the professional staff of the Hospital would be nominated by Union University (actually the Executive Faculty of the College) and appointed by the joint Administrative Board. This agreement was the foundation of the close relationship of Albany Medical College and Albany Hospital which exists to the present. In a sense, it was the fulfillment of the plan which Dr. March had at the time the College was founded in 1839.

The Comittee of five Trustees (Huyck, Chester, Lansing, Gibson, and Smith) who were appointed to oversee the construction of the new building agreed that the costs were not to exceed the Building Fund. At this point, the minutes of the Board become puzzling. At a meeting of the Board in May, 1926, the estimated cost of the building had been placed at $170,000 and the Building Fund was reported to be only $130,000 which seems to place the Committee at a $40,000 negative variance from its goal of having the cost of the building not exceed the Fund. Less than a month later, the construction contract was awarded to the firm of Feeney and Sheehan for $129,000. The confusing part of the record occurs in the meeting of October of the same year when the Board granted authorization to the Finance Committee to borrow $40,000 to complete the building. If the Fund contained $130,000 and the contract for construction was $129,000, why the necessity to borrow $40,000 for completion? However, as events turned out, it was not necessary to obtain the $40,000 mortgage. The Board was able to meet its goal as a result of Dr. Ordway's thrift. On June 10, 1927, the Committee was able to report that the $40,000 anticipated deficit was avoided because Dr. Ordway had saved that amount on the cost of furnishing the building. This would seem to indicate that with these latent abilities, Dr. Ordway would have been a financial genius had he not chosen the medical profession, or at least an outstanding purchasing agent. The Board gave further recognition to Dr. Ordway's prowess for "economical management" when they stated that the building was

(Fig. 63) The "new" Albany Medical College, 1928.

completed without incurring debt by virtue of his having saved $62,000 during his management. In general, the accounting is difficult to follow because of the substantial funds which seem to fortuitously tumble from unsuspected sources.

NEW BUILDING

It would be expected that the archives of Albany Medical College would contain numerous newspaper clippings and photographs of the construction and dedication of the new building *(Figure 63)*. Such is not the case. There is not a single photograph or description of the usual removal of the first shovel of earth or cornerstone-laying ceremony. There is a logical explanation of this gross oversight. The new school building was first occupied in 1928, the same year and possibly the same time, that Albany Hospital completed exensive additions to the existing Hospital facilities. This may well have distracted from the new College facilities. A second factor may have been that the College did not move directly from the Lancaster School to the new building. After the sale of the property on Eagle Street, the College was conducted, pending the erection of the new building, in a portion of the Bender Hygienic Laboratory, the Almshouse, and an amphitheater in the Hospital. Whatever the reason, the archives are bare of any direct reference to the new building which had been so long needed and deferred.

Fortunately for history, two other sources do contain information concerning the funding, erection, and physical description of the new

*Left and Below: (Figs. 64 & 65) Fire-
places and mantles removed from the
Lancaster School and installed in the
new building in 1928.*

*(Fig. 66) Former Lancaster School entrance
relocated to current Albany Medical College building.*

College. One source is the minutes of the Board of Trustees, the other is a publication entitled, "Methods and Problems of Medical Education." It is the fifteenth in a series of similar publications issued by the Rockefeller Foundation. On pages 1 through 19, there is a description of the building and several photographs and detailed floor plans outlined by Dr. Ordway.

It may be recalled that during Dr. Vander Veer's administration, a concerted effort was made to erect a new building to the extent that architectural plans were drawn. However, the building, completed approximately twenty years later, is much more utilitarian in appearance than the earlier plans.

The new building is described by Dr. Ordway in the Rockefeller Foundation publication as being six stories high, 50 feet wide by 125 long, and containing 35,000 square feet of floor space. The basement and attic were fully utilizable for laboratory and shop purposes having ample daylight lighting. (The architects were more energy conscious than many of their successors.) Dr. Ordway continued by stating that "two fine old mantels from the original school building" were used in the construction of fireplaces in the library and reception room *(Figures 64 and 65)*. While the construction of fireplaces in a commercial building may be viewed as an extravagance, they were installed to create a more attractive appearance for those working during long periods of time in the building. Certain other memorabilia were built into places in the new school building, notably the front steps and doorway, the latter an example of the Philip Hooker architecture constructed for the old Lancaster School built over one hundred years prior to the new building *(Figure 66)*. The fireplaces and mantels still remain in the building where they were installed. However, only a knowledgeable person can find them or relate their origin. The front steps and doorway, also remain in place even though the front of the building has been extended after the original structure was completed. Dr. Ordway, in his description, did not mention the many memorial tablets which were also removed from the old building to adorn the walls of the passageway to the Hospital. They are so numerous and their design so resembles headstones that one using the passage has the feeling of walking through a cemetery with his feet a few feet below the level of the sod.

The following is a verbal description by Dr. Ordway of the building and its use:

Floor Plans

In assigning space for the different departments it seemed important to do this on the basis of technical requirements. Thus, various departments may use facilities for histological, physiological, chemical, pathological, or bacteriological techniques. This makes for economy in equipment and maintenance and favors interdepartmental cooperation.

Basement Floor

The basement contains the students' locker and toilet rooms, rooms for physical apparatus, carpenter and machine shops, stack room, animal rooms, and unassigned space for a large laboratory or cafeteria.

First Floor

The first floor is made up of the dean's office, general office, reception room, library and conference rooms.

Second Floor

The second floor is devoted almost exclusively to the Department of Physiology , including an office and private laboratory for the professor and his assistants, a large room for students for general physiology, histology, and embryology, a special room for mammalian work, and two private laboratories for clinical pathology and research.

Third Floor

The chemistry department is located on the third floor which included the private office and laboratory for the professor and his assistants, a larger laboratory equipped for students' use in the study of biological chemistry and certain phases of clinical pathology and another larger student laboratory used for bacteriology, pathology and clinical pathology.

Fourth Floor

The greater part of the fourth floor is devoted to rooms for pathologic, anatomic, and embryologic histological technique. The private offices and laboratories of the professors of anatomy, neurology, gynecology, and pathology and a small amphitheater for anatomical demonstrations are also on this floor.

Fifth Floor

A large dormer running almost the entire length of the building on the north and small dormer windows on the south have provided the attic, or fifth floor with ample daylight. The major portion of it is used as the dissection room, separated into smaller units by movable partitions. Smaller rooms toward the south are provided as special dissecting rooms for graduates and advanced students. A small amphitheater for anatomical demonstrations will be provided between the general dissecting room and the rooms for embalming and preservation of anatomical material.

Future Development

The College building has been so designed and constructed that future requirements for additional space may be cared for by the addition of wings to the north and south. These would allow for lateral expansion of departments without disorganization of their present facilities.

GROWTH OF ENDOWMENTS AND THEN THE "CRASH'

In 1928 the Board of Trustees for the first time employed a professional fund raiser. The goal of the effort was to establish a $2,000,000 endowment. While the full amount was not realized, the failure was not for want of effort. In the archive files are two boxes which contain copies of letters written to prospective donors to the fund. These are not the usual form letters of solicitation but each is a personal letter. Unfortunately, to trace the success or failure of each letter would require massive research. The effort might be worthwhile because somewhere in this pile is the prototype of the successful letter of solicitation. The John Price Jones Corporation was considered for the purpose having performed in a similar capacity for Johns Hopkins University for $10,000 year. Apparently, the practice at the time was to pay a flat fee for the service rather than a percentage as is now customary. For whatever reason, the task was instead given in 1929 to H.J. Seymour to be performed for $6,000 annually. Mr. Seymour must have been very effective because the endowment fund began to grow at an impressive rate, as endowment funds went at Albany Medical College. On January 24, 1928, the fund totalled $370,000. On January 5, 1929, when the decision to employ Mr. Seymour was made, the fund had increased by $72,000 over the amount reported a year prior. In the first six month's of Seymour's employment, the fund was increased by approximately $190,000 reaching the comparatively magnificent sum of $630,000.

While Mr. Seymour performed ably, the John Price Jones Corporation came into the financial picture in 1930 with a bang. That year and for the first time the endowment fund exceeded a million dollars, reaching $1,071,090. Presumably, for its effort in attaining this height, the John Price Jones Corporation received $30,794. A reasonable guess might be that the fund raiser received 10 percent for the effort, the endowment fund having increased by roughly $300,000 between 1929 and 1930. Exclusive of tuition, the College enjoyed an annual income of $84,000 that year. Tuition was $305 annually and compared favorably with tuition in other medical colleges. Rochester Medical College had a tuition of $300 and other small schools had annual tuitions of $400. Medical colleges in New York City had set tuition at $500 and Johns Hopkins topped the list at $600—almost double that at Albany Medical College. The reporting of the comparison of tuitions in the Board's minutes of January, 1930, was not just to satisfy the idle curiosity of the members. That spring it was announced that tuition would be increased by aproximately 33 percent to $400. The reason for the increase is a matter for conjecture as the minutes do not elucidate on the change beyond recording the increase. Two possibilities for the increase present themselves. First, the Trustees may have believed that they were the unwitting directors of a bargain basement medical education and decided to place Albany Medical College closer to the downstate colleges' tuition and nearer to the category of the much esteemed Johns Hopkins. More likely, the reason was the loudest bang heard in the finanical history of the United States—the Stock Market crash of the previous year. The Trustees, being sagacious men, probably realized that funds would not flow freely to the College from benefactors who were affected by the diminished return from their portfolio. In addition, the return from the invested endowment was reported to be down $38,335 from the previous year. The following year, 1931, the funds in the endowment trust had decreased to $800,000. While the loss of approximately $200,000 was not a small loss, the fact that the loss was contained at 20 percent is silent testimony to the wisdom of the investors. During the 1929-31 period, complete bankruptcy was the order of the day throughout the entire Nation.

During the balance of Dr. Ordway's administration, the financial position stabilized and the endowment fund of the College improved slightly. In 1932, the income from the fund rose to $42,000 and the principal recovered from the earlier loss to reach $861,627. However, a substantial portion of the increase can be attributed to the generosity of Edmund Niles Huyck, Chairman of the Board of the Trustees, who on his death on July 15, 1930, had left a bequest of $50,000 which the College received in 1931. Tuition fees continued to provide insufficient income by far to support the College and contributions which might have come to the College were going to maintain soup kitchens for the prevention of starvation. The Roosevelt administration was in its second term when Dr. Ordway resigned in 1937 and while it was making tremendous social reforms, its efforts were strained to the utmost. Young men who in other times might have been studying medicine were thankful to be members of the CCC (Civilian Conservation Corps).

In retrospect, during the period 1915 and 1937, the College faced up to the necessity of establishing a sound financial base on which some long-range plans could be made and the hand-to-mouth existence of the past put to an end. The struggle had its "ups and downs" before a stable financial program was established in the late twenties. During the first five years of the Ordway administration, the $50,000 fund provided by the Trustees was exhausted. However, at the time substantial funds from foundations and private donors began to flow into the College's bare financial cupboard. The endowment drive began in 1928 for the first time provided a steady annual income subject to minor fluctuations. Had the drive not been initiated at that time, the College might have failed. Nineteen twenty-eight and the first three quarters of 1929 were years of great prosperity. Following the Stock Market crash in October, 1929, would have been a most inopportune time in which to try to raise substantial sums of money. When Dr. Ordway resigned in 1937, the College had survived the precarious years.

QUALITY EDUCATION AND DISCIPLINE

There can be no question that if the academic standards of Albany Medical College had remained at the level of the period between 1910 and 1914, the College would not have survived much longer. When anything approaching 50 percent of the students fail to pass a licensing examination, something is missing other than lack of application by the students. It was to bring a quick turnabout in academic achievement that Dr. Ordway was appointed Dean of the College. Being a scholarly person himself, he saw this as the primary challenge confronting him. The pride and satisfaction which he derived in achieving the improvement stands out in his annual reports to the Board of Trustees. In 1925, Dr. Ordway stated that no student had entered the College since 1915 and failed to pass the licensing board. The identification of the year 1915 is important because this is the first year that the Ordway administration controlled admissions. The careful wording of the statement is significant and particularly the phrase, "entered the College since 1915." Therefore, the statement does not exclude the probability of some failure during the first three years of the Ordway administration by students who were admitted to the College prior to his taking office. In 1926, the Ordway report states that eight successive years had passed without a failure, so it may be concluded that the last failure of a student to pass the licensing examination occurred in 1918—the last year for students admitted by the previous administration. In 1927, the remarkable record came to an end. One student failed the licensing examination in bacteriology. Dr. Ordway reported this failure to the Board but said that it was most likely due to carelessness, the student being of outstanding academic achievement.

That the College was run as a tight ship is illustrated by the publication of the student yearbook "Skull" being subjected to censorship by the Dean. Presumably, any double entendre passages were "blue penciled" as quickly as they were detected by the Dean through his steel rimmed glasses. Perhaps this accounts for the discontinuance of the publication after 1916. The publication did not resume until 1947. In 1916, the Dean requested that students stop smoking in the building. This regulation was imposed well before the carcinogenic effect of tobacco was recognized. With the imposition of strict regulation and the record of high academic achievement, one might mentally picture the student body as stern faced young men walking through the halls of the College wearing grave expressions and heavily laden with texts. They appear in photographs to be to the contrary, rather relaxed and enjoying life without undue tension. Perhaps the fact that most wore derbies at jaunty angles even in the dissecting room gave them an almost rakish appearance. Remember that this was the era of airplane pilots wearing leather helmets and white scarves; "flappers" with their frizzed hair styles, helmet-like hats and recently shortened skirts.

The reduction and almost elimination of academic failures when the graduates were confronted by the State Board of Examiners was in part due to the requirement in 1918 that entering students were to have completed two years of pre-medical studies. This eliminated some that may have progressed through medical college only to come a cropper at the licensing examination. Further culling was automatically performed by academic attrition. Of the 40 students in the first year, only 30 "survived" to be in the second year. Five more were lost after the second year and an additional five in the third year, leaving 20 to graduate. If this reduction was consciously enforced, the 50 percent that had been failed by the State Board had already been removed by the College.

WORLD WAR I

The first acknowledgement of World War I that appears in the recorded minutes of Albany Medical College Board of Trustees is in the record of January 10, 1917. There was a discussion of the possibility of war service and that consideration should be given to initiating a course in military training for the students. It is assumed that the training was to be of a medical nature and not close order drill.

The second acknowledgement of World War I that appears in the recorded minutes of Albany Medical College Board of Trustees is in the records of February 14, 1917, some three years after the war had begun and less than two months before President Woodrow Wilson would ask Congress to declare a state of war between the United States and the German Empire and its allies. Because of the proximity to the declaration by the United States to enter a war of three years duration at that point in time, the content of the entry is strange. The minutes state that Washington authorities had notified Dr. Ordway, "that on account of the unsettled conditions abroad, military training in medical colleges would not be started at present." The reference to "unsettled conditions abroad" should qualify for consideration by the Guiness Book of Records for the understatement of all times. Several millions had been slaughtered in three years of trench warfare and the war was in a stalemate. Perhaps on his own initiative, on March 26, Dr. Ordway suggested that some training in military medicine be started for the students at Albany Medical College.

BASE HOSPITAL UNIT NO. 33

The civilian reaction to the medical need to meet the war crisis was much more direct than that of the Government. On June 5, 1917, Base Hospital Unit No. 33 was established from members of the Albany Hospital staff and the faculty of the College and other persons from the

(Fig. 67)
Members of the United States Base Hospital No. 33

Albany area *(Figure 67)*. Thirty-five thousand dollars were raised by the Governors of Albany Hospital to equip the Unit which was headed by Dr. Elting. The Unit consisted of the following: 24 physicians and surgeons, 152 enlisted men, 65 nurses, and 6 civilians. The Unit was mobilized in November, 1917, at the cavalry armory on New Scotland Avenue, Albany. The Unit had the capacity to administer medical aid to 500 patients.

Its equipment included three ambulances, four automobiles, six fire extinguishers, power-driven wood cutters, meat choppers, laundry machines, a fully-equipped portable kitchen, two x-ray outfits, and a telephone system with forty different connections. The 500 bed capacity was increased to 1000 when the unit arrived overseas. It was one of the best organized in the United States. The Thirty-Third General Hospital arrived at Portsmouth, England in May, 1918. On July 26, it was formally accepted by Sir Willian Osler of Johns Hopkins fame.

Sir William Osler wrote of the Unit:

Elting made things hum at first, and Corning (Dr. Erastus) was an unqualified success as his successor. The clinical and pathological laboratory was one of the very best I have ever seen, and the x-ray outfit was extraordinarily good.

Of the 24 physicians and surgeons in the Unit, 21 were members of the teaching staff of the College granted leave for active war service. They were: Doctors Andrew McFarlane, Henry L.R. Shaw, Edward W. Becker, Erastus Corning, Malcolm Douglas, L. Whittington Gorham, Clinton B. Hawn, Joseph P. O'Brien, Joseph A. Lanahan, Arthur Benson, Joseph L. Hemstead, Arthur W. Elting, J. Lewi Donhauser, James N. Vander Veer, Edwin L. Draper, Peter L. Harvie, John F. Southwell, John E. Heslin, William G. Keens, Thomas W. Jenkins, and Lawrence J. Early. A year later, the Government acknowledged the presence of war had caused a shortage of medical teachers and declared all teachers to be an essential branch of industry and exempt from the draft. The war was to end two months later.

THE WAR EFFORT AND FLU EPIDEMIC

Earlier in 1918, all medical students were declared members of the Enlisted Reserve Corps. It was further ruled that no student could be admitted to a medical college or advanced without the approval of the War Department: a long step into the grey fog of bureaucracy. In September, the students' Army Training Corps was established and all students were inducted into the Corps on October 1, 1918. The students of Albany Medical College were ordered to live in barracks at Union College in Schenectady where they were issued food and clothing. At the same time, the notorious influenza epidemic struck the United States. To help meet the demands for medical aid for those stricken, third and fourth year students were released from classes for five weeks. Albany, like many other population centers, was overwhelmed by those stricken by the highly contagious disease. Of the medical students from Albany Medical College who worked with the sick, 16 became infected and two lost their lives. Second year students were called on to perform post mortems during the epidemic. After the declaration of armistice, the Corps was dissolved and student life returned to a normal condition with the return of the instructors from military service. Acknowledgement must be made of this chaotic period during which Albany Medical College was making its revival.

World War I affected the Hospital in several ways. In order to staff the Army Hospital Unit No. 33, it was necessary to reduce the Hospital staff in most sectors. In addition, expenses to operate the Hospital were increased. Salaries had to be raised to meet the competition for employees by industry. Because of the demands of the war theater for medical supplies, the cost of those items increased. Coal rose $2 per ton. Perhaps the most severe effects of the War were the demands on the Hospital as a result of the influenza epidemic that devastated the Nation. For six months, the Hospital operated over capacity and was staffed in part by medical students and lay volunteers. The financial burden of caring for those stricken by the epidemic who could not pay for the care was an additional burden on the Hospital.

Two interesting sidelights illustrating the effects of the War were reported in newspaper articles. The first dealt with the increase of insanity. For the years 1915-16, 118 cases of insanity were treated in Pavilion F. The numbers increased to 132 in 1916-17 and 144 cases in 1917-18. The increase was attributed to the pressure of wartime on those with weak minds or mental defects. The belief was that the war pressure accelerated the breakdown resulting in insanity. A second newspaper article entitled, "Another Evil of War," cited that the number of illegitimate births had increased from 14 to 17 and then to 18 in Albany County during the period 1915-16, 1916-17, and 1917-18. The article included the following quotation; "Commissioner Alvin C. Quentil, in giving out the figures, stated that from last July to the present date the marked increase in bastardy cases has been traced directly to the war." It would be interesting to follow this obviously tedious process of detection pursued to support this so definite statement.

ALMSHOUSE IS MOVED

In 1928, the inhabitants of the Almshouse were moved from the location near the College to the Shaker Farm, depriving the College of clinical material. In 1926, when the move was proposed, Dr. Ordway declared the move to be little short of criminal because the inmates would not receive the medical care which they had received because of their proximity to the College. A committee was appointed to appear before the Supervisors to oppose the move but their effort was in vain and the move was effected two years later. Edmund N. Huyck, then President of the Board, said that the move was inevitable and that the College should turn to the out-patient clinic of the Albany Hospital for the needed clinical material. A year later the out-patient clinic had increasing use by the residents of Albany and the College was able to avail itself of the necessary clinical material. From this time forward, the out-patient clinic grew to become an important adjunct to the Hospital and a valuable source of study for Albany Medical College students.

COLLEGE SUFFERS LOSS OF TWO LEADERS

If 1929 was the high water mark of the Ordway administration, 1931 was the beginning of the ebb tide. In 1930-31, the College suffered the loss of two of its stalwart leaders. In 1930, Edmund Niles Huyck, then President of the Board of Trustees, died. Dr. Ordway and Mr. Huyck had worked together harmoniously for sixteen years, during which time the College had been revitalized. They were close friends and shared many common interests.

That next year, 1931, Dr. Hermon Camp Gordinier, Professor of Medicine, also died. Dr. Gordinier had served as Professor of Medicine since 1914 and had made substantial improvements in that department. Coincidentally, that same year, 13 of the 36 first year students failed to pass. As stated earlier, Dr. Ordway had established desirable class sizes at 40 students in the first year and 30 in the second year. As the first year class was 36, four below the goal, with 13 failures the second year class became 23, seven below the desired number.

Mr. Huyck was succeeded as President of the Board by Mr. A. Page Smith in January, 1932. Mr. Smith had been a member of the board since 1921. He resigned three months later and was succeeded by Lewis S. Greenleaf, who was also a member of the joint Administrative Board of the College and Hospital. In 1933, John A. Manning was elected to membership on the Board of Trustees and also the joint Administrative Board. He was a member of the Board of Governors of the Hospital prior to this time and continued to serve on that Board also. Thus, the close working relationship to which Dr. Ordway was accustomed had been changed. It is reasonable to assume that these men may have had goals for the College which, while meritorious, differed from those of Dr. Ordway and Mr. Huyck. In the best of circumstances it is difficult to establish a new pattern with incoming team members after many years of a close working relationship has been broken.

Undoubtedly pressed by the stringent financial condition of the

College at the time of Dr. Gordinier's death, Dr. Ordway took on the additional duties as Professor of Medicine. The Department of Medicine is generally recognized because of its scope as being the most demanding of time and attention of any in medical education. To perform in the capacity of Dean and Professor of Medicine is too much of a burden for one man. The combination of these two responsibilities probably contributed to the calamitous events of 1937.

CHANGES IN ADMINISTRATIVE PHILOSOPHY

When Mr. Manning joined the Board of Trustees he requested that a member of the Board serve on the Board of Admissions. Dr. Elting agreed to the proposition but said that the new member must justify his presence on the Board. Dr. Elting was not a man to mince words with anyone. This may have been another bubble which culminated in the eruption four years later.

Changes continued to grow in the administration of the College. In 1935, the first student committee was formed and recognized by the faculty. The committee consisted of four students who were admitted to faculty meetings to present the requests of the student body. While the requests submitted would today be regarded as innocuous, the Student Committee presented another new factor with which Dr. Ordway and the faculty had to reckon. A more serious threat to the autonomy of the faculty was the presence of Trustees as members of the Executive Faculty. This change began in 1934 and was the only instance of the Executive Faculty being invaded by lay persons. In September, 1936, Dixon Ryan Fox, Chancellor of Union University and a member of the Executive Faculty of the Medical College, protested the membership of Trustees in the administrative council of the College. He called a meeting to be attended by all professors, associate professors, clinical professors, and assistant professors. The purpose of the meeting was to vote on the continuing presence of Trustees as members of the Executive Faculty. Before the voting, he let his opinion be known by stating that if the vote was in favor of the continuation of the Trustees in the Executive Faculty, he would move to have the College dissociated from Union University. The vote was an overwhelming 36 to 2 that the Trustees should withdraw. The three lay persons, Messrs. Manning, Greenleaf, and Adams withdrew from the Executive Faculty.

Meanwhile, other affairs of the College were moving along at a somewhat normal pace. The incoming class of 1936 consisted of 31 students (9 below the desired 40 showing a further decline in enrollment). The first year students represented 18 different colleges and six states. Graduation in 1936 was once more returned to Albany, the ceremony being held in the Albany Law School auditorium instead of on the campus of Union College in Schenectady.

THEOBALD SMITH MEMORIAL LABORATORY

In 1935, a letter was written by Mr. Greenleaf, President of the Board of Trustees, to Mr. Manning, President of the Board of Governors, requesting Albany Hospital to grant the use of the old County Hospital to the College for $1.00 per year. The lease which extended for the next 20 years was granted by the Hospital to the College. The request was made so that the building, renamed the Theobald Smith Memorial laboratory, could be used by the Department of Physiology to perform research work for the purposes of both the College and the Hospital. It was planned that $100,000 would be invested in the research work provided that an additional $175,000 could be obtained from the Rockefeller Foundation to further support the undertaking. This action accomplished two ends. First, it provided the College with a needed research facility. Second, it recognized the College's preeminent graduate, Dr. Theobald Smith. Unfortunately for the College, he had never returned to his Alma Mater in any official capacity other than to deliver the 86th Commencement Address in 1917. The title of his address was, fittingly, "The Significance of Laboratory Research in Medical Education."

MANDATORY RETIREMENT INTRODUCED

The first step that was to result in the retirement of three of the College's most eminent men was taken in January, 1937. The Board of Trustees discussed the retirement age of faculty members. After considerable discussion, a resolution was unanimously adopted that effective September 1, 1938 the limitation would be 65 years. In April, Mr. Manning called to the attention of the Board, the resolution passed in January and suggested that it be amended to make 62 years the mandatory retirement age for executive heads of clinical departments and that retirement for other professors remain at 65 years. The same age limitation would also apply for basic science teachers and other full time teachers. The Board agreed with Mr. Manning's proposal with the exception that the 62 year limitation for executive heads of clinical departments be advanced one year to 63. The Board further decided that the new regulation become effective on July 1, 1937. In addition, they specified that before final action was taken, a committee of three members be appointed to consult with Dr. Elting. Dr. Elting at the time of the discussion was vacationing at his estate in North Carolina. The reason for consulting with Dr. Elting was because of his intimate relationship with the College for so many years. The action of the Board during Dr. Elting's absence in view of his fiery temperament may not have been coincidental and the duty of the committee of three who were to confront him on his return was not enviable.

RETIREMENT OF DOCTORS ORDWAY, ELTING AND SAMPSON

At the same meeting, the Board accepted an agreement concerning Dr. Ordway that the Executive Faculty submitted as a result of their meeting earlier that year on February 25. The Ides of March came early in 1937. In that meeting, Dr. Ziegler, Professor of Neurology and Psychiatry, made a motion seconded by Dr. Wright, Professor of Pathology and Bacteriology. The motion stated that, "The Executive Faculty desired to recommend to the Board of Trustees of the Albany Medical College that Dr. Ordway be relieved of his duties as Dean of Albany Medical College on July 1, 1937. The motion was carried by a vote of 10 to 2 with Doctors Ordway and Sampson dissenting. A second motion was then introduced by Dr. Knudson, Professor of Biochemistry, and seconded by Dr. Wright, recommending to the Board that Dr. Ordway be relieved as Executive Head of the Department of Medicine effective September 1, 1937. This motion also passed, the voting being 9 in favor and 3 dissenting. The dissenters were Doctors Sampson, Hun and Ordway. Present at the meeting with the voting right were Doctors Ordway, Sampson, Donhauser, Gorham, Hun, Knudson, Wright, Ziegler, Wallingford, Himwich, Schwind and Klinck. Dixon Ryan Fox was another who was present, being Chancellor of Union University, but he did not have the voting right.

In the subsequent meeting of the Board of Trustees, the recommendation of the Executive Faculty concerning Dr. Ordway was accepted. An agreement was reached on his behalf concerning his retirement. The agreement provided that he would be appointed Emeritus Professor of Medicine without any executive duties for 5 years and payment of an annual salary for that time be made to him. A subsequent motion reduced the continuation of his salary from five to two and also reduced the amount. Thus was the sad ending to a brilliant association brought about. Because of the diversity of his efforts, Dr. Ordway may have begun to fall off in some areas. Had it not been for financial pressure, he would probably have not taken the responsibility of Professor of Medicine on the death of Dr. Gordinier in 1931. Had the Executive Faculty demonstrated a more patient attitude, Dr. Ordway would have retired in a few short years under the mandatory age limitation. Dr. Ordway, as would be expected of one of a gentle, scholarly nature, quietly withdrew from the College to private practice.

It is not clear as to whether Dr. Elting was ever personally contacted by the committee appointed to notify him of the new regulation concerning mandatory retirement. However, after learning of the

Board's action through whatever medium, he did request a letter defining the agreement and said that he would consider the proposal set forth by the Board concerning the status which they proposed he hold after retirement. He further clearly stated that no definite assurance of acceptance should be understood in the interim.

The Board responded by sending what amounted to a form letter to Doctors Elting and Sampson. The letter expressed the regret of the Board in bringing about the retirements and asked them to accept the posts with no executive duties and stated that they would be "under" no one individual officer. Dr. Sampson responded to the letter by agreeing to accept the proposal of the Board and expressed his approval of the plan. Dr. Elting replied, refusing to accept the position and declared it to be a title without function. He retired completely and asked that his name not be used in any connection with the College. Thus, Albany Medical College lost a man regarded by some as a martinet, but by all as an outstanding surgeon.

Growth and Emergence of the Medical Center Concept

DR. ROBERT SIDNEY CUNNINGHAM

When Dr. Ordway resigned as both Dean and Professor of Medicine in 1937, his successor as Dean was Dr. Robert Sidney Cunningham *(Figure 68)*.

Dr. Cunningham had accepted the appointment to become Professor of Anatomy at Albany Medical College in February 1937. Dr. Wesley M. Baldwin had been Professor of Anatomy until 1935 and the post was vacant in 1936. The offer, made by Mr. Manning, provided a salary of $7,000 per year. Though the College was not in the dire financial straits of previous times, Mr. Manning offered $10,000 to the College for each of the next three years to cover any deficit that might be caused by the addition of Dr. Cunningham to the faculty at the relatively high salary.

Dr. Cunningham was one of several eminent anatomists at Albany Medical Center. On becoming Dean, he was succeeded by Dr. Jack Wolfe as Chairman of the Department of Anatomy *(Figure 69)*.

Before he came to Albany in 1937, to become Professor of Anatomy and, as events turned out, Dean of the College, Dr. Cunningham had achieved an enviable record in his chosen field of anatomy, histology, and hematology. Graduating in 1915 from Johns Hopkins Medical School, he remained there until 1925 interrupted by an interval for military service between 1917 and 1919.

At Johns Hopkins, he rose through the ranks from Instructor in Anatomy to Associate Professor before going to Vanderbilt University in 1928 as Professor of Anatomy. Dr. Cunningham never lost the high pitched nasal accent of his native region which is permanently imprinted on his students' minds. First year students in Histology at Johns Hopkins, remember his favorite response to a difficult question: "I don't know—nobody knows—it just is not known." It almost sounded similar to one declining the verb "know." At Vanderbilt he developed a strong Department of Anatomy where research became diversified and stimulating and where he accumulated a notable collection of lantern slides to be used in teaching.

But his interests included other areas of Vanderbilt's medical school

225

(Fig. 68)
Dr. Robert Sidney Cunningham

and he developed and demonstrated the administrative ability which was to serve him so well in later years. He became chairman of the library committee and suggested plans which made the library outstanding. He served also on the school's committees of admission, instruction, promotion, and scientific publication. His was a major voice when reorganization made Vanderbilt University a major education center in the South.

Dr. Cunningham was well fitted for his chosen career. Born and reared in Anderson, South Carolina, he was the only child of Robert Campbell Cunningham and Annie Cooley. From his parents he absorbed a proud Scottish ancestry and the graciousness of the ante-bellum South. His father died when he was eighteen years old. Henceforth, he became especially devoted to his mother. She encouraged him through his college years at Davidson, where he received a bachelor's and a master's degree and on through his work at Johns Hopkins from which he received a medical degree in 1915. The close association of mother and son continued through the remainder of his life. When he came to Albany, Mrs. Cunningham lived with him and when he left Albany, his mother returned with him to the South.

Dr. Cunningham was of medium height and solidly built. Like his predecessor, Dr. Ordway, he was of a shy nature and did not mix well in a social sense. He was always intent on the job at hand and did not spend words in light exchange. As a result, many people were not comfortable in his company and departed quickly when business matters were completed as though to avoid a reprimand from him.

This direct and sometimes brusque manner stood him in good stead to cope with the situation confronting him when he became Dean. A certain independence of authority had developed in the faculty during Dr. Ordway's administration and a firm hand was required to restore the members to an even pulling team.

A testimony to his administrative ability was the fact that while fulfilling his obligations as Dean of the Medical College in 1942, he was appointed Chief Administrative Officer of Albany Hospital. The burden of the dual responsibility must have been especially heavy as the faculty was being depleted by the needs of the war effort. At the time of the Hospital appointment, Dr. Cunningham had been receiving $10,000 annual salary as Dean. In 1943, the Board of Governors of the Hospital agreed to pay him $6,000 per year as Chief Administrative Officer of the Hospital. This offer was contingent upon the College paying him the same amount as Dean. The Board of Trustees readily agreed to the proposal and reduced the Dean's salary to $6,000 annually. As a result, Dr. Cunningham netted a gain of only $2,000 for assuming the added responsiblity. Financial reward must not have been a primary motivating factor for Dr. Cunningham.

Recognizing that the imposition of the dual responsiblities on one man would be an excessive burden, it was agreed by the Trustees and Governors to provide some assistance to Dr. Cunningham by establishing the post of Assistant to the Dean. The Governors of the Hospital in turn appointed Mr. E.W. Jones to provide help in the business related operation of the Hospital, and Dr. Charles E. Martin to provide support in medically related problems.

In a similar situation, the Board of Trustees demonstrated a

(Fig. 69)
Dr. Jack Wolfe

econsistent logic in regard to the salary of one Dr. Richard T. Beebe. When, at the invitation of Dr. Ordway, he joined the faculty, his salary was $2,000 per year as an Instructor in the Department of Medicine. In 1938, the Executive Faculty and the Board of Trustees advanced him to an Associate Professor of Medicine. Using the same logic as in the instance of Dr. Cunningham, on promotion, young Beebe's salary was reduced from $2,000 to $1,250. Apparently the thinking was that the improvement in title was worth some sacrifice on the part of the recipient.

Dr. Cunningham envisioned a great medical center which would serve upper New York State. He never wavered in his efforts toward that goal and was able to withstand the criticism of some who did not clearly understand the future accomplishments toward which he was striving.

A colleague who appreciated his qualities described him as exacting of himself and of others. He respected worth and helped and praised those who demonstrated this quality. He was forthright, basically generous and loyal.

At the time of Dr. Ordway's resignation, there was criticism of the College's academic achievements from various quarters. That the condition, if the criticism was justified, was corrected early in Dr. Cunningham's administration is attested to by the results of the National Board Examinations in 1938 and 1939. In 1938, Albany Medical College students attained an average of 81.8 percent on Part I versus a National average of 78.5 percent and in Part II of the examination, the Albany Medical College students averaged 84.3 percent versus the national average of 81.3 percent. The results were repeated in 1939 when Albany Medical College averaged 84.8 percent and 82.6 percent, respectively, for Parts I and II, bettering the National average of 81.0 on each of the two Parts.

He involved himself deeply in whatever he undertook: poker, rehabilitation of a sick crow, helping a person in need of guidance, planning an education program, laying cement or raising parsley, home entertainment of his classes, or study of oriental rugs, etchings, philosophies, religions. Medical research and medical teaching were the interests to which he was most devoted.

In 1951, Dr. Cunningham resigned as Dean of Albany Medical College to become Director of Albany Medical Council which was comprised of Albany Hospital, Albany Medical College, and Union University School of Nursing. The college contributed $500 per month as its part of the expenses of the Council. Incidentally, this amount ($6,000 per year) is the same as Dr. Cuningham's salary as Dean in 1943.

When, because of ill health, he relinquished this post, he returned to his native state, South Carolina. He resumed his teaching career at

South Carolina College of Medicine in Charleston where he taught histology. He subsequently moved to Richmond, Virginia where he taught anatomy and histology at the Medical College of Virginia. Beset by an almost incredible series of ills, including a cardiac episode, refractory anemia, eye problems and diabetes, he continued to teach until death closed the classroom door to him.

In May 1963, approaching 72 years of age, the career of this brilliant but shy man who shunned the limelight and whose personal concerns centered in his home, his garden and his intellectual pursuits came to an end. Following his wishes, his family announced that those who desired to honor his memory might make contributions to The Memorial Arms Hospital of Richmond, which is especially dedicated to the treatment of older persons. But a greater memorial to his talents and personality resides in the memories of those who knew him and who continue to inculcate in young persons the standards of excellence that he exemplified.

DR. JOSEPH LEWI DONHAUSER

Dr. Joseph Lewi Donhauser was the second generation of his family to graduate from Albany Medical College *(Figure 70)*. His father, Alois Donhauser, had graduated in 1877. Two uncles, Maurice J. Lewi and William G. Lewi, graduated in 1877 and 1892, respectively. Dr. Donhauser's father died in 1890 and the seven year old Lewi and his mother moved from Washington, D.C., where he was born in 1883, to Albany.

After graduating from Albany High School in 1900, he entered Union College receiving his A.B. degree in 1904. Three years later he graduated from Albany Medical College. After internship and residency in pathology at Pennsylvania Hospital, Philadelphia, he returned to Albany and became associated with the man who was to be his predecessor as Chairman of the Department of Surgery at Albany Medical College, Dr. Arthur W. Elting.

Dr. Donhauser was active in the military. He served during the Mexican Border Incident in 1916-17; was promoted to Major during World War I serving with U.S. Base Hospital Unit No. 33; and in World War II he was appointed Senior Surgeon, U.S. Public Health Service, with equivalent rank of Lieutenant Colonel, and was Commanding Officer of Unit No. 1.

Like Dr. Elting's, Dr. Donhauser's surgery was voluminous, varied, and strictly accountable. When transporation of a patient was unavailable or impractical, he performed emergency operations in the patients' homes somehow avoiding the possible complications of ether fumes and kerosene lamps.

Dr. Donhauser enjoyed the classroom and association with students. He was enthusiastic in meeting the challenge of inculcating his learning

(Fig. 70)
Dr. Joseph Lewi Donhauser

and patient relationship in his students. In 1929, he published a textbook on surgical diagnosis. Appointed Professor of Surgery and Chairman of the Department, he succeeded Dr. Elting and served in that position from 1937 to 1946. During his Chairmanship, departures from previous customs were accomplished and surgical specialties were formed into sub-departments. After retiring as Chairman, he remained a Professor of Surgery and Senior Surgeon. Dr. Donhauser never retired; he remained active physically and intellectually until his death on December 1, 1964.

En route through life he was student, teacher, professor, soldier and worthy citizen.

DR. L. WHITTINGTON GORHAM

Dr. L. Whittington Gorham was born in Albany, the son of Dr. and Mrs. George E. Gorham *(Figure 71)*. After graduating from Albany Academy in 1902, he attended Yale University receiving his A.B. degree in 1906. He then studied at Johns Hopkins University completing studies for his M.D. degree in 1910. The next three years Dr. Gorham studied in Boston and Europe returning to Albany in 1913. On his return, he established his medical practice and a long association with Albany Medical College.

At that point, there began an interesting paralleling of his career with that of Dr. Donhauser. Dr. Gorham, like Dr. Donhauser, served in World War I with Base Hospital Unit No. 33 with the rank of Captain, U.S. Army Medical Corps. In 1937, after the resignation of Dr. Ordway as Dean and Chairman of the Department of Medicine, Dr. Gorham was appointed to the latter position. That same year, Dr. Donhauser was appointed Chairman of the Department of Surgery. He served as Department Chairman from 1937 to 1948. In 1948, he retired from the Chairmanship and was appointed Head of the Division of Oncology in the Department of Medicine. He served in that capacity until 1951.

During his career, Dr. Gorham specialized in cardiology, internal medicine and allergy. He was secretary-general of the second World Congress of Cardiology, established in conjunction with the American Heart Association, which convened in Washington, D.C., in 1954.

Nineteen fifty-one brought to a conclusion his professional career and he moved to New York City. He continued some research, never being able to relinquish his love for medicine. On July 23, 1968, at the age of 83, he died at his home after several months of illness. His remains were returned to Albany and after funeral services at All Saints Cathedral, he was interred in the Albany Rural Cemetery.

DR. THOMAS HALE

Dr. Thomas Hale succeeded Dr. Sidney Cunningham as Director of the Albany Hosptial and Executive Vice President of the Albany Medical Center and Associate Dean of the Medical College *(Figure 72)*.

A graduate of Princeton University, Columbia Law School and Vanderbilt University Medical School, he practiced surgery one year before he was enticed here by his former teacher at Vanderbilt. Dr. Cunningham chose well. Dr. Hale's medical and legal background protected him from many assaults by the staff. He stood his ground and came out on top, always having the respect and trust to complete any worthwhile projects. He fought stubbornly for the continuation of nursing training schools for Registered Nurses in medical centers when there was a great effort to require all nurses to obtain Bachelor of Science degrees.

Dr. Hale was President of the Hospital Association of New York State from 1955 to 1956 and, as an indication of the trust this organization felt in him, he was elected treasurer of the same organization from 1955 through 1964. It was with a feeling of great loss and anxiety when Dr. Hale retired, but he like Dr. Cunningham, had planned the future well and selected Dr. Thomas Hawkins to succeed him.

DR. THOMAS L. HAWKINS, JR.

Dr. Hawkin's career was similar to Dr. Hale's. Dr. Hawkins is a graduate of Union College and Albany Medical College *(Figure 73)*. Because of his great interest in hematology, he spent a year of fellowship

(Fig. 71)
Dr. L. Whittington Gorham

(Fig. 72)
Dr. Thomas Hale

(Fig. 73)
Dr. Thomas L. Hawkins, Jr.

with Dr. Maxwell Wintrobe, at the University of Utah. Dr. Hawkins then gave up his career as a hematologist, as Dr. Hale had given up his career as a surgeon, and continued as Director until his retirement because of health problems in 1981.

The staff and Governors of the Hospital during the years plagued by inflation and financial crises were confident in his leadership. Dr. Hawkins seemed always to find a solution to maintaining the high standards of the Hospital during his administration.

PROBLEMS CONFRONTING DR. CUNNINGHAM

The situation confronting Dr. Cunningham when he became Dean in 1937 was not as tumultuous as that which faced Dr. Ordway in 1915 but it was not exactly a rose garden into which he stepped. A substantial problem confronting the new Dean was the condition of confidential probation imposed that year by the Eduction Committee, headed by Dr. Herman G. Weiskotten, of the American Medical Association. The probation was acknowledged in the June 11, 1937 meeting of the Board of Trustees. The basis for the criticism was that the College had erred or fallen short in four conditions. They were:

1. Control of the College was largely in the hands of the Education Committee.
2. Executive Faculty never met alone without trustee representation, thereby, opening the door to lay domination.
3. The Department of Pathology was understaffed.
4. Inadequate material was available for obstetrical teaching.

This first reason given for the probation was considered to be the most serious and it is difficult to determine why the seriousness was weighted in that direction. The solution to that problem appears rather simple—have the Education Committee retire from the scene. The Committee did disband; however, the problem ran deeper than the existence or interference of the Committee. The American Medical Association was actually criticizing the College for its lack of firm university participation and direction. In this Nation, medical colleges are associated with universities to some degree. The reason may boil down to the fact that medical colleges are notorious money eaters and through association with a university they may, when the occasion demands, look to the university for financial assistance. The association is not wholly parasitical because the university through its association with the medical college can nicely round out its collection of colleges with medical college the prestigious frosting on the cake. Dr. Hutchinson of Chicago Unviersity on one occasion described a university as a group of colleges joined by a common heating system.

RELATIONSHIP WITH UNION UNIVERSITY ON TRIAL

The association of Albany Medical College with Union Unviersity could not even point to common use of a utility other than Niagara Mohawk Power Corporation. It is true that the Chancellor of Union University was a member of the Executive Faculty of the Medical College but beyond that there was little interaction between the two organizations. Dr. Ordway, when Dean, had recommended that graduation exercises be held in common with other graduates of Union in Schenectady. Other than the availability of a ready made larger audience, this may have been an attempt to draw more interest from the University to its member organization in Albany.

By comparison, the College had a hand-in-hand association with Albany Hospital. The College and Hospital occupied attached buildings; they shared a common staff in that the faculty of the College was the medical staff of the Hospital; the students of the College used the Hospital as its primary clinical training facility; and the Board of Trustees and Governors of their respective organizations appointed members from their body to serve as a joint Administrative Committee. A portion of the reason for the gulf betwen the College and the University may have been geographic and another reason may have been the basic educational field of the two. Union University is primarily an educational institution devoted to preparing students for the business arena or the field of liberal arts. The Medical College's sole purpose is to prepare its graduates for the practice of medicine which is a scientific field.

AFFILIATION WITH
RENSSELAER POLYTECHNIC INSTITUTE DISCUSSED

In a meeting on June 10, 1938, with the exception of one day, exactly a year after the discussion of the probation, the Trustees had a lengthy meeting. The subject of the meeting was the possibility of terminating its affiliation with Union to become a member college of Rensselaer Polytechnic Institute. The Chancellor of Union University had been informed by the Trustees of their inclination and he said there would be no objection by Union University to their conducting an open discussion between the Medical College and Rensselaer Polytechnic Institute.

At the meeting, numerous reasons were given to support the proposed change in the affiliation. The major reason for considering severing the connection with Union was that the Trustees believed the cause for the probation status by the American Medical Association was the lack of university participation in the affairs of the College. They also felt that Union had no real interest in strengthening the bonds between the two. The Trustees were also of the opinion that the most affluent foundations were sparing in their support of the College for the same reason held by the American Medical Association.

On the positive side, the Medical College and Rensselaer Polytechnic Institute had in common the emphasis on the scientific fields such as physics, chemistry, biology and electricity. It was reasoned that the results of research conducted in chemistry and biology in the Medical College would strengthen the courses in undergraduate work at Rensselaer Polytechnic Institute. Then too, the role of public health was growing and the amalgamation of medical and engineering talents would hasten progress through mutual research by the two disciplines. A final reason for the change of affiliation was the example of success demonstrated by the working relationship of the Massachusetts Institute of Technology and Harvard Medical School.

The planning was worked out in some detail during numerous conferences between the two institutions. Albany Medical College was represented in the discussion by a committee comprised of Messrs. Renshaw, McNamee, Eldridge, Greenleaf and Dr. Cunningham. It was proposed that a Board of Trustees be established with 12 representatives from Albany Medical College and 24 from Rensselaer Polytechnic Institute. The Medical College was willing to accede numerical superiority on the Board to Rensselaer Polytechnic Institute. Funds were to be solicited for use by both institutions as the needs of either dictated and finally, Albany Medical College would retain its name, but it was requested that Rensselaer Polytechnic Institute change its name to Rensselaer Scientific Institute.

For whatever reason, the move appears to have died in committee. Somewhat mysteriously, the suggesion is never again mentioned in the minutes of the Board of Trustees or elsewhere in the archives. In 1962, there was a relationship established between Albany Medical College and Rensselaer Polytechnic Institute where by agreement of the two, a student could complete an accelerated course of study and obtain a Bachelor of Science and Medical Degree in six years. The program was first offered to Union University who rejected the proposal after lengthy discussion. The reason was that it would require a substantial alteration in Union's curriculum which the faculty was unwilling to make. Rensselaer Polytechnic Institute welcomed the proposal, which has been highly successful since its inception.

OTHER AFFILIATIONS ESTABLISHED AND CONSIDERED

In regard to the remaining reasons for the imposition of probationary status, the Department of Pathology was strengthened and a new agreement between the College and the Brady Maternity Hospital was made to provide greater opportunity for the students to obtain obstetrical training and experience. In 1942, the College approved the following institutions to be used by the faculty for clinical instruction of the students:

Ann Lee Home and Hospital
Anthony N. Brady Maternity Hospital
St. Margaret's House and Hospital for Babies
The Mary Imogene Bassett Hospital
New York State Hospital for Incipient Tuberculosis
St. Peter's Hospital
Samaritan Hospital
Ellis Hospital
Homer Folks Sanitarium

Of this list, all except the last four had been previously approved.

In 1949, it again seemed possible that Albany Medical College would sever its ties with Union College and become a member institution of the New York State University System. New York State was seeking the location for a medical center in the upper part of the State. The Board of Trustees with majority, but not unaminous approval, elected to seek the selection. The obvious advantage to the College was the availability of State funds which would have permitted immediate expansion of the physical plant of both the Medical College and the Hospital. The advantages offered to the State were the following:

1. A day-to-day working partnership already was present between the State Department of Health and the Medical College.
2. The Trustees were willing to turn over all of the assets of the College to the State.
3. Albany Medical College had a close working relationship with General Electric Company and Winthrop Laboratory.
4. In the academic field, close ties had been formed with Rensselaer Polytechnic Institute.
5. The College had working relationships with hospitals from Kingston in the southern part of the State to Ticonderoga in the north.

However, after due deliberation, the State selected the Syracuse University School of Medicine to become a member of its university system. One of the reasons why Albany was not selected was that its remote physical location from its university affiliation was not conducive to encouraging research. This lack of close affiliation with a university had, since the turn of the century, retarded the growth of Albany Medical College in several instances.

ADMISSIONS POLICIES REVISED

Almost immediately after his appointment as Dean, Dr. Cunningham recommended that all previous actions concerning the admission of students be revised. Specifically, he recommended removing the restriction on the number of students admitted, cease the granting of admission on the basis of geographical origin of the applicant, and disregarding the religious preference of any individual applying for admission. He recommended that the admissions committee be permitted full discretion in their selection of applicants. As recently as February 25 of that same year, the Executive Faculty had recommended to the admissions committee that exceptional students of the Hebrew religion should be admitted even if this required that the 10 percent quota of Hebrews be exceeded. Dr. Cunningham's recommendations were accepted and an era of enlightenment and growth began.

In regard to admission, the 1936 Catalog had stated succinctly that "Women are admitted." In 1937, that statement was broadened to say "Women are admitted under the same conditions as men." The door was open and the welcome mat was now fully extended.

The new admission regulations were first effective in 1938 when 36 students were admitted to first year studies. In 1939, first year class size increased by one to total 37 students selected from 544 applicants. Of that number 60 had been approved for admission of whom 23 apparently declined. Graduates increased overall during Dr. Cunningham's administration in the following numbers:

1938 - 25	1943 - 34	1948 - 40
1939 - 23	1944 - 39	1949 - 41
1940 - 29	1945 - 40	1950 - 52
1941 - 29	1946 - 44	1951 - 39
1942 - 32	1947 - 43	

DEPARTMENTS AND SUB-DEPARTMENTS IN 1940

In 1940, the Board of Trustees, as a matter of record, identified the departments and sub-departments of the College. The ten departments were: Anatomy, Biochemistry, Pathology and Bacteriology, Physiology and Pharmacology, Medicine, Neurology and Psychiatry, Pediatrics, Radiology, Gynecology and Obstetrics, and Surgery. Of these, the Departments of Medicine and Surgery had sub-departments. The Department of Medicine had three sub-departments: Dermatology and Syphilology, Preventive Medicine and Public Health, and Tuberculosis. The Department of Surgery consisted of seven sub-departments: Anesthesia, Dentistry, Ophthalmology, Orthopedics, Physical Therapy, Urology, and Neurosurgery. It is interesting to note that of the then three sub-departments in Medicine, only a portion of one, Dermatology, remained in 1975. Preventive Medicine and Public Health had become a department in 1968 and syphilis and tuberculosis had been rendered curable by modern drugs so that there was no longer the need for concentration in those fields. Of the then seven sub-departments of Surgery, five remained in 1975 and two, Anesthesia and

Physical Therapy had developed into departments. Earlier in 1940, Radiology had been separated from Surgery to become a department, and the Department of Pediatrics had emerged from the Department of Medicine. By 1975, the ten departments of 1940 had grown to seventeen. However, 1940 can be regarded as the year that inaugurated the growth period of departments and sub-departments in the College. At a later time the designation "sub-department" was changed to "division."

Albany Medical College was not a pioneer in this breadth and depth of organization, for in 1940, it was only coming abreast of organizations in other advanced medical colleges. Two factors had heretofore hampered the growth of Albany Medical College. They were the absence of funds to staff the departments and sub-departments, and, equally restrictive was the unavailability of personnel of the calibre required.

FINANCIAL SITUATION OF THE COLLEGE IN 1938

And to the point of finances, in 1938 the College had an income of $136,000 of which $45,000 came from tuition. However, expenditures for that year were $151,000 resulting in a net loss of $15,000 which had to be deducted from the assets of only $110,800. It requires no financial genius to conclude that the College would be hard pressed to sustain itself during an extended period of similar or more severe losses. This is not to imply that the funds of the College were restricted to the unsubstantial amount mentioned but the balance of the funds was "tied-up" in various trust funds whose use was restricted by the terms of the donor or the particular trust. In 1943 and 1944, the financial situation happily reversed its previous direction. In 1943, the Board of Trustees reported a gain in cash of $24,649 and in 1944, an additional improvement of $21,390. In view of the dire significance of earlier losses, these gains were a substantial reversal.

The straitened financial condition of the College could in no way be attributed to profligate spending by the administration. In 1939, the annual tuition was increased from $400 to $500. This increase could have yielded nothing in excess of the loss of $15,000 in 1939 and since that amount would have required an enrollment of 150 students, the increased tuition did not balance the loss. Reflecting back to 1839 reveals that during the following 100 years tuitions had been gradually increased by 500 percent. But what costs had not increased by more than that?

However, it must be remembered that the Nation was still in the grips of the Great Depression precipitated by the Wall Street Crash of 1929. In recognition of the financial burden imposed on the student and his family by the expenses of medical education, the College continued to lease microscopes to students who could not afford or did not elect to purchase one for their use. The total cost for three years use was $117 payable in three installments. Forty dollars was required at the time of registration, a second payment of $40 at the start of the second year, and $37 for the third year of use. If the microscope was returned in good condition, the $117 was returned to the graduate. This provided a small dowry to the young doctor at the time of his wedding to private practice. A fairly decent automobile which was a prerequisite for practice in those days of house calls, could be purchased for $400. In effect, the trusty microscope could be at least traded in as a down payment on a car. First things first.

The Government had not yet initiated any programs offering financial aid to students. However, the College did have 21 scholarships which were available to qualified applicants. Of these, eight were Fuller Scholarships awarded by Union College, one was the Julia G. McNutt Scholarship for Women of New England Ancestry, another was the Isaac S. and Catherine E. Becker Scholarship, and the remaining eleven were the so-called Trustee Scholarships. To retain these scholarships, a student was required to maintain a "B" average. It is possible that the question of reverse discrimination may have reared its head because it is noted in the recitation of the scholarship list that "on advice of council," the Julia G. McNutt Scholarship, etc., must be awarded to women.

DEPRESSION WAGES

To provide some benchmark as to wages paid by the College in 1937, the night watchman received $960 per year—$80 per month or less than $20 per week. A stenographer received substantially more at $1,200 per year. The switchboard operator did little better than the watchman, recieving $85 per month. Dr. Cunningham requested that the Trustees approve the appointment of a Miss Mary E. Carroll as registrar of the College (Figure 74). Miss Carroll was paid $1,800 per year. From the description of Miss Carroll's assignment, it appears that the thinking of the administration was that idle hands are the devil's workshop. Miss Carroll was secretarial assistant to the Dean, in charge of editing the College Catalog, and responsible for publicity and extension programs as developments would demand. If not a one woman band, she was at least a string quartet. The foregoing emoluments were not in addition to retirement benefits, lengthy vacations, sick days, various insurance programs or other ancillary benefits of employment. The total paid faculty comprised 59 members, of whom 17 were doctors and for whom the payroll was $102,459 an average of slightly less than $1,730 per year. So, Miss Carroll need not feel put upon, being somewhat above average at $1,800. And the 17 doctors

(Fig. 74) Miss Mary E. Carroll

were not threatended by the burden of impending wealth in return for their service on the faculty either. As mentioned earlier, one member of the faculty had his salary reduced from $2,000 annually to $1,250 when promoted from Clinical Instructor in Medicine to Associate Professor. Pursuing that logic, one hesitates to calculate the potentially staggering financial impact of promotion to full professorship.

The tightness of the ship or more appropriately the financial reins is exemplified by a letter from a Mr. R.J. Almy to Dean Cunningham written in 1937. The subject of the letter concerned the Department of Experimental Surgery expenditure. The letter explained the over-expenditure of the Department of $22.20. It also explained in detail the reason for the overexpenditure. It was caused by the replacement of the Department's porter's assistant and the necessity of a retraining program to properly equip him for his duties. The records do not contain a reply from Dr. Cunningham, so the degree of dissatisfaction is not known, nor whether he accepted the over budget expenditure with resigned complacency.

RESEARCH GRANTS IN LATE THIRTIES

Quite obviously to maintain any semblance of a research program, there had to be some extramural financial support. In the latter period of the 1930's, the College began to receive grants for research in specific fields. The grants came from drug manufacturers such as Winthrop Chemical Co., Hoffman-LaRoche, Emerson Drug Co., Belhuber Chemical Co., and Miles Laboratory. Of these, Winthrop Chemical Co. was the most generous. The American Medical Association in 1940 granted $200 for research in physical therapy and foundations such as the Josiah Macy, Jr., Dazian Foundation for Medical

Research, the Council of American Academy of Arts and Sciences, and the International Cancer Research Foundation contributed funds for various research efforts. Of these, the latter was the largest contributor.

An interesting grant was made in 1940 by the Consolidated Car Heating Co. for the purpose of research in the application of Ticonium to surgery. The initial grant was for $650 and a year later, perhaps encouraged by some development now lost in time, the grant was renewed. Consolidated Car Heating Co. offered to give the College $248.58 per month for a continuation of research on the subject until further notice. In an effort to rationalize the amount of $248.58 curiosity forced the multiplication of that figure by 12 on the basis of one year's extension. The amount was an equally unexplainable $2,982.96.

While the amounts of the grants do not bear favorable comparison with those of later years, they must be viewed in the proper perspective. These were the times when tuition was $500 per year and the annual salary of College employees was below $2,000.

WORLD WAR II

The winds of war were again scattering the ashes of the cities of Europe and the holocaust of a second global war soon to engulf the Earth. Unlike the government's action in World War I, when it made no effort to prepare for the demand for more doctors until the war was in its final days, in World War II the effort was made early in the conflict. In 1942, the Army-Navy Program was started. It was based on a 12 month school year and the Armed Forces would select the students to be admitted. Of those admited, 55 percent would be sponsored by the Army and destined for service in that branch, 25 percent were selected for Navy service. The remaining 20 percent were to be civilian students and the eligible were women and physically handicapped men. The students received free tuition and books which were paid for by the government in addition to $2.75 per day for board and lodging. Fifty dollars per month was given to the students for incidental expenses. The Army assigned students were required to practice close order drill and the Navy students, in the absence of available ships, were presumably permitted to stand about and comment on the lack of precision of their marching fellow students. In 1943, the College recessed for 17 days. The Army granted 10 of the 17 as a furlough for their students and required them to spend the remaining seven doing calesthenics.

The faculty of the College and the staff of the Hospital had no need for calesthenics having already been "thinned out" by the demand on them for extra duty because of reduction in their numbers as a result of the formation of Albany Base Hospital Unit *(Figure 75)*. It was designated as the 33rd General Hospital and was comprised of 693 members.

(Fig. 75) Members of the Base Hospital Unit formed at Albany Hospital: Left to right, first row, Maj. Hermon Gordinier, Maj. Howard Berg, Lt. Col. Eldridge Campbell, Maj. Paul Schulze Jr., and Maj. David Hunn; second row, Capts. John F. Filippone, Henry C. Engster, William H. DeRouville, Stewart C. Wagoner, and Sigmund H. Smedal; third row, Capts. John J. Lyons, William H. O'Brien, James H. Flynn Jr. and Stuart MacMillan, and First Lt. William McGuire.

Of this number, 48 were doctors and 120 nurses. Fourteen thousand dollars was raised to provide some of the material necessary to equip the 1,000 bed capacity of the Unit. Dr. Eldridge Campbell, Professor of Surgery in the College, was appointed Unit Director and Chief of Surgical Service with the rank of Colonel. As a rather pointed inducement, all doctors under 45 years of age were offered the choice of enlisting and receiving a commission, or being drafted and receiving $20 per month as any other draftee. The option was there, but decidedly one sided. Nurses were not, of course, subject to the draft and their enlistment was totally voluntary. All nurses were commissioned second lieutenants at the time of enlistment. As a result of this demand, the nursing staff in the Hospital was reduced to 120 from the normal staff of 210. The attending staff of doctors was reduced more drastically, their number shrinking from 80 to 40.

The requirement to make do with less extended beyond the reduction in staff to conservation in medical supplies. There is an old adage that the meat packing industry used every part of the pig including the tail from which a whistle was fashioned. Those practicing medicine were urged to equal this approach in regard to the use of rubber gloves in surgery. Those in surgery were urged to use gloves until they were beyond repair *(Figure 76)*. Exactly what "beyond repair" implied was left to the bounds of ingenuity of the user. When that point was reached, the glove was then dismembered for further use in the following manner: fingers (presumably those intact) were cut off and used as finger cots, dismembered palms and backs were to be used as bottle and flask tops, and wrist parts were to be cut into rubber bands. The latter could have been used to bind efficiency reports. Had there been a tail on the glove, it would probably have been given to patients to be used to call for a bed pan.

Mobilization of Albany Hospital Medical Unit had taken place prior to the entry of United States in World War II and thereafter the Hospital suffered from a shortage of staffing. In 1943, it was reported that 80 percent of the orderlies had been lost to the Hospital. To relieve the situation, 534 volunteer workers that year contributed 9,590 hours of service in one month. Floor staffing was reduced to one graduate nurse per floor after 5:00 p.m.

Concurrent with the shortage of staff was the pressing need for more beds. In 1944, the bed shortage became acute. In 1945, patients were waiting 2 and 3 months for admission for elective surgery because of the shortage which was to continue. On April 30, 1946, 613 patients were awaiting admission to the Hospital. Albany Hospital was not alone in this regard. Every hospital in the City had waiting lists. An Emergency Admission Committee was formed to act on admissions. A second Committee was formed to maintain surveillance on length of hospitalization. Each admitting doctor was required, "in his own handwriting within 48 hours," to state the reason for admitting a patient. The Veterans' Hospital, which was to become a part of the Medical Center complex, had not yet been built. This imposed a further burden on admissions as veterans with service related disabilities were to be treated at Albany Hospital. The Veterans' Administration was respon-

(Fig. 76) Sterilizing surgical gloves for reuse.

sible for the expense of hospitalization. Further intensifying the situation was a report that the shortage of nursing staff might require 80 much needed beds to go unoccupied. The War had reduced the number of general staff nurses to 40 percent of that before the War. Nursing and beds were not the only shortages. The Government allowed the Hospital only 66 2/3 percent of the interns that were employed prior to the War. Sixteen year old girls were encouraged to volunteer to handle flowers, arrange bedside tables, replace drinking glasses and water pitchers, as well as to deliver luncheon trays to the patients. The call for male volunteers had been answered with an excellent response.

WARTIME MEDICAL ADVANCES

In would seem as though man rises to his greatest proficiency during times of adversity. As a biproduct of World War I, the medical profession had made great strides in the treatment of shock victims which may have contributed substantially to the development of the trauma unit. Great strides were made in the treatment of wound victims in the prevention of tetanus infection as well as numerous other advances. The period of World War II was to provide a similar impetus. In 1937, sulfonamide was first used to cure gonorrhea, and in 1939, at the outset of the War, there was a period of many advances in the treatment of wounds and traumatic infections, sanitation methods, and improvements in prosthetic limbs. In 1939, P. Müller introduced DDT insecticide (without which the World may have suffered catastrophic epidemics spurred by the War), and in that same year penicillin was developed to the stage of therapeutic use.

Fortunately for mankind throughout the world, penicillin had been discovered and was being used to both cure and prevent a myriad of illnesses. However, due to the demands of the battle fields, the Hospital was allocated only 360 ampules of the precious drug as a month's supply. Twenty-five to 30 ampules were being prescribed for daily use by the doctors. As a result, a notice was circulated requesting a curtailment of use of the precious drug or rationing might be imposed by the Hospital. On October 25, 1945, the Hospital was faced with the possibility that on the next day no penicillin would be available.

ALBANY HOSPITAL PLANS EXPANSION

It was impractical to enlarge student enrollment in the Medical College to alleviate the shortage of doctors. The volunteers could not replace the shortage of nurses but they did do many of the menial time consuming jobs previously performed by staff nurses thereby freeing the nurses for those tasks which required their training. In the midst of the chaos, the Board of Governors in 1944 started planning expansion of the Hospital to provide 1,000 beds. Two new buildings were to be added and designated as the North and West buildings. In addition, a building was to be erected for the Medical College and a new residence building for the Nursing School. The following year a fund raising drive was launched — the goal placed at $3,000,000. As with earlier expansion programs, this amount was to prove inadequate to fulfill the plans. The final cost of the expansion was in excess of $4,000,000. The drive was "kicked-off" with the preparation and distribution to potential donors of a brochure explaining the history of the Hospital and the intended use of the funds to be raised. Income tax during the War had become a substantial burden. The fund raisers, aware of this, included in the brochure a rather complete schedule of tax deductions that could be claimed by the donor based on the amount given, and the donor's income which was also shown in numerous income ranges.

The nursing staff and Ladies' Auxiliary conducted a Charity Bazaar in the Troup B Armory for the benefit of the Hospital. The affair was held on December 11 and 12, 1946 and raised $5,000.

An interesting sidelight on the fund raising drive was revealed in a survey of City residents. The question asked was: did they favor a compulsory government insurance program to cover the cost of hospital care as a substitute for a voluntary program to meet financial shortages? Seventy percent responded to the effect that they would prefer the voluntary way of providing Hospital support. It would be interesting to follow-up on this survey to determine if those people were willing to put their money where their votes were. It would be even more interesting to conduct a similar survey today.

A lesser problem than raising funds for expansion of the Hospital developed in 1945 with the return of doctors to the hospital from military service. The parking space in front of the rotunda entrance to the Hospital is limited and reserved for doctors. However, this was the most convenient parking space. Perhaps as a result of the War with its officer status and "rank has privilege" mentality, executive status with its "perks" became more prevalent in America. In industry, executives were awarded corner offices. Office furnishing was to replace officers' bars and chevrons as an outward mark of rank or status. What doctor finding the current and prestigious parking spaces filled would drive around the "block" to find a parking space? The solution was found only with much thought and resultant "bent noses" that plastic surgery could not correct.

HOSPITAL DEVELOPS PATIENT RELATIONSHIP

In 1946, the Hospital became increasingly patient-relationship conscious. Each patient was given a booklet on admission explaining the workings of the Hospital. A portion of the booklet was devoted to the "do's and don'ts" for both patient and visitors. Patients were encouraged to report less than satisfactory service of food. It was explained that occasionally coffee might not be as hot as one might desire. The reason being that nurses might be delayed in serving the meal because of some emergency condition. That particular problem, like warm coffee, has proved to be insurmountable because, as of this time, it has yet to be solved.

Brochures of this sort routinely have one peculiarity in common— the photographs of patients and attendants. First, the patients always appear to radiate good health and a smiling attitude to the world. The nurses are always the most beautiful women who exceed in attractiveness the Hollywood representation of their profession.

In 1947, the Hospital surpassed its previous printed communication with its patients. "Good morning" cards were distributed, presumably, with the breakfast trays. In addition to the cheery salutation, the greeting card included an attractive reproduction of a painting done in an oriental style by the artist Chang Shu-Chi. The reproduction was accompanied by a variety of Chinese proverbs which may have been intended to fortify the patients against the events of the day or a philosophical acceptance of their coffee should it not happen to be piping hot. In somewhat the same vein, post cards were available with an aerial view of the Hospital. It would be interesting to know of the number sent by patients to friends bearing the usual post card message, "Wishing you were here," with a postcript "instead of me."

CIGARETTES SEEN AS A DANGER

In view of the public's later perception of the dread effect of smoking the evil weed—cigarettes—a rather surprising warning was issued to Hospital personnel on June 11, 1947. The warning forbade smoking in the operating rooms or corridors of the seventh floor. The warning resulted from a notice issued by the insurance carrier earlier that year in April. It is assumed that the warning excluded not only cigarettes but cigars and pipes as well. At the time, the basis for the 1947 warning was the possibility of fire or explosion due to the presence of ether or oxygen in the air from the operating room. However, a new danger from cigarette smoking was later discovered. On April 29, 1965, Drs. Kenneth Olson and John Hosley who were working in lung cancer research at Albany Medical College, called cigarettes the greatest tragedy of the 20th century. They were among the first to recognize the causal effect of cigarette smoking in lung cancer. In 1968, the Medical Center initiated its campaign against cigarettes. Employees wore a button with the picture of a burning cigarette and the word "No" above the cigarette.

In 1947, an awareness of malpractice litigation was also developing and another edict stated that doctor's prescriptions without the doctor's signature or those accompanied by only the nurse's signature had no standing in court.

CHANGES IN ORGANIZATION AND PERSONNEL

As a result of these discoveries and improvements, the very basics of medical education and the structure of the curriculum were to be altered. Specialties such as syphilology and the treatment of tuberculosis were eliminated or reduced in scope and were replaced by other specialties and areas of research. However, these advances were not reflected in the structure of Albany Medical College until the decades of the '50's and '60's. The most significant changes during the preceding decade had been those which took place in 1940. In 1940 Radiology became a department, the subject having been taught by the Department of Surgery since 1915. Additionally, Pediatrics was detached from the Department of Medicine that same year, 1940, to become a full department. The Tumor Clinic was established in 1942 and continued under that title until 1948 when it was organized as the Department of Oncology. Dr. L. Whittington Gorham, who was Professor of Medicine and head of that Department as successor to Ordway in 1937, was appointed Professor and Head of the newly formed Department of Oncology. Dr. Richard T. Beebe was appointed Professor of Medicine and Department head to replace Dr. Gorham in 1948. At the same time, Dr. Beebe was appointed Physician-in-Chief of Albany Hospital.

The Department of Anesthesiology was formed in 1953, having been a sub-department of the Department of Surgery since 1938. Nine years earlier, in 1944, it was proposed as a separate department and the proposal was rejected. In 1952, the sub-departments of Plastic and Thoracic Surgery were both formed in the Department of Surgery.

In 1935, the sub-department of Public Health was established under the Department of Medicine. It continued as such until 1939 when its field was expanded as reflected in its new title, the sub-department of Preventive Medicine and Public Health. In 1948, it became a full Department. While it continued as a department through 1975, it is identified as the Department of Preventive and Community Health in 1958. There were probably good reasons for the numerous changes in title but the cost of discarding stationery and door plates must have been substantial.

ROBERT B. LAMB CHAIR OF MEDICINE

In 1948, Dr. Robert Brockway Lamb, a graduate of Albany Medical College in the Class of 1891, contributed $2,000 to establish a course in doctor-patient relationships *(Figure 77)*. Dr. Lamb was very sensitive of a patient's apprehensions and desired to develop that sensitivity in

(Fig. 77)
Dr. Robert Brockway Lamb

students. The Lamb Foundation also awarded annual prizes to three graduating seniors who demonstrated the greatest proficiency in their professional relations with patients.

By 1955, the Lamb Foundation had increased its funding of the Doctor-Patient Relationship Program to $10,000 annually. That year, the Lamb Foundation also provided a permanent trust fund to establish the Robert B. Lamb Chair of Medicine at Albany Medical College. The generous offer was accepted and the Chair was established. Dr. Richard T. Beebe was the first Robert B. Lamb Professor of Medicine. He was followed by Dr. Stuart Bondurant, Dr. Wallace N. Jensen, and the incumbent, Dr. John A. Balint.

In 1982, the College received $800,000 from the estate of the deceased Dr. Lamb. This is the largest bequest ever made to the College by a graduate.

POSTWAR EXPANSION OF THE HOSPITAL AND COLLEGE

During this period the finances of the College improved, due in part to a gradual increase in tuition fees. In 1946, annual tuition increased from $500 to $600. Two years later another $100 increase brought the annual fee to $700, and again two years later, in 1950, the tuition was increased by $50 to a total of $750. However, while the increased income from tuition did contribute to the finances of the College, more substantial aid came from the Federal Government and various foundations. The public in general was becoming more "health" conscious and the Government responded with financial aid to hospitals and medical schools throughout the Nation.

As stated earlier, in 1944 the Governors of the Hospital started planning for expansion of the facility. In 1945, the Governors of Albany Hospital undertook an expansion program. They employed Will, Folsum, and Smith as fundraisers and appointed Messrs. Schmidt, Gardner, and Erickson to design the new additions. The Trustees of Albany Medical College endorsed the development and participated in the effort, the end result being visualized by them as the formation of a unified medical center. A portion of the expansion was to be built on land owned by the College. It may be recalled that the Theobald Smith Laboratory Building belonged to the Hospital and had been leased to the College. Since 1936, the College had invested $85,000 in renovation of the Laboratory and in 1944 had requested that the Hospital deed the building to the College. After all, a tenant is willing to make only so much improvement to a property before gaining some equity for the investment.

As part of the negotiation for the expansion of the Hospital, the College granted the necessary land to the Hospital and, in return, received the deed for the Laboratory Building. In addition, the College pledged $450,000 to the Hospital Expansion fund to be paid in three isntallments of $150,000 each on February 1, 1950, August 1, 1950, and February 1, 1951. The first $300,000 was paid from accumulated funds of $150,000, $100,000 cash on hand, and the balance of $50,000 was borrowed. In return for this generous support, the College was granted free use of space in the bulding expansion for 99 years rent free.

The culmination for this unified and mutually beneficial effort was the formation in 1950 of the Albany Medical Center Council.

The College's need for additional space may have originated in a request in 1949 by the Trustees of New York State University that the nine medical schools in New York State graduate 200 more students each year. If the request could not be satisifed by the then existing schools, the Trustees further stated that the State would establish new medical schools for that purpose. The Trustees of Albany Medical College agreed to participate in the effort with the other eight schools.

DR. JAMES A. CAMPBELL

When Dr. Cunningham became Executive Director of the Albany Medical Center Council in 1950, Dr. James A. Campbell was appointed Dean of Albany Medical College *(Figure 78)*. The appointment was effective May of that year.

Dr. Campbell was born in Moweaqua, Illinois in 1917. He graduated from Knox College, where he received a Bachelor of Arts degree. He then attended Harvard Medical School, graduating in 1943. After an

Assistant Resident in Pathology at Billings Hospital in Chicago, Dr. Campbell had his internship at Boston City Hospital where he was later Assistant Resident and Resident in Medicine.

In 1946, he was appointed Executive Officer of the Medical Division of the Clinical Research Section of the Army Chemical Center, Edgewood Arsenal, Maryland. A year later, he was named Harvey Cushing Fellow at Johns Hopkins Hospital and Medical School. In 1948, he joined the staff of Presbyterian Hospital in Chicago as Assistant Attending Physician, and, in 1949, Attending Physician of that Hospital. A year later, in 1950, at the age of 33, he became the youngest person to be Dean of Albany Medical College.

On his appintment to Dean, he was faced with a not unusual circumstance for Albany Medical College—straitened finances.

For many years Albany Hospital had enjoyed literally free use of laboratory facilities and personnel in the College for laboratory tests of patients treated in the Hospital. Of course, the Hospital charged for the tests. Like unrequited lovers, this unrequited service had long since been a sore point with the faculty of the College. The youthful Dean, with undeniable insistence, informed the Board of Governors of the Hospital that henceforth the College must be compensated for its laboratory service. The Governors, without feigning their reluctance, agreed. The income to the College brought some welcome financial relief.

Dr. Campbell was active in medical research and encouraged the growing research work being done in Albany Medical College. He is the author of a number of papers on cardiovascular and other diseases.

In 1953, he left Albany to become Professor of Medicine and President of Rush-Presbyterian St. Luke's Medical Center and Professor of the Department of Medicine of Rush Medical College, Chicago.

PUBLICITY AND ETHICS

An interesting insight into the strict adherence to the ethical codes of the times took place in 1950. Dr. Eldridge Campbell was then professor of Surgery and Chief Surgeon in the Hospital. Research was being done in replacement of heart valves with plastic valves and the replacement had been successfully performed on laboratory animals. *Life* magazine proposed doing an illustrated article on the accomplishment. As *Life* leaned heavily toward pictorial reporting, the article was to be copious in the use of photographs. Dr. Campbell refused permission for the article that would have certainly enhanced the public perception of research by the College. His reason for refusing permission was based on the appearance in one picture of a doctor involved in the research. The general opinion of the time was that the acceptance of personal publicity would afford an unethical advantage

(Fig. 78)
Dr. James A. Campbell

to the recipient. In subsequent years, lesser medical breakthroughs have become front page news with no noticeable reluctance on the part of the individuals involved. It can be argued that this has resulted in a more informed, though at times confused, public.

CHANGING WORLD OF COLLEGE FINANCE

The financial history of Albany Medical College has been a series of moderate highs and plunging lows. It is like a small ship on a stormy sea, rising to the crest and then sinking into the trough of the wave. But each time it plummets, it miraculously steadies and begins another rise.

The financial support which gave sustenance to the College during its birth struggle came from modest contributions of those interested in its beginning. The relative financial tranquility after launching was primarily due to the modest objectives of the College which was to educate a small number of students in a short course primarily by rote. The building which housed the College was donated by the City of Albany and the only expense to be met by the College was the cost of maintenance and heat. The instructors' primary contribution was to lecture, and the students' main job was to listen to the lecture, watch demonstrations in the lecture hall, and observe treatment of patients in the Almshouse. None of these activities required a great financial outlay by the College.

The income from tuition was sufficient to support the College's modest expenses and compensate the instructors who were primarily devoted to the better education of aspiring doctors. The satisfaction that the faculty derived from a job well done was sufficient to keep each of them steadfast to his post and none left a great estate at his death.

However, by the early twentieth century, medical science had advanced to the point that the previous method of education was no longer sufficient. The curriculum had expanded, the body of knowledge to be imparted had grown, and the student had to participate more actively in the learning process. As a result, there was need for laboratory facilities for the students beyond that afforded in the Lancaster School. Albany Hospital had moved to a new location and the physical separation of School and Hospital made clinical work inconvenient. The little ship was headed into a deep and threatening trough. Again the City and the contributions of private citizens avoided a sinking. The City granted land to the College adjacent to Albany Hospital and private donations provided the necessary funds to erect a new home for the College.

Not unlike other institutions and most individuals early in the decade of the 30's, the College's finances again tilted downward. The Great Depression eroded income to the College from endowed investments and on this occasion the public sector was unable to respond with its usual generosity. The ability to avoid disaster at that time came from two sources. First, Dean Cunningham was a man possessed of remarkable organizational resources. His clever management provided the stabilizing hand which was needed. Secondly, the Federal Government, anticipating war in Europe, recognized the urgent need for more doctors. As a result, the necessary infusion of funds for the College's survival came in the form of tuition grants to students who, after graduation, were bound to serve at the Government's pleasure.

At the conclusion of the war, the Nation had emerged from the Great Depression and the College was financially sound. It was not then and never was as secure as many of its affluently endowed peers, but neither was it threatened by financial disaster.

EXPANDED FEDERAL ROLE

The world, which had suffered previously unsurpassed torment and destruction, suddenly awakened to the need and blessing of health. In addition, the surviving governments were faced with the task of mending the maimed of the war and restoring health to those who had suffered the great physical deprivation of war. The Government of the United States began to give unprecedented funds for the expansion of medical schools and for the support of medical research. The demands of everyone for medical attention had grown and the ability of medical science to provide treatment for heretofore incurable physical ailments had developed. The need for more doctors was imperative.

Albany Medical College was lifted by this tremendous wave of support in the form of State and Federal grants in addition to those from industrial organizations and charitable foundations. As a result of this outpouring of funds, the College was positioned to launch research programs, and, in general, provide an academic atmosphere that would attract scientists who would enhance the faculty and enable improvements in the teaching responsibility of the College.

Simultaneous with these developments, the Veterans' Hospital was built by the Government adjacent to the growing Albany Hospital in 1947 *(Figure 79)*. This facility provided an almost doubling of clinical opportunities for the College's medical students and its increased research effort. The advent of the Veterans' Hospital provided a great step toward the launching of the Albany Medical Center.

The working relationship between Albany Medical College and the Veterans' Hospital has always been excellent. The Veterans' Hospital had access to the consulting services of the College staff. In return, the College had the advantage of the Veterans' Hospital for clinical teaching. Dr. James H. Cullen was Head of the Department of Medicine at the Veterans' Hospital *(Figure 80)*. Dr. Cullen, a specialist in pulmonary physiology, was a dynamic teacher. The students of Albany Medical College learned much from their contacts with that always genial man. Dr. Stanley Wallach was appointed Head of the Department of Medicine at the Veteran's Administration Hospital in 1973 after Dr. Cullen's death.

(Fig. 79)
Veterans Administration Hospital

(Fig. 80)
Dr. James H. Cullen

The Time of
Growth and Development

DR. HAROLD C. WIGGERS

It was at the time of incipient growth that Dr. Wiggers was appointed Dean *(Figure 81)*. Through the fortunes of fate, the right man was available to be appointed Dean of the College at the right time. Harold C. Wiggers was Dean of Albany Medical College from 1953 to 1974, years of the College's most dynamic growth physically and academically, and most significantly, during its growth in medical research.

Dean Wiggers was born in Ann Arbor, Michigan in 1910. At the age of 22 he received his A.B. degree from Wesleyan University. Four years later, in 1936, he was awarded a Ph.D. degree in physiology from Western Reserve University. In his choice of physiology, he was following in the footsteps of his father, Dr. Carl Wiggers, a noted physiologist and author of, perhaps, the first text on the subject.

Before accepting the invitation to Albany Medical College, he had developed in other schools his talent for teaching. For the year 1936-37, he held the W.T. Porter Research Fellowship granted by the American Physiological Society, at Harvard Medical School. For five years thereafter he instructed in physiology at the College of Physicians and Surgeons of Columbia University. Then he served for a year as Assistant Professor of Physiology in the School of Medicine at Western Reserve University until he was called to become Associate Professor of Physiology at the University of Illinois, where he remained from 1943-47.

When Dr. Wiggers joined the faculty of Albany Medical College in 1947, as Professor and Chairman of the combined Departments of Physiology and Pharmacology, he had other offers in hand. Georgetown University had offered him a similar post but the opportunity for development seemed greater at Albany. Subsequent to his acceptance and during his service at Albany Medical College, he had opportunities from Detroit, New York City and Chicago. Pleasant living conditions in the smaller Capital District was one among other reasons which caused him to decline the moves.

Thus, when Dr. Wiggers assumed the Deanship of Albany Medical College in 1953, he had been on its faculty for six years. From his new

(Fig. 81)
Dr. Harold C. Wiggers

position, Dr. Wiggers observed a relatively amorphous organization, almost casually staffed by part-time teachers, and without the physical equipment that a first-rate institution would present. But, though he had no experience in raising funds, and little administrative background, he had been assistant to Dean James Campbell and had developed perspectives by serving on various College committees, including Admissions.

Thus prepared, Dr. Wiggers lost no time to invigorate the faculty seeking the best men available. In 1955, Dr. John A. Muntz was appointed Professor and Chairman of the Department of Biochemistry *(Figure 82)*. Dr. Muntz, after graduate training at the University of Chicago, had been a faculty member of Western Reserve School of Medicine in the Department of Biochemistry, then under the chairmanship of Harland G. Wood for nine years. Dr. Muntz held the position at Albany Medical College until his retirement in 1974. With Dr. Robert S. Alexander he developed a highly sucessful program for correlated teaching in biochemistry and physiology. Dr. Alexander had also arrived in 1955 from Western Reserve University as Professor of Physiology *(Figure 83)*. Besides Dr. Muntz' appointment to the Chairmanship, he served as Director of Laboratories at Albany Medical College and pioneered in enhancing the sophistication of the clinical laboratories. His efforts paved the way for Albany Medical Center Hospital to become one of the first institutions in the country to adopt automated and computerized laboratory procedures. His lectures set high standards for his staff to follow. He was the first chairman of the

(Fig 82)

Dr. John A. Muntz
Professor of Biochemistry

Dr. Joseph L. Glenn
Professor of Biochemistry

(Fig. 83)

Dr. Robert S. Alexander
Professor of Physiology

Dr. Rudolph M. Anker
Professor of Biochemistry

(Fig. 84)
Dr. Stuart Bondurant

Graduate Studies Program to coordinate and encourage graduate programs in the other basic sciences in the Medical College.

For whatever reason when Dr. Wiggers became Dean, the Department of Physiology and Pharmacology of which he had been Professor and Chairman became two separate departments. Dr. Frank Currier Ferguson was appointed Chairman of the Department of Pharmacology in 1953. At the time of his appointment, Dr.Ferguson was the youngest chairman of a department of pharmacology in the United States. Dr. Ferguson remained Chairman for the next twenty years, retiring in 1973. During those years, he developed an interesting teaching program which provided students with an insight into the relationship between fundamental pharmacology and therapeutics that is seldom found in medical school courses in pharmacology.

An applicant for entrance to the College in 1948 recalled his first meeting with Dr. Wiggers, one of a seven member screening group: "Questions ran the gamut from why we wanted to become doctors to what we thought about sex, gambling, drinking and the Cleveland Browns. Today, if the most hardened criminal were indicted for the most heinous felonies, all he would have to do to gain his freedom would be to show that his initial questioning took place under circumstances similar to those used in the admissions process of those days."

Dr. Wiggers' incumbency as Dean was less complicated at the beginning than it later became. During its first years, he still found time to teach a class in physiology.

The appointment of Dr. Wiggers was made with reservations from some quarters. Dr. Wiggers derived his title of "Doctor" as a result of a Ph.D. and not an M.D. degree. He was the first and only Dean to date who did not have an M.D. degree and some thought that his lack of the medical degree might be a handicap in controlling and directing the faculty and College. This was not the case. A newspaper reporter who knew Dr. Wiggers for more than a quarter of a century considered him an ideal Dean for the Medical College because of his specific abilities. He was described as having the characteristics of a planner, an administrator, a spender-penny-pincher, a visionary, a pragmatist, a soft-spoken diplomat, a hard-nosed executive, a teacher, a learner, the possessor of a strong stomach and a sense of humor. He was equally at ease before a class, at the head of a faculty, at a Board of Trustees meeting, at a meeting in Washington with Government representatives, or in a gathering of academia. His sense of where grants and gifts were available made him a premier fund raiser.

Coming to the office of Dean, Dr. Wiggers learned and grew on the job. He found that, "running a department does not necessarily prepare a man for supervising the administration of a variety of departments and divisions, many with conflicting viewpoints and needs that must be adjudicated, and for maintaining smooth and effective relationship with affiliated institutions, with the local, state, and federal governments, with foundations and other private resources of research funds, with trustees and staff and students, and with the many greatly divergent factions of the community and the area." When one considers the full implications of the statement, the conclusion reached is that the driver of a team of 60 mules had a picnic directing his 60 associates.

Dr. Wiggers retired in 1974 after 21 years as Dean of Albany Medical College. The sum of his contributions to the development of this College is impossible to state without fear of omission. Many of his salient accomplishments, however, are easily recognized.

The 1953 budget of the Albany Medical College was less than a million dollars. By 1974, it had grown to $16,000,000. Diverse research activities accounted for $6,000,000 of that sum—a large amount in contrast to what had been spent in 1953. The size of the physical plant had more than tripled, and the facilities had become immensely more varied and sopisticated.

Honors came from many sources to Dr. Wiggers and he accepted them modestly. At the close of his career in the Albany Medical College, those honors were augmented by naming the Chair of Physiology for him, and through the establishment of the Harold C. Wiggers Scholarship Fund by David and Eleanor Falk, members, respectively, of the Classes of March, 1943, and January, 1975. The fund is a recognition of Dr. Wiggers' contributions to medical education in general, and his devotion to the College in particular.

The Class of 1971 created a fund in honor of Dr. Wiggers for his specific contribution to education and " to medicine in our Nation." It is used to bring to the College commencement speakers who have contributed notably to the fields of medicine, medical education, and public health. A plaque bearing the names of the speakers is displayed in the Schaffer Library. In 1971, Dr. Stuart Bondurant, Professor and Chairman of the Department of Medicine at Albany Medical College, gave the commencement address. The next year, Dr. John H. Knowles, physician, educator, and administrator, received the honor.

That he might enter retirement equipped for healthful exercise, the American Society of Physiology, holding its annual meeting in Albany in 1974, presented Dr. Wiggers with a set of golf clubs. Many friends and colleagues attended parties to wish him well. At one of these, his portrait was unveiled. It hangs in the library of the Department of Physiology. At another gathering, the College's Executive Faculty gave him an engraved gavel and sounding board. The Faculty Wives' Club, founded by Mrs. Wiggers, sponsored a dinner dance where a purse for the History of Medicine Room of the Schaffer Library was presented.

The Albany Medical College played host at a reception to honor Dr. Wiggers and Dr. Stuart Bondurant, his successor as Dean *(Figure 84)*. Guests were happy to learn that Dr. Wiggers would remain active in academic circles after leaving Albany.

He had been invited to Greenville, North Carolina, to be Acting Dean of a proposed four-year medical school at East Carolina University. There his expertise would assist in the selection of architects, the planning of a curriculum, the hiring of key staff members, and the choosing of a dean.

Relinquishing his duties at Albany Medical College, Dean Wiggers applauded the appointment of his successor, Dr. Stuart Bondurant, praising him as, "one of the most able, nationally respected and sought-after leaders in American medicine," and asked support for him from alumni, faculty and students, "in one of the most uncertain periods, economically, politically, and energy-wise in the history of the United States and the world."

If he thought back to the founding of Albany Medical College as he was about to leave it, Dr. Wiggers must have been satisfied that the complex medical center, with the College at its hub, carries out the directive of Alden March, "to communicate and receive instruction in the science of medicine, and to preserve and restore the health of man." He could depart with the reasonable hope that the center will keep abreast of new discoveries in medicine and in collateral disciplines because of the enlightened minds and the spirit of dedication in each new generation of teachers and physicians.

(Fig. 85)
Dr. Robert L. Friedlander

DR. ROBERT L. FRIEDLANDER

In 1973, Dean Harold C. Wiggers asked Dr. Robert L. Friedlander to join his administration as Assistant to the Dean *(Figure 85)*. Dr. Friedlander had become a member of Albany Medical College faculty in 1962 as Resident, Obstetrics and Gynecology. In 1963, he served as Chief Resident and in 1964 he was appointed Instructor, Department of Obstetrics and Gynecology. During the preceeding nine years, he served in various positions in Albany Hospital and Albany Medical College until his appointment in 1973 as mentioned earlier.

Dr. Friedlander was born in 1933 in Detroit, Michigan. He was awarded a B.S. degree (Chemistry) by Wayne University in 1955 and three years later his M.D. degree from the same University. He subsequently interned at Mount Zion Hospital and Medical Center, San Francisco, California, before becoming Junior Assistant Resident, Obstetrics and Gynecology, University of Chicago Clinics, Chicago Lying-In Hospital, Chicago, Illinois. In 1960, Dr. Friedlander began two years active duty in the United States Navy Reserve as a medical officer with the rank of Lieutenant Commander. After completion of military service, he became a member of Albany Medical Center Hospital in 1962.

Before being appointed Dean in 1979 to succeed Dr. Bondurant, Dr. Friedlander had a progressively more demanding position in the administration of the College. When appointed Dean, Dr. Friedlander's previous experience equipped him well for the task which confronted him.

(Fig. 86)
Dr. Alice Fruehan

DR. ALICE ELIZABETH FRUEHAN

Another who served as Assistant to the Dean during Dr. Wigger's administration was Dr. Alice Elizabeth Fruehan *(Figure 86)*. Dr. Fruehan was appointed to that post in 1966 having joined the Albany Hospital Staff in 1957 when she served as Assistant Resident in Medicine and Resident in Medicine. Dr. Fruehan graduated from Johns Hopkins School of Medicine in 1956 and served her internship in the Osler Medical Service (Ward Medicine) at Johns Hopkins Hospital. In 1957, Dr. Fruehan joined the faculty of Albany Medical College serving in various assignments principally in the Department of Medicine. In July 1976, she was appointed a Professor of Medicine and in November of that year Professor and Chairman of the Department of Family Practice. Dr. Fruehan is a member of numerous committees and has found time in her active career to publish many papers on her work in medical research.

RESEARCH AND THE DYNAMIC GROWTH OF KNOWLEDGE

During the latter part of the 1940's and early 1950's, there was a tremendous growth in medical research and, as a result, medical science or medical knowledge. This growth was reflected in the expansion of medical schools performing research, the teaching of the results of the research, and specialization of medical practice to apply the knowledge. Perhaps the growth of specialization can best be described by the use of an imaginary martini glass, the bottom of the container portion of the glass comes to an exact point and therefore has no surface dimension. This was the state of medical and all scientific knowledge at the time of creation. When the first cave man twisted a vine about his arm to stop bleeding, or plastered mud on a bee sting, the first drop of knowledge was added to the empty glass. The surface at the bottom was now extended by virtue of that one drop. With each successive droplet of knowledge, the liquid in the glass rose and presented a broader surface of knowledge. While this hypothetical glass will never be filled, by the mid-point of the twentieth century the content had reached a height so that the total surface of knowledge was exceeding the grasp of any one man and the multitude of questions that were presented by the new breadth of knowledge exceeded the capability of one man to perceive.

As a result, the total which had already been divided into reasonable dimension had to be further divided both to perceive the question presented, to teach the knowledge acquired, and to put the knowledge in practice.

Albany Medical College was not the first or the last to be faced with and accept this challenge. But to meet the challenge it had to attract the personnel to perform the research which it could then contribute to the body of knowledge and to teach what was being discovered there and throughout the medical world. To attract the personnel necessary to do this work, the College had to provide facilities, direction and the intense academic atmosphere to foster the end result. Money may not be the answer to every problem but it helps solve many.

The necessary money came in abundant, and heretofore, unprecedented amounts.

DEPARTMENTS IN 1953

In 1953, the year in which Dean Wiggers took office, Albany Medical College was comprised of the following thirteen departments: Anatomy, Medicine, Neurology, Obstetrics and Gynecology, Pathology, Physiology, Surgery, Anesthesiology, Biochemistry, Pediatrics, Pharmacology and Experimental Therapeutics, Psychiatry, and Radiology. The first seven listed had existed since 1916 at the time the College was reorganized under the direction of Dr. Ordway, then Dean. In 1932, the Departments of Obstetrics and Gynecology were joined into one department. For one reason or another, the teaching of obstetrics had frequently suffered from the lack of clinical work in Albany Hospital with the majority of obstetric cases going to the Brady Maternity Hospital. At one time, pediatrics had been taught under the subject title of Diseases of Women and Children. A rather indiscriminate

(Fig. 87)
Dr. William L. Holt

combining of gender and age group. Also in 1941, the Department of Radiology was established. Earlier in 1930, Biochemistry had been elevated to full department status. From 1941 until 1952, no further additions were made. The eleven year hiatus in the growth of academic departments is probably largely explained by the demands of World War II which had depleted the faculty and Hospital staffs. After the war, no additions could be made until the original faculty strength was restored and funds became available for further growth.

Until 1952, neuropsychiatry covered both neurological and psychiatric problems. That year, Neurology and Psychiatry became separate departments. Dr. Robert Graves became the first head of the Department of Neurology and Dr. William L. Holt was appointed head of the newly established Department of Psychiatry *(Figure 87)*.

In 1953, two more departments were added to the roster: Anesthesiology, and Pharmacology and Experimental Therapeutics. Anesthesiology had, since 1938, been a sub-department of the Department of Surgery.

DEPARTMENT EXPANSION, 1956-63

From 1956 through 1963, four more departments were established: they were Microbiology and Immunology (1956), Community Health (1958), Ophtalmology (1963), and Physical Medicine and Rehabilitation (1963). The Department of Community Health was re-named the Department of Preventive Medicine and Community Health in 1963. The Department of Preventive Medicine had been a sub-department of the Department of Medicine since its inception in 1952.

In 1975, the departments with the greatest population of sub-departments, or divisions as they were later titled, were Medicine, Pediatrics, and Surgery. Examining each of the three in turn, the first will be Medicine. (To avoid the accusation of bias, it is hereby stated that the order of discussion is based on alphabetical order.)

DEPARTMENT OF MEDICINE

The Department of Medicine under the chairmanship of Richard T. Beebe was the theater for dynamic growth during the 1950's and early 1960's. In 1950 the sub-department of Cardiology was established under Dr. John Filippone who was joined by Dr. Joseph T. Doyle from the Harvard School of Medicine. Dr. Filippone had studied under Dr. Paul White, the world renowned cardiologist then practicing at Massachusetts General Hospital. Dr. Doyle later succeeded Dr. Filippone who returned to private practice. In 1952, three main sub-departments were added in a single year. They were Endocrinology, Hematology, and Oncology. The first head of Endocrinology was Dr. Thomas Frawley who was succeeded in 1964 by Dr. A. David Goodman *(Figure 88)*. The sub-department of Hematology was under Dr. Simon Propp, who had been a Professor of Medicine since 1936. He was succeeded in 1977 by Dr. William Scharfman *(Figure 89)*. The sub-department of Oncology had its origin in the Tumor Clinic which was founded in 1942 and was under the direction of Dr. L. Whittington Gorham, following his retirement as Chairman of the Department of Medicine in 1948. When founded, the Tumor Clinic was a department in the College and functioned as such until 1952 when it became a sub-department of the Department of Medicine. Dr. Kenneth B. Olson was appointed head of the sub-department of Oncology in 1952 *(Figure 90)*. Dr. Olson developed the sub-department and also developed the Tumor Registry. Dr. John Horton who had been an Associate Professor and Attending Oncologist at Albany Medical Center, succeeded Dr. Olson in 1972 as Chairman of the Division of Oncology.

In 1953, the Division of Pulmonary Diseases became the sixth division in the Department of Medicine. Dr. Rubin Erickson, formerly head of the Divison of Tuberculosis was appointed head. He was succeeded by Dr. Frank Maxon. In 1954, the sub-department of Physical Medicine and Rehabilitation was organized by Dr. John Ghormley. In 1963, it was given Department status. Dr. Ghormley was succeeded by Dr. Policoff until 1967 and Boris J. Paul until 1975. The Department is now headed by Dr. Radu I. Ghiulamila.

The Division of Syphilology and Dermatology was established in the Department of Surgery in 1935. At that time, syphilis was a common and widespread disease for which the only cure was a long series of

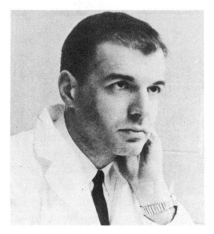

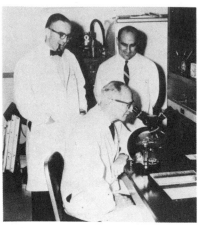

(Fig. 88)
Dr. A. David Goodman

(Fig. 89)
Drs. William B. Scharfman,
Simon Propp and
Anthony P. Tartaglia.

(Fig. 90)
Drs. Kenneth B. Olson and Arthur Wright.

injections of arsphenamine. Each week there would be a long line at the out-patient clinic of persons awaiting the injection. With the discovery of penicillin and better public education, the decrease in the incidence of the disease was dramatic. As a result, the division was eliminated. In 1956, the Division of Dermatology was assigned to the Department of Medicine where it logically belonged.

Growth of the Department of Medicine continued. In 1960, the Division of Renal Diseases under Dr. John Kiley was formed. In 1961, two more divisions were added. The first was the Division of Rheumatology under Dr. Curtland Brown *(Figure 91)*. In 1971, Dr. Lee E. Bartholomew succeeded Dr. Brown *(Figure 92)*. The second division added that year was Infectious Diseases headed by Dr. John Miller, who was succeeded in 1970 by Dr. James Tillotson. In 1963, Gastroenterology joined the ranks of divisions in the Department of Medicine. At its origin, the Division was directed by Dr. John A. Balint *(Figure 93)*. In 1981, Dr. Balint was appointed Chairman of the Department of Medicine and Dr. John Rodgers replaced him in the former post.

The most recent addition, as of 1975, is the Division of Allergy, which was established in 1965. Dr. Robert Raymond was appointed head of that Division.

Thus, from 1950 when the Department of Medicine had one division, by 1965, it had grown to twelve divisions. This growth was made possible by two factors; increased financial support for the College and Hospital through grants and gifts, and most significantly, by the availabiliy of dedicated and highly qualified people to man the growth.

This growth is clear evidence of the rapid development of medical science in a few decades. One might rightly conclude that the body of knowledge had increased six-fold. At the same time that these developments were taking place in the College, similar developments were made in the Hospital *(Figures 94, 95 and 96)*.

DEPARTMENT OF PEDIATRICS

Compared to the Department of Medicine and Surgery, pediatrics was a newcomer, having been established on July 1, 1941. Dr. Henry Larned Keith Shaw was the organizer of the Department and logically became its first Head. Dr. Shaw was followed by Dr. Otto Faust *(Figure 97)* as Chairman of the Department of Pediatrics until 1950 and then he was succeeded by Dr. Edward S. Goodwin until 1953 and Dr. Paul R. Patterson until 1967 *(Figure 98)*. Thirty-one years after the department was established, in 1972, it had been developed into seven areas of specialization or divisions. These developments were accomplished largely under the direction of Dr. Patterson and Dr. Ian H. Porter who was appointed Chairman of the Department in 1968 *(Figure*

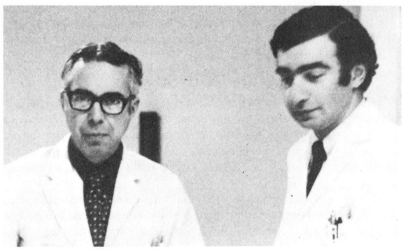

Top:
(Fig. 91) Dr. Curtland C. Brown

Above:
(Fig. 92) Drs. Lee Bartholomew
and Richard Rynes.

Left:
(Fig. 93) Dr. John A. Balint

99). It is interesting to note that of the seven divisions of the Department of Pediatrics; Ambulatory Pediatrics, Clinical Immunology, Endocrinology and Metabolism, Medical Genetics, Newborn Service, Pediatric Cardiology and Renal Diseases; Endorcrinology and Metabolosm and Renal Diseases have conterparts in the Department of Medicine.

DEPARTMENT OF SURGERY

The Department of Surgery in 1975 consisted of eight divisions namely; Dentistry, Neurosurgery, Orthopedic Surgery, Otolaryngology, Pediatric Surgery, Plastic Surgery, Thoracic Surgery, and Urology. Of these, the most recent additions were made in 1953 and 1955, when the Divisions of Thoracic Surgery and Plastic Surgery were added to the roster *(Figure 100)*. Dr. W. Brandon Macomber was the first clinical professor and Head of the Division of Plastic Surgery *(Figure 101)*. Dr. Macomber was largely responsible for the establishment and development of the "Burn Unit" in the Hospital. Plastic Surgery performs a vital role in the recovery of burn victims. Dr. Adrian Ehler organized the Division of Thoracic Surgery. After his death, he was succeeded by Dr. Allen Stranahan and later by Dr. Ralph D. Alley *(Figure 102)*. Dr. Alley formed a nucleus for the performance of open heart surgery at Albany Medical Center. Dr. Thomas M. Older trained with the group and then became responsible for much of the open heart surgery *(Figure 103)*.

Another surgeon of vision, Dr. C. Stuart Welch, had joined the faculty in 1938 *(Figure 104)*. He was an eminent author on surgery. He was the author and co-author of over 90 scientific papers and monographs, probably the most outstanding of which are "History of Surgery," "Christopher's Textbook on Surgery," 12th Edition; Section on Surgery, Encyclopaedia Britannica, 15th Edition; co-author with Dr. Samual R. Powers of "Essence of Surgery."

Dr. Welch came to Albany in 1938 and was an Associate Professor and attending surgeon until 1942. From 1942 to 1945, he served as Lieutenant Colonel in the U.S. Army Medical Corps. He returned to Albany Medical Center as Professor of Surgery and attending surgeon until 1947. From 1947 to 1952, he was Professor of Surgery, Chairman of that Department at Tufts College Medical School. In 1952, he, for a third time, came to Albany Medical Center and resumed the positions he held in 1945. Dr. Welch retired in 1972.

Dr. Welch was a pioneer in liver surgery. In association with Dr. John H. Carter, he contributed to a new surgical procedure which enabled the correction of portal vein obstruction which occurred primarily in cirrhosis of the liver.

Dr. Welch made an important contribution to the Hospital which was

(Fig. 94)

(Fig. 95)

(Fig. 96)

Facing page, top:
The 1948-49 medical house staff: (Front row, left to right) Drs. John Runyon, George Hemstead, Richard Beebe, Ralph Reynolds, William Diefenbach III; (Back row, left to right) Drs. Ronal Germain, Louis Jensen, David Cugell, Mary Hall, J. Thomas Grayston, Clayton Rich, Curtland Brown.

Facing page, bottom:
The 1967 Department of Medicine subdepartment heads: (Front row, left to right) Drs. Kenneth Olson, Simon Propp, Alice Fruehan, Richard Beebe, Joseph Doyle, John Kiley, John Balint; (Second row, left to right) Drs. David Goodman, James Cullen, Harold Wiggers, Robert Raymond, Curtland Brown; (Third row, left to right) Drs. Paul Formel, Frank Maxon, Joseph Demis, John Miller.

Above:
The 1960-61 medical house officers: (Front row, left to right) Drs. Joseph Dougherty, Robert Milora, Anthony Tartaglia, William Donahue, John Hornblower, Orlando Hines, David Pankin, Robert Allen; (Second row, left to right) Drs. George Reardon, Dominique Allerand; (Third row, left to right) Drs. Charles Norland, Adrian Grubs, Samuel Spitzer, David Siebert; (Fourth row, left to right) Drs. John Horton, Gilbert Geir, John Poggi, Martin Bruskin, Alice Fruehan; (Fifth row, left to right) Drs. Henry Tulgan, Robert Yerry.

out of context with his many contributions in surgery. He devised a portable scale which enabled bed ridden patients to be weighed. He is memorialized by that scale. When in the Hospital, at least once a day, one will hear these exact words over the call system: "Attention, everybody, anyone knowing the whereabouts of the Welch's scale please notify the operator." The design has withstood the test of time, the call is not for *a* Welch's scale, it is always for *the* Welch's scale.

Ophthalmology, which had been a division of the Department of Surgery, was elevated to Department status in 1963. Dr. Harry M. Judge was the first Chairman of the sub-department. He was succeeded by Dr. Walter Mott. Dr. James E. Miller succeeded Dr. Mott as chairman of the then formed Department of Ophthamology. Dr. Robert D. Reinecke became Professor and Chairman in 1970 following Dr. Miller's retirement. Dr. Richard S. Smith became Chairman of the Department in 1981. The appendices include a list of the Department and Division Chairmen and the years served.

NEED FOR RESEARCH FACILITIES

As a result of the growth which took place in the 1950's, the need for laboratory space in which to conduct research was absolutely necessary. Except for the conversion of the Theobald Smith Building for laboratory space, no addition had been made to the College facilities since the move to the new building in 1928. The growth in number of students was not a prime factor in the need for enlargement of College facilities. There had been a modest increase in the number of graduates from 47 in 1953 to 61 in 1962.

While the number of graduates from 1915 to 1962 had shown a small increase the number of students had increased substantially. The disproportionate increase of students to graduates during certain periods of this time is accounted for by the extension of years of study required for graduation.

Prior to 1950, little pure research was performed in Albany Medical College. The College's primary contribution was the education of persons for the profession. Developments in the science of research was brought to the College by adding new members to the faculty who had been trained in other colleges. In addition, those who were faculty members maintained growth in their knowledge by attendance at outside symposia and close attention to medical journals and papers.

With the availability of funds following World War II the transformation of the College from a teaching center to that of a research center as well took place. This change was clearly stated in 1953 at the time that the Medical Center was developing. The primary concern of the College was the teaching of medical students, and the primary concern of the Hospital was care of patients. Each institution was, in a sense,

(Fig. 97)
Dr. Otto Faust

(Fig. 98)
Dr. Paul R. Patterson

(Fig. 99)
Dr. Ian H. Porter

*(Fig. 100) The members of the 1955 Department of Surgery: (Clockwise from
far left) Drs. Stanley Alderson, J. Lewi Donhauser, Eldridge Campbell,
John Heslin, Pelham Glasier, Walter Mott, Crawford Campbell,
Allen Stranahan, C. Stuart Welch, Benjamin Volk, W. Brandon Macomber.*

supporting the other. It was recognized that the end result of both of
these efforts would be enhanced by an atmosphere of medical research.

To meet the need for more space, in 1957, the Board of Governors of
the Albany Hospital proposed a joint fund raising campaign with
Albany Medical College. The goal of the campaign was set at
$5,000,000. The agreement reached was that the Medical College
would receive the first $1,500,000 raised; the Hospital the next
$3,000,000; the College the remaining $500,000; any funds received
thereafter would be evenly divided. The Trustees of the College agreed
to participate and to the division of the receipts. The firm of Lawson
Associates of Rockville Center, Long Island, New York was employed
to manage the drive. Mr. Gates Aufsesser was appointed Chairman of
the Committee. Mr. Aufsesser established goals of $250,000 to be
raised from members of the Boards of the Hospital and College, and
$1,000,000 to be contributed by staff doctors.

ESTABLISHMENT OF ALBANY MEDICAL CENTER

This joint fund raising was the result of efforts to further amalgamate
the College and Albany Hospital which already had close working
relationships. At the time of Dean Wiggers' appointment, the College
and Hospital Board formed a joint committee of three men from each

(Fig. 101) Dr. W. Brandon Macomber

(Fig. 102) Drs. Ralph Alley, Allan Stranahan, and Harvey Kausel.

(Fig. 103)
Dr. Thomas Older

(Fig. 104)
Dr. C. Stuart Welch

of their memberships. The objective of this effort was to form a New York Northeastern Medical Center. Twenty-six names for the proposed center were considered. Some of these were:

> March Medical Center
> Philip Schuyler Medical Center
> Peter Gansevoort Medical Center
> Sampson Medical Center
> March-Sampson Medical Center
> Physicians' Center
> The Doctors' Center of Medicine
> The Patients' Center of Medicine

Of the 26 names proposed, Albany Medical Center was not included.

The Center was established as a charitable corporation, the purpose of which was to improve the care of the sick and to promote the means, and the better learning of the means for the care of the sick in the northeastern region of New York State. Albany Hospital and Albany Medical College were the constituents of the Corporation. The basic functions of the Corporation were to coordinate the related work of both; to formulate and define policies of mutual concern; to arbitrate differences; to regulate appointments serving the center of both institutions; to regulate development and appointment of facilities used by both; and to solicit and administer funds. The Board of Trustees of the Center were not to be members of either constituent bodies.

Without question this new concept of medical care and education provided impetus to the growth and development of both institutions. It is probable that without the joint effort neither the College nor the Hospital alone would have been able to build the present Albany Medical Center *(Figure 105)*. By the joining of the two institutions a mass of sufficient weight was established to attract the attention and financial support of the State and Federal Governments, charitable foundations, and private contributors.

CHANGING CLINICAL DEPARTMENT CONTROL

As a result of the agreement of July 1, 1953, the Albany Hospital assumed financial and operational responsibility for the Clinical Departments of Medicine, Surgery, Pediatrics, Psychiatry, Gynecology, and Neurology. It was further agreed that the income from any of the previously listed Clinical Departments would be applied against the expense of operation. Also, grants for salaries of Clinical Department Heads would be applied to the salaries being paid to those persons, thereby relieving the Hospital's financial burden. This arrangement lasted only three years and the financial "hot potato" was handed back to the College. The Clinical Departments sustained a loss of approximately $10,000 for the fiscal year 1956-57 when expenses totalled

(Fig. 105) An aerial view of the Albany Medical Center complex with the Empire State Plaza and Hudson River visible at the top of the photo.

$1,056,573 and income $1,045,642. During this time, the Hospital had contributed $120,000 to maintain the Departments. The Board of Trustees of the College agreed to reassume the financial responsibility.

UNBALANCED BUDGET AND TUITION INCREASES

Despite all of the high finance and legalistic jargon, the Medical College was still confronted with deficit budgeting. It found itself in much the same plight as the Federal Government of recent times, but without the resources of being able to print its own scrip. When Dean Wiggers submitted a deficit budget for 1953-54, the Chancellor of Union University did not approve it. This disapproval was not an unusual occurrence because the Chancellor had registered disapproval on other occasions in regard to the budget. His attitude was forced by the Board of Trustees of Union who insisted on a balanced budget throughout Union University. The approval or disapproval was strictly pro forma because Albany Medical College frequently operated in the red as far as budgeting was concerned. Indeed, as the record shows, Union University did nothing to help alleviate the financial woes of the College beyond frowning on the lack of fiscal restraint. An interesting sidelight to the attitude of Union University to Albany Medical College is provided in the minutes of the March 18, 1955 Board of Trustees meeting. The Committee of the Association of American Medical Colleges had issued a questionnaire on the subject of Federal aid to medical school building programs. Senator Hill was advancing a bill in Congress to that end. At that time, the idea of a new medical science building was at least a gleam in the Dean's eye. Dean Wiggers was authorized by the Trustees to appear before Congress in support of the bill. Chancellor Davidson, who was opposed to Federal funds for education, voted as opposed to Dr. Wiggers' appearance before Congress.

To help in a small way to counter the downward financial slide of the College, Dean Wiggers requested permission of the Board of Trustees of the College to increase tuition from $800 per year to $1,000. The increase, which was effective for academic year 1954-55, was approved. Applications for admission fees remained at $7.00. The $1,000 tuition continued for only four years. In 1958, the tuition was increased to $1,200 per year effective September 1, 1959. In 1961, tuition was again increased to $1,450 to be effective January 1, 1963.

Of this increased tuition, $8,000 was to be set aside and made available to the Medical College Scholarship Fund. The student loan fund of $10,000 had been established in 1960. It stipulated that there would be interest charged on the unpaid balance of the loan equal to the Federal Discount Rate and thereafter to be the same as the going mortgage rate. Since 1957, sons and daughters of faculty members who received 50 percent or more of their salary were granted free scholarships to the College. This indicates rather directly that faculty members could receive more for their services elsewhere. A further condition of the scholarship is that students so admitted must meet normal entrance requirements and maintain satisfactory grades.

DISPARITY BETWEEN COST OF
MEDICAL EDUCATION AND TUITION

At the time of inception of Albany Medical College, many medical schools were financially rewarding businesses to the operators of the schools, some of which were really diploma mills providing only a minimum education and an attractive diploma for framing and display. As the standards were raised and licensing came into being, the cost of education gradually surpassed the amount received from tuition. Naturally the "business enterprises" disappeared and the full burden of educating doctors fell to the "sincere" institutions. Any businessman who buys apples at $1.25 per bushel and sells them at $1.00 per bushel is in deep trouble. Were it not for the grants and gifts the cost of medical education for the individual would have been beyond the reach of many. Salt was added to the financial wounds of medical colleges by the report of the Bane Committee, which in 1959 reported that medical schools should increase enrollment to 100 students per class. It also recommended that because of the critical need for more doctors, funds be made available for 20 more medical colleges. Funding for the expansion of medical colleges would be provided by the Federal Government. Four years later, another report submitted by the Muir Committee recommended the establishment of two more medical colleges in New York State. Dean Wiggers responded by suggesting that it would be more practical for the state to provide economic aid to existing medical colleges even at the inconvenience of their increasing present enrollment. As a further reply to the Committee, the Deans of medical colleges in New York State met to discuss the report of the Committee. The Deans recommended that the state consider the two requests which were as follows:

1. That matching funds be provided to the colleges by the State for any new construction or renovation necessary to accommodate larger classes.
2. That the State provide to the colleges $700 for each student enrolled and that the fund be not contingent on State residency.

In addition, seven private medical colleges believed that through this plan they could accommodate 100 additional students per class. Had either of the reports been pursued in the direction of more medical colleges, the demand for new facilities would have had a disadvantageous effect on the existing colleges.

It is interesting to note that in regard to support of medical colleges, the State of Pennsylvania paid $2,600 to medical schools in that State for each student attending.

Of the total estimated income for 1962-63, $320,000 or only approximately 20 percent of the total income to the College was from student tuition. That same year, the College had a deficit budget of $66,472. No statement is recorded of the Chancellor's reaction to the budget but it can be assumed that a deep frown accompanied his reading of the report. The administration of the College was certainly not profligate in dispensing funds. In 1961, a rather extensive survey was conducted to determine how much of the total budget was being directed to education and how much to research. Research for the year 1959 consumed $881,000 and $390,000 was spent for student education. With 235 students in the College, educational cost per student was set at $1,600 per year. This figure is further substantiated by a similar survey conducted by medical colleges in New York City which established the annual cost per student at $2,000. Allowing for the higher cost of everything in New York City, the two figures seem to validate each other. At that time the 235 students in Albany Medical College were paying $1,200 per year, or a total of $282,000 against an incurred expense of $390,000. The College that year sustained a loss of $108,000 as a result of disparity between tuition and the cost of education.

MEDICAL SCIENCE BUILDING

When the Medical Science Building was dedicated on October 5, 1963, it marked the occasion of only the second building to be erected by Albany Medical College during its 124 years of existence. Dean Wiggers had been head of the College for ten years and as related earlier was a man who maintained a keen awareness of potential sources of funds for the College's maintenance and growth. There is little doubt that one of the enabling factors for the erection of the Medical Science Building was the Health Research Construction Bill. Another factor was Dean Wigger's recognition of the opportunity.

The Health Research Construction Bill as the title implies provided money for research facilities. The College received $1,300,000 for construction of the Medical Science Building from the Health Research Facilities Division of the U.S. Department of Health, Education and Welfare. Dean Wiggers, in the formal application for funds had requested $1,312,000 so it may be concluded that his request was thoroughly substantiated. A sidelight to this largest grant that Albany Medical College had received to date is that in 1921, Johns Hopkins had received $3,000,000 from the General Education fund. A dollar in 1921 purchased much more than did a dollar in 1960. This places the grant in perspective. The balance, $3,700,000 was raised by gifts from corporations, private donors, the alumni and faculty members.

It is interesting to note that the first discussion of the new building with the Board of Trustees was October 1958. That was three years after Dean Wiggers' appearance before Congress. Five years after that Board discussion, the building was completed. The proposal placed before the Board was that a structure containing 128,000 square feet could be built for $2,300,000 and as 70 percent of the building would be used for research, $1,000,000 to $1,200,000 could be expected to be granted by the Federal government. However, Dean Wiggers was not a man to let grass grow under his feet or to let an opportunity pass because he was not prepared to seize it. On January 13, (hopefully not a Friday) 1956, two years before approaching the Board on the proposal, Dean Wiggers had shown to the Executive Faculty sketches of an eight story addition to the Medical College, thereby indicating that the Dean had given detailed thought and some action (the architectural drawings) to the expansion. The building was to be built as a wing to the existing school building and was planned to be 50 feet by 100 feet. A photograph on the cover of the Winter, 1958, Alumni Bulletin shows an aerial view of the growing Medical Center complex with an artist's conception of the proposed new building. For some reason, the site of the actual structure is turned 90 degrees north of the original plan. The extent of the proposed floor space was based on the expressed need of the several department heads of the College. Dean Wiggers had asked each head to submit a detailed plan which outlined his needs for research facilities, the floor space to house them, and office space.

At the time of Dean Wiggers' presentation of the sketches to the Executive Faculty in 1956, the Governors of the Hospital were planning a fund drive to raise $4,247,000 for construction of additional units to the Hospital. Obviously, if both the Hospital and the Medical College simultaneously launched fund raising campaigns, the result would be counterproductive for both. The Board of Trustees and the Board of Governors of their respective institutions agreed on a joint drive to be conducted under the aegis of the Albany Medical Center. It was related earlier how the division of funds would be made with.

It was after the agreement on the joint fund drive that in 1958, Dr. Wiggers formally applied to the Federal Government for the funds to be provided by the Health Research Construction Bill. Without the combination of those funds, it would have been financially impossible to erect the building as planned. The eight story building had been modified to five stories, but the total floor space was increased to 105,000 square feet. The cost was estimated to be $2,860,000 with air conditioning, or $2,500,000 without.

Perhaps inflation was already becoming a fact of life because in 1960, Dean Wiggers revised the cost estimate upward to $3,600,000. One year later in 1961, the estimate was jumped to $4,848,364—close to the $5,000,000 final cost. In 1961, another baleful fact was presented; cost to operate the Medical Science Building might run as high as $200,000 per year. This would add substantitally to the College's budget for fiscal year 1961-62 which was $1,494,071, with a deficit of $27,463. In short, unless additional income was quickly realized upon completion of the new addition, the annual deficit would approach a quarter million dollars annually.

At this point there was no turning back, regardless of mounting cost of construction and the substantial cost of operation. In fact, as early as 1957, the necessity to expand was unavoidable if the College was to maintain its academic position. The Council on Medical Education and Hospitals of the Association of American Medical Colleges jointly issued a guide for the use of the "Accrediting Survey Team," entitled "The Function and Structure of a Modern Medical School." The guide stressed seven areas in which the Survey Team was to evaluate a school. The report of the Survey Team in 1958 was complimentary and encouraging in the majority of areas measured. However, the report did recognize the inadequacy, qualitatively and quantitatively, of the present physical plant in terms of space and modern facilities. In its discussion of the physical plant per se, the survey report states, "The present space appears inadequate, both quantitatively and qualitatively for the basic science departments, particularly in regard to office-laboratory, teaching conference rooms and seminar quarters. Certainly, an immediate critical need that applies to all departments, clinical as well as basic science, is for additional space, despite the efficient utilization and excellent maintenance of the present plant." This report left little option for Albany Medical College.

A second reason for the expansion was the increasing volume of grants for research. Research had a two-fold reward: Successful research advanced medical science sometimes a step, sometimes a league, but always forward toward cures for disease or the prevention of them. An ancilliary benefit of research is the prestige that accrues to researchers and the institution supporting them. So research was essential not only because of the decree of the American Medical Association, but also because it is one of the basic reasons for being a medical college. But as research effort grows, so does the need for suitable space in which to conduct the research. In 1959, Albany Medical College received grants for research and teaching that totalled $1,005,780. To continue to attract grants, it was necessary to assure adequate facilities in which to conduct the research. Teaching was still, nonetheless, the primary function of the College. In the May, 1957 Alumni Bulletin, Dean Wiggers reported that the college's primary objective was education and, secondarily, research. Research was necessary to attract faculty, but was not the primary objective of the College.

As stated earlier, the Medical Science building was completed in 1963, but not without some of the difficulties attendant on most projects of that scope. Test boring of the site revealed a sub-structure of the type of clay soil that has plagued the building of many of the large structures in the Albany hill area. To provide a proper foundation for the building, it was necessary to install a massive concrete platform to distribute the weight and, in a sense, upon which to float the structure. The thickness of the foundation caused constant concern to one scientist who would occupy the building. For the purpose of his research project, he needed a perfect electrical "ground." Before the concrete was poured, a large copper rod was driven deep into the subsoil. Each day as the foundation was poured and the structure grew, the wary scientist would examine his precious "ground" to assure that nothing had been done to interfere with its perfection. Happily, all went well and errant electrical charges can still be harmlessly discharged deep in the clay beneath the building.

When on October 5, 1963, the Medical Science Building was dedicated, the principal address was delivered by the President of the Rockefeller Institute and former President of Johns Hopkins University, Ditlev W. Bronk *(Figure 106)*. The Rockefeller Institute had been very generous to Albany Medical College. As is usual with dedications—invocations, musical fanfare and interludes, as well as remarks by notables in attendance provided a program of appropriate duration. Tours of the building followed the ceremony. It is not noted in the imposing program for the dedication, but it would only be reasonable that after the sound of trumpets, weighty proclamations, and tramping up stairs and down long hallways that there was a room somewhere that provided satisfactory refreshments for all who had perservered.

The new building provided 122,000 square feet, more than doubling the floor space in the other College building and was an integral part of the existing building being connected by corridors with all five floors of its predecessor. As stated in Dean Wiggers' proposal, approximately 75 percent of the building is committed to research purposes. For students, provision was made for two new lecture rooms, a large and well equipped laboratory for the teaching of Biochemistry, Physiology and Pharmacology, and several seminar rooms. Administrative offices are on the first floor. The basement houses the latest in animal care facilities. In spite of the cost, the building is fully air-conditioned. The cost of installing air-conditioning later would have been prohibitive. The building is "T" shaped, with the main wing 275 feet long. Among the attractive features created by Schmidt, Garden and Erickson, the Chicago based architectural firm which designed the

(Fig. 106) The ribbon-cutting ceremony for the Medical Science Building with, from left to right, Col. McNamee, Chancellor Davidson, Board of Trustees President James Adams, Dr. Bronk and Dean Wiggers.

building, is the landscaped courtyard at the main entrance. In the courtyard are four marble pylons, standing in sharp contrast to the lateral sweep of the building. On gentle days students frequently eat carry-out lunches or just enjoy the sun in the pleasant surroundings of the courtyard. During inclement weather, people awaiting a ride crouch by the pylons which shelter them from the wind. Even beauty has practical aspects.

JOINT MEDICAL-LAW SCHOOL DORMITORY PROPOSED

During their founding years, Albany Medical College and Albany Law School had shared occupation in the Lancaster School. The Law School moved to a separate location on State Street in Albany in 1879. While both institutions paid allegiance to the same University at that time and since then, each pursued its individual way until 1959. The only sharing between the two institutions was the use of the Law School auditorium for Medical College graduation ceremonies *(Figure 107)*. In December 1959, Dean Clements of Albany Law School proposed that the two schools share in the building and use of a dormitory building for their students. A committee representing both interests was appointed to pursue the proposal.

In 1961, approximately eight acres of land became available for the construction of the dormitory. The location was adjacent to the Law School property and within short walking distance of the Medical College. The cost of the land was estimated to be $8,000 to $10,000 per acre. A year later, the two institutions agreed to share in the purchase of the land for $5,000 per acre or $38,500 for the entire plot. In consideration of the earlier estimate, the $5,000 per acre price was a bargain. The deal was closed in January 1963.

It was not until five years later, in 1968, that the dormitory became a reality. It provides living quarters for 98 medical students and an equal number for law students. It seems to have been the continuing objective of both the Board of Trustees and the Board of Governors to construct buildings of eight stories height, as in the instance of the Medical Science Building and other expansion plans. However, in the instance of the Dormitory, the seeming ideal was achieved. It is eight stories in height.

It is true that "a rose by any other name would smell as sweet," but Dean Wiggers in 1956, prior to the building expansion program, was of the opinion that a medical college with a less restrictive name than Albany Medical College would grow more quickly. He proposed consideration be given to changing the name of the college to one which was less provincial such as Union University School of Medicine or Northeastern New York School of Medicine. However, this seed of

(Fig. 107) The procession to
Albany Law School for Medical College graduation in 1964.

change must have fallen on barren soil for the records maintain a stoney silence concerning the renaming of the College until February 1957 when Dean Wiggers agreed to drop further consideration of the change.

STATE AID IN EXCHANGE FOR INCREASED ENROLLMENT

Having completed the major expansion of the physical plant and, with the abundance of grant funds for research, the 1960's might have been expected to be halcyon days for the College. This was not the case. Financial problems as well as other factors, though not threatening the continued existence of the College, did constitute a worrisome atmosphere. In March 1964, Dean Wiggers reported that the financial picture was far from bright. The cost of the Medical Science Building had exceeded early estimates and projections of the high cost of its maintenance had been proven only too true. On top of these problems was the need to increase salaries and the burden of increased charges by the Hospital for the use of utilities. To augment the College income, Dean Wiggers requested of the Board and received approval to increase tuition to $1,700 per year to be effective February, 1964. The previous tuition increase to $1,450 had been effective since January, 1963. Even with the increase to $1,700 per year, Albany Medical College's tuition was the lowest of the seven private medical colleges in New York State. The tuition at State operated medical colleges was $1,000 less and as a result private schools were at a distinct disadvantage in their effort to attract some superior students to whom educational financing was a prominent consideration. Medical college tuition in New York State was not inexpensive. In 1960, tuition at Johns Hopkins Medical Institute, one of the Nation's most prestigious, was $1,200, the same as Albany Medical College.

A further threatening possibility was the State's plan to establish another medical college. The establishment of another State medical college would not only have its effect on student enrollment because of lower tuition, but it would also have an effect on the faculty by attracting some to greener pastures, as it were.

The State had been pressuring the medical colleges to admit larger classes to the schools. As mentioned earlier, tuition only covered a fraction of the cost of medical education and, therefore, larger classes would only worsen the financial condition of those private schools that did not enjoy the advantages of large endowments or substantial State aid. In reply to this pressure, the New York State Medical Deans submitted a proposal to the Governor of the State. The proposal requested that the State provide matching funds to the College for any construction or renovation necessary to accommodate larger classes. A second part of the proposal requested that the State provide $700 for

(Fig. 108)
Dr. Frank Woolsey

each student enrolled and that the fund not be contingent on State residency of the student. In a 1965 meeting, Governor Rockefeller was receptive to the plan that the State would provide funds for medical college building expansion and an amended basis for operating expenses. In return, the seven private medical colleges would accept 44 more students in 1967 and 117 in 1970. As expected, New York State opened not one but two medical colleges.

BIOMEDICAL PROGRAM INSTITUTED

Perhaps in anticipation of the future competition for top candidates for medical education, Albany Medical College in 1962, concluded an agreement for Rensselaer Polytechnic Institute for cross registration of students for a Biomedical Training Program. A student of the Program could, in six academic years and five years of summer study, obtain a Bachelor of Science degree and Medical doctorate. A similar program had been discussed earlier with Union University but the proposal was rejected by Union University after a three day seminar held in Williamstown by representatives of Union and Albany Medical College. In 1976, Union University reconsidered their decision and joined the Biomedical Program. The Biomedical Program was initiated in 1964. That year 75 applications were made for the 25 available places for the joint Medical College-RPI program. The Program has enjoyed complete success. The students are of high intellectual calibre.

GROWTH OF
POST GRADUATE MEDICAL EDUCATION PROGRAM

As related earlier, during Dr. Ordway's administration, he and other faculty members frequently traveled throughout the State, particularly to rural areas, to lecture on medical advances. The sites for the lectures were small local hospitals to which the area doctors would come to listen to the lectures and join in the discussion. Dr. Ordway's efforts were in keeping with the concept and reason for establishing the Medical College—to improve the quality of medicine practiced in Upstate New York by continuing education of doctors.

As so often happens, far reaching effects are precipitated almost by accident and explained only as a whim of fate.

The graduate education program now so widely accepted at Albany Medical College was given great impetus by a strictly coincidental happening. In 1953, Dr. Albert Harris became ill and was admitted to Albany Veterans' Administration Hospital for what was anticipated to be a long stay. Dr. Harris was a ham radio fan of long experience and much equipment. To counter the usual boredom of a prolonged hospital stay, one of Dr. Harris' colleagues, Dr. Frank Woolsey, Head of the Department of Medicine at the Veterans Administration Hospital suggested that Dr. Harris set up some of his radio equipment in his room *(Figure 108)*. The suggestion not only filled Dr. Harris' hours with entertainment but opened the door on a "first" in medical graduate education. Why not use radio as a media for disseminating developments in medical education which had previously required so much travel time?

On December 4, 1955, the series of two-way conferences between Albany Medical College and six participating hospitals was initiated. The program met with immediate success and one month later the number of participating hospitals had grown to 13 with others interested. The College had been granted a license earlier in 1955 to operate a radio station with the call letters being appropriately WAMC-FM. The station manager was Albert P. Fredette who ran the station from one room located on the fourth floor of the College building *(Figure 109)*. The 10,000 watt transmitter was located atop Mt. Greylock, Massachusetts. Programming was not restricted to medical subjects but included programming of an educational-cultural nature for lay persons. The non-medical programs cost the College $12,000 to $15,000 each year.

Because of technical limitations, only five hospitals could participate in the lectures and discussions at one time. The lectures were conducted on Monday, Wednesday and Friday of each week. By 1957, 24 such programs were conducted yearly. Dr. Frank Woolsey was appointed Associate Dean and Director of Postgraduate Medical

*(Fig. 109) Dr. Charles Eckert (left) and Dr. John Balint (right)
during one of WAMC's interview programs.*

Education in 1954 and as such, the radio program came under his
direction. After the initial few programs, Dr. Woolsey issued a survey
form to measure the effectiveness of the innovation. The returns were
gratifying. Approximately 70 physicians participated in each of the
three programs or a total of 210 per week. Of this number, 58 percent
were specialists and the balance were general practitioners. Of the
respondents to a questionnaire, 60 percent voted the programs as
excellent, 36 percent good, 3.6 percent fair, and 0.4 percent poor. The
latter evaluation proving again that no one can please all of the people
all of the time. As a result of this initial success, an ultimate audience of
35,000 to 40,000 physicians was projected.

The lecturers were, in later programs, sometimes put on the "spot"
by questions presented by the audience and to which immediate answers
were expected. One lecturer was said to have had a medical student
accompany him before the microphone with medical texts to which
reference could be made to answer a "loaded" question.

The program was praised by the report of a special committee which
visited the College to determine the School's proficiency in various
areas. The Rockefeller Foundation expressed a willingness to pay for
two-way postgraduate programs for 11 hospitals in the area. Four years
after the inception of the program in 1956, a representative of the
National Institutes of Health met with Dr. Woolsey to get more

information concerning the radio program. He asked why the College had not requested financial aid for the program and said that a grant of $40,000 to $50,000 might be obtained without difficulty. Heretofore, the cost had been underwritten by a subscription paid by the participating hospitals. No mention is made in subsequent minutes of the executive committee concerning an application for funds. However, with such an expression of encouragement from the granting source, it may be assumed that an application was promptly submitted.

There are always occasions when the cart temporarily precedes the horse. In one instance, television preceded radio. In 1954, a year before the initiation of the medical lectures via radio, the Mohawk Valley Council of Television Education, of which Albany Medical College was a member, sponsored a 13 week series on medical education which began in September at 10:30 a.m. over WRGB in Schenectady. Is it possible that from such beginnings television viewers later got Dr. Kildare, Ben Casey, Medical Center and the numerous soap opera programs centered about the interrelationships of patients, doctors and nurses?

Dr. March would unquestionably be pleased by the use of all the modern media to promote medical education. However, it is just as well that the mass media was not available during the early, tempestuous period of the history of the College. The vying factions who had to settle with expressing their opinion in pamphlet form might have demanded equal time on "the tube."

Expansion and Renovation of Albany Hospital

In 1917, the Hospital launched a fund raising program which resulted in $300,000 being donated for general improvements to the Hospital. Recognition of the necessity for those improvements may have resulted from a report requested by the Hosptial and submitted by Dr. Winford Smith, Superintendent of Johns Hopkins Hospital. The amount raised in that single campaign is in marked contrast to amounts raised in the annual fund drives which were in the neighborhood of $6,000. Among the improvements afforded by the $300,000 was the replacement of the horse drawn vehicle used for trucking, by a motor truck and the installation of a time clock. To improve the efficiency, nine departments were established to operate the Hospital. They were:

Administration	Real Estate and Building Maintenance
Nurses' Training School	Machinery and Tools
Dietetic	Ambulance
Housckeeping	Pharmaceutical
Purveyors	

Significant in this listing is that of Dietetics. For the first time Albany Hospital formally recognized the importance of scientific dietary planning for the care of patients. This is not to suggest that the Hospital did not recognize the importance of proper nutrition prior to the reorganization. Perhaps it was the first time that the Hospital could afford the salary of a professional dietician and staff.

It being pointless to just install a department without proper guidance, Miss Alice Mitchell of Peter Brent Brigham Hospital was installed as Dietician. Miss Mitchell could organize into the menu the fresh vegetables from the Hospital farms. There probably was a marked decrease in the feeding of ham and pork products which heretofore had comprised a substantial part of the patient's food trays. Grunts of relief must have been measurable from the Hospital's piggery.

In 1973, Dr. Lyn J. Howard came to Albany Medical College as a member of the Department of Medicine *(Figure 110)*. Nutrition having been recognized as extremely important, became a part of the curriculum and is taught by Dr. Howard. People with extreme nutrition

(Fig. 110)
Dr. Lyn Howard

problems are studied by Dr. Howard and her staff and recommendations are made.

These recommendations frequently involve elaborate methods of improving calorie intake which may have resulted from disease or surgery of the gastrointestinal tract, or individuals who have matabolic forms of obesity.

In 1917, the Hospital had accommodations for 400 patients, which were soon to be recognized as insufficient for a city of Albany's population. However, the accumulated debt had reached $79,000 and without the infusion of substantial financial assistance, major improvements were out of the question. The Hospital still carried substantial expenses for the care of indigent patients. The City and County paid only a portion of charity cases. In addition to in-hospital non-paying patients, in 1916, Albany Hospital had taken responsibility for the operation of the Albany City Free Dispensary. The Dispensary was located at 2 Ash Grove Place *(Figure 111)*. The property was turned over to the Hospital. The Hospital renamed the Dispensary, the South End Dispensary of Albany Hospital. Persons were asked to contribute whatever they could afford for the attention and medication they received. In many instances, this was nothing, in others 10 cents. However, it would be recalled that an office call at that time was $1.00 and a house call but $3.00. Nonetheless, these were expenses that the Hospital could ill afford.

Courtesy of Arthur O'Keefe

(Fig. 111)
2 Ash Grove Place

MAJOR EXPANSION PROGRAM IN 1925

The renovations resulting from the $300,000 raised in 1917 provided temporary bolstering to the Hospital, but during the next seven years, the situation again deteriorated. The Hospital had become over-crowded being able to accommodate only 550 patients. Patients were turned away if not critical and operations were delayed if possible. The Governors again appealed for funds to make the necessary improvements. The goal was set at $700,000 and perhaps to the amazement of many, quickly oversubscribed. Seven hundred and thirty thousand dollars were realized from the drive. George C. Hawley contributed $50,000. William N. Cary, an Albany brick manufacturer, donated 100,000 bricks.

As a result, the now familiar entrance and main building were erected. Work was begun in 1925 with the demolition of the administration building to make way for the eight story replacement *(Figure 112)*. The bed capacity was increased to 600 patients by the addition. The first floor provided space for offices and lobby, four elevators, a medical library, staff rooms, a pharmacy and drug section, and a dining room for guests and medical staff. The second, third and fourth floors were devoted to private rooms and small wards of 44 beds. The fifth floor was for maternity cases and contained 35 beds. The sixth floor was for pediatric cases and the front portion was a roof garden for those patients. The seventh floor consisted of seven operating rooms for major surgery, one of which provided space for observations by students. A ninth operating room was established for clinic operating cases (minor surgery). The eighth floor was a solarium for the use of

(Fig. 112) The current Albany Medical Center entrance.

those able to walk or be wheeled into the non-hospital atmosphere.

Of the four elevators in the new building, two were restricted to the use of patients going to and being taken from the operating rooms. The reason given was that persons coming into the Hospital as patients or visitors would not see those going to or coming from surgery. This could have been to provide privacy to those on the stretchers or to protect sensitive visitors or apprehensive admissions. Another hindsight observation concerns the operating room provided with seating for student observers. The seats were so removed that the observers could only have been certain that a surgical procedure of some sort was taking place at a point well below and beyond the ability of non-telescopic sight to see. A final point on the addition: it may be recalled that kitchens had been located throughout sections of the Hospital where "dainties" could be prepared on request for the patients. The addition housed a central kitchen in which all of the food was prepared: end of the "dainties" on request. The addition was completed and with all due ceremony, it opened January 19, 1928.

DR. ALBERT VANDER VEER
RESIGNS FROM BOARD OF GOVERNORS

In 1927, a relationship of more than 50 years was dissolved when Dr. Albert Vander Veer resigned from the Hospital's Board of Governors. Years later, the incident, which in all likelihood precipitated his resignation, may be regarded as a tempest in a teapot, but at the time, it received unwarranted publicity and strongly held positions by both sides of the disagreement. The *Albany Evening News* made public the demotion of Albany Hospital to secondary rating by the American College of Surgeons. The reason for the demotion was the lack of staff meetings by the Hospital. Dr. James M. Vander Veer, the son of Dr. Albert Vander Veer, and Dr. Arthur J. Bedell had advocated the holding of staff meetings. It was said that, "The staff meetings were intended to provide a check on whose patients were getting better and whose were dying." As a result of their advocacy of staff meetings and the outspoken attitude, they were both removed from the Hospital staff and the College faculty. The Albany Hospital and Albany Medical College thereby lost the services of an eminent surgeon, Dr. James N. Vander Veer, and a world recognized ophthalmologist, Dr. Arthur Bedell, and one of its most devoted founders, Dr. Albert Vander Veer. Within the year, the staff meetings were resumed. Much ill will could have been avoided had the issue been resolved promptly.

OUT-PATIENT DEPARTMENT

In 1929, the South End Dispensary was moved from Ash Grove Place to the Hospital. During the next ten years, the dispensary or Out-Patient Clinic, as it became known in 1933, assumed an increasingly important role in the medical care offered to Albanians. The Stock Market Crash and the ensuing Depression fell upon the Nation. Many of those who could previously have afforded to pay for medical care were now forced to depend on the Hospital charity. As in earlier years,

(Fig. 113) The Out-Patient Clinic in 1933.

those who could afford to pay something were expected to do so. However, as before, the most frequent payments were dimes and quarters.

Indirectly, the Out-Patient Clinic located in "old" building D, floors one, two and three, did save the Hospital greater losses in this way *(Figure 113)*. Albany City paid $3.00 per day for the treatment of patients whom they sent to the Hospital. Four dollars per day would have just barely met the cost of patient care. As a result, the more patients sent to the Hospital by the City, the greater the loss to the Hospital. Because of the dire financial plight of many of these cases, after being released from the Hospital, in short time they were back in the Hospital again not having been able to provide any recovery period medical care for themselves. The Out-Patient Clinic provided the needed post-hospital medical care. In addition, the Clinic also provided a source of "preventive maintenance" wherein persons could obtain medical care for illness before it progressed to the point of requiring hospitalization.

The Clinic was staffed by doctors who were members of the Hospital staff and who volunteered their services. Students from the College did the preliminary examination as required and obtained specimens when necessary and performed laboratory analyses. A small laboratory was included in the Clinic area. After the preliminary work, the attending doctor then made further examination and specified treatment and medication. Brewers yeast from nearby Dobler Brewery was donated and frequently prescribed and dispensed to the patients to enrich their all-too-often impoverished diet.

The Out-Patient Clinic in 1929 was in the tradition of Albany Hospital's care for the indigent. In 1873, an advertisement in the Albany City Directory offers the services of the Eye and Ear Infirmary gratuitously to the "poor" *(Figure 114)*.

DECENTRALIZED LABORATORIES ESTABLISHED

At the same time that the Out-Patient Clinic was developing, a number of small laboratories were established throughout the Hospital. These small laboratories occupied areas little bigger than closets and each was equipped with a microscope, a centrifuge, bunsen burner and basic reagents for blood, urine, or spinal fluid tests. The performance of these tests was taught in medical school so that interns or residents could perform them. The advantages of these satellite laboratories are obvious. Blood work and other tests could be performed on admission and diagnosis was not delayed until the specimen could be sent to the laboratory in the College and there analyzed. The central laboratory was not manned 24 hours each day or seven days a week. These small laboratories provided a certain immediacy of attention and a certain

ALBANY CHARITABLE
EYE AND EAR INFIRMARY,

Connected with the Albany Hospital,

CORNER EAGLE and HOWARD STREETS,

ALBANY, N. Y.

This Public Charity, recently established in connection with the Albany Hospital, is open daily (Sundays excepted,) for gratuitous advice with Medical and Surgical treatment for all diseases of the EYE and EAR.

Patients may apply from 10 to 12 o'clock A. M.

Patients not residing in the city, who require continued treatment, will be received in the Hospital on the payment of $5 per week for board.

DISPENSARY
OF THE

ALBANY HOSPITAL,

Corner Eagle and Howard Streets.

Medical and Surgical advice, medicine and attendance will be furnished gratuitously to the POOR, between the hours of 10 and 12, daily. Cases of deformities, club foot, &c., will be treated at the Dispensary.

ATTENDING PHYSICIANS TO THE DISPENSARY.

GEO. T. STEVENS, M. D., *Surgeon in Charge Eye and Ear Department.*

F. C. CURTIS, M. D.,	WM. HAILES, M. D.,	B. U. STEENBERG, M. D.,
T. D. CROTHERS, M. D.,	WM. H. MURRAY, M. D.,	W. G. TUCKER, M. D.,
JOSEPH H. BLATNER, M. D.,		LORENZO HALE, M. D.

The Medical and Surgical Staff of the Hospital constitute the Consulting Board.

(Fig. 114)
An advertisement from the 1873 Albany City Directory.

directness or participation by the attending physician which was not previously possible. However, with the sophistication of today's laboratory equipment, decentralization would not be practical. The laboratory is now manned by specialized technicians on a 24 hour basis.

HOUSE STAFF SALARIES

The decentralized laboratories also tapped a source of economically priced help even for those depression days. In 1933, a resident doctor received $50 per month and full maintenance (board and room). Assistant residents were paid half of the resident fee, $25 per month. A laboratory appointees $6.75 per week, second year interns $2.50 per week and first year interns nothing as usual. In all other months, their maintenance. A second year intern moved up the financial ladder to $10 per month in addition to room and board. All of these categories were provided with uniforms. Therefore, in February which alone has four weeks, residents were paid $12.50 per week, assistant residents and laboratory appointments $6.75 per week, second year interns $2.50 per week and first year interns nothing as usual. In all other months, their incomes were reduced because of the two or three extra days. First year interns could derive some satisfaction during eleven months of the year because nothing cannot be reduced further regardless of the devisor. In view of today's experience, it might be concluded that these were good times for the financial health of the Hospital until recognition is given to the income of the Hospital.

ALBANY HOSPITAL VS. THE CITY

In 1937, the question of admitting paying patients came to a head. Emergency patients were, of course, admitted without concern for their financial condition. The real problems of deciding priorities for admission were presented in the case of elective surgery. The determination of "who comes first" is not recorded. One can only presume. Then there were the instances of patients admitted on a paying basis whose days of hospitalization eventually exceeded their ability to pay. The City countered the request by the Hospital for the City's assumption of the cost of maintaining these patients with a clever proposition. At the time, the City paid $3.00 per day for the maintenance of a patient admitted by its request. Paying patients were charged $4.25 to $5.00 per day depending on their type of accommodation — wards, semi-private, or private room. In the case of a hypothetical paying patient who was admitted to a $4.25 room, after 20 days the bill would be $85.00. At this point, his funds are exhausted and he is no longer able to pay thereby becoming a City patient. The City proposed that instead of picking up the cost at $3.00 per day after the 20 days, the first 20 days of hospitalization be computed at $3.00 per day or a total of

$60.00. This left $25 of the patient's payment to cover another eight and a fraction days at no expense to the City. The Hospital countered with a request for a payment of $4.00 per day for City patients. Such was the thrust and parry of the City and Hospital for support.

LEGACY OF GEORGE CLEMENT HAWLEY

In 1934, at the depth of the financial depression, the Hospital received a financial bonanza. The legacy of George C. Hawley provided the funds, $1,075,000, to pay the outstanding debt of the Hospital. In the midst of worldwide financial chaos, the Hospital was able to pay its debts and be free not only of principal payment but interest as well.

HOSPITAL CHARGES IN THE THIRTIES

The record of the number of beds in the Hospital during the period depends somewhat on which report is read. In 1938, one source places the bed count at 617. In 1940, the count was 600 beds and 56 bassinets. Perhaps the bassinets were not counted in 1938. But whatever the number, they were a bargain compared to today's cost of hospitalization. For some obscure reason, a patient's bill for hospitalization in 1938 is included in the Medical College archives. The period of the hospital stay was 32 days. Board at $4.25 per day totalled $136. The use of the operating room twice during this period was $8.00−$4.00 each time. Laboratory fees were $4.00. The item that brought the total to its $148.20 was $.20 for "extra medicine." It would be interesting to know what the "extra medicine" was.

Incidentally, had that patient requested private or special duty nursing, the charge would have been $7.25 for 12 hours of nursing. Of the $7.25, $1.25 was paid to provide three meals to the nurse during the 12 hour period. That same year, 1938, special duty nurses requested that their hours be reduced to eight hours per shift from the previous 12 hours. For this reduction, they offered to accept a reduction in fee to $5.00 per shift and only two meals for an additional $.75.

EMERGENCY ROOM

The emergency room might be said, in 1939, to be doing a lively business if such a description were not inappropriate. Total number treated reached 4,278 persons, an increase of 710 cases over 1938. The following year, 1940, the number reached 4,428, another increase of 150 over 1939. The automobile or the drivers of them had begun to make a substantial contribution to emergency room care. In 1938, casualities of the automobile received in the emergency room of Albany Hospital were 280. In 1939, the figure was 345. In 1940, surprisingly, the number dropped by seven to 338.

In view of the foregoing, the now seeming minimal charge of $24 for annual medical insurance for a husband, wife, and dependent children is understandable. The medical insurance offered by Blue Cross, Blue Shield, and the many industrial medical programs was perhaps the greatest single factor to enable hospitals to emerge from dependence on organized charities and private benefactors. Medicare and Medicaid yet to come were also major contributors to the financial self-sufficiency of today's hospitals.

ALBANY HOSPITAL RAISES $4,000,000 FOR EXPANSION

When during Dean Cunningham's administration, Albany Medical Center was formed by the joining of Albany Medical College and Albany Hospital, the two institutions grew apace. The College had received funds for the erection of the Medical Science Building from the joint fund raising drive. From the same drive, the Hospital raised the $4,000,000 necessary to erect the new "K" building. However, contrary to the earlier survey of Albanians and their preference for sources of support for the Hospital, only $1,000,000 came from citizens' donations. The balance of the needed funds came from bank mortgages and $1,200,000 from a federal grant. Incidentally, the Troy Savings Bank was one of the principal lenders making $750,000 available to the Hospital. The Board of Governors, seemingly confident that the money would be raised somehow, had let the bids for erection of the eight story addition while the drive was underway. Originally, the cost of the addition had been estimated at $3,000,000 but this was $1,000,000 short of the actual $4,000,000 finally needed. If a lesson was to be learned from this estimating on the low side, it was not. The next addition, in 1955, was again estimated initially at $3,000,000 and shortly thereafter increased to $4,000,000. The K Building was dedicated on October 21, 1951 at a final cost of $4,500,000 — approximately 50 percent in excess of the original estimate. Perhaps this can be best explained that unlike residential housing, a hospital cannot be purchased after completion when all costs are accumulated and the final price established. Frequently, partitions after erection are needed to be moved, wiring must be added to meet newly realized requirements, and one coat of paint is just not enough.

When finished, the K Building was five stories high instead of the eight originally planned. The building provided additional space for the Medical College and 132 more beds for the Hospital. The bed total was now 705. In addition, the K Building housed a new out-patient clinic which would treat 20,000 patients who made 60,000 visits that year. A new diagnostic clinic, a new mental health center, additional nursery space for the newborn, new emergency rooms and additional operating rooms were also housed in the K Building. The building, while dedicated in 1951, was not completed or fully occupied until

1952. Much of the delay was due to the installation of piped oxygen to rooms throughout the building. This was a modern concept and provided immediate access to oxygen for patients in distress.

HOSPITAL STAFF REORGANIZED

With the return of physicians from military service, the appointment roster was revised organizationally. Specialty boards were established and the Chiefs of Service were appointed from the Heads of Departments in the Medical College. The attending Staff consisted of Chiefs of Service, Consultants, Attending Physicians, Assistant Attending Physicians, and Clinical Assistants. Together with varying degrees of responsibility, the Attending Staff was responsible for the care of public patients and maintenance of quality medical care in the Hospital. The Dispensary Staff for the most part was constituted of members of the Attending Staff. A Courtesy Staff and the House Staff completed the medical staff of the Hospital in the reorganization. A year later, 170 physicians cared for the indigent and the House Staff had grown to 65 doctors.

INCREASED EXPENSES IN POST-WAR ECONOMY

With the conclusion of World War II, America went on a spending spree. War-caused shortages ceased and automobiles and appliances were available in abundance. Food rationing had ended and the supermarket shelves were heaped with staples and delicacies to satisfy the public appetite. Unfortunately, the prices of these things, so much in demand, also increased and the inflation spiral shifted into high gear. In 1950, Dr. Hale, Hospital Administrator, circulated a message concerning the effect of inflation on the cost of food. He cited the statistic concerning the cost of beef steak. In 1940, one could buy four pounds of steak for a dollar; by 1950, the price had quadrupled to just one pound for a dollar. What a tremendous bargain that would be today when dog and cat food exceeds the 25 cent per pound of steak in 1940. Unfortunately for Dr. Hale and the balanced budget, the piggery had ceased to exist along with its inhabitants and no longer could the Hospital call on that convenient source of fresh pork. Also, the gardens had been abandoned and the fresh vegetable supply from that source had ceased.

The cost of food was only one source of increased operating expense. For the first time since 1940, the salaries of interns were increased in 1950. First year interns now received $25 per month, second year $35, assistant residents $50, and residents the princely sum of $100 per month. Nurses' salaries, which were approximately $100 per month, were boosted to average $200 for the same period. It is interesting to note that a nurse received twice the compensation of a resident.

However, it may be rationalized by the fact that the nurse was at the apex of her earning potential but the resident was on the threshold of his. To offset in part the mounting expenses, room charges were increased by $2.00 per day. However, hospital stays were substantially reduced. In 1941, a patient undergoing a routine appendectomy was hospitalized for 12.3 days; in 1949, hospitalization was required for only 8.3 days. In the same period, hospitalization for maternity cases was reduced from 11.2 days to 6.7. Blue Cross increased family charges to $3.40 per month.

MISCELLANEOUS CHANGES AT THE END OF THE DECADE

In a much more mundane area of medical care, the Hospital daily processed six tons of laundry each day. This apparent record amount of soiled linen may have been attributed to the increase of 140 beds with the completion of the K Building.

Some things come and others go. The Cerebral Palsy Treatment Center was transferred to the Albany Hospital—a new arrival. The ambulance service, however, which had metamorphosed from horse drawn wagons to motorized coaches complete with walnut trim, was discontinued. Ambulance services from outside sources had become available to serve all of the hospitals in the City and was more financially feasible.

Non-medical changes were also taking place. The Hospital was suffering an unexplained loss of supplies. To curb the losses and catch the culprits, the Pinkerton Detective Agency was called in on the case. The record of the success of their detection is not readily available. However, more than twenty years later, the Hospital was plaintively appealing on luncheon doilies for help to stop the thefts. One idle wit wrote a suggestion to the Hospital administration that the redesign of some things might reduce the thefts. Among other recommendations, he suggested that water pitchers be redesigned to resemble bedside urinals and that all blankets and linens be stamped with the words, "Property of Contagious Diseases Department." These suggestions are yet to be implemented and are no doubt reserved as a course of last resort. Another non-medical change was the extension of insurance coverage for malpractice suits brought against the House Staff. The new coverage extended to payment of judgments whereas the previous insurance provided only funds for legal expenses.

Medical Discoveries and Their Impact on the Hospital

POLIOMYELITIS

Nineteen forty-nine was the 100th anniversary of the founding of Albany Hospital and during those hundred years, cures had become available and even routine for most of the killing diseases of the past. But others, such as poliomyelitis and cancer, were on the increase. In 1949, a record number of poliomyelitis cases was reported.

The epidemic proportions of poliomyelitis in the early 1950's had a role in accelerating the development of sub-departments in the Department of Medicine. Before the development of the Salk vaccine and the Sabin attenuated virus, poliomyelitis was a deadly stalker of both the young and the mature. It left in its wake death and life-long crippled bodies. As a result of the disease, a wide array of physical and neurological problems developed. Therefore, treatment of the victims required special knowledge in excess of that obtainable by one man or groups in the field of general internal medicine. It was during this period that much of the expansion of the Department of Medicine took place in the Medical College. As a result of the growth of departments in the College, specialists could be called for consultation from the growing number of specialties. Orthopedic, pulmonary disease, physical medicine, cardiology, urology, neurology and others were dispatched by the Chief of Medicine to cope with the numerous complications of poliomyelitis. In 1948, Drs. Gilbert Dalldorf and Grace M. Sickles of the New York State Department of Health isolated a virus responsible for an illness frequently confused with poliomyelitis *(Figure 115)*. It was named the Coxsacki Virus. As complete recovery generally followed the Coxsacki Virus infection as compared to poliomyelitis, the identification of the Coxsacki Virus relieved much of the anxiety from the patient and family. This was not the first time that the New York State Department of Health made a substantial contribution to medical science. Earlier, Dr. Augustus Wadsworth organized the founding of the research laboratories in the Department of which he was its first Director *(Figure 116)*. It was there that pneumococcus serum was developed *(Figure 117)*. It was extracted from horses and

(Fig. 115)
Dr. Gilbert Dalldorf

(Fig. 116)
Dr. Augustus Wadsworth

(Fig. 117)
The New York State Department of Health Laboratories,
located on New Scotland Avenue across from Albany Medical Center.

was effective in the treatment of certain types of pneumonia.

In 1949, a cancer detection center was opened at Albany Medical Center and a year later, in 1950, Albany Hospital installed one of the first of six artificial kidney units in the Nation.

DIALYSIS

The need for an artificial kidney was recognized shortly after World War II. Dr. W.J. Kolff was able to prolong the lives of patients who had suffered severe injuries during the bombing of London. Dr. Kolff used a primitive machine to remove waste products from the blood replacing the function of failed kidneys. When the patients survived three or more weeks through the use of the machine, the kidneys often returned to normal functioning. This forerunner of the modern kidney machine unlike its modern-day successor was a large bulky device which required permanent installation in a room large enough to accommodate it and a bed for the patient.

In 1949, the availability of the kidney machine became known to officers of Albany Hospital. At the time, the financial books of the Hospital were balancing, but just barely. The machine would cost $1,000 and only after an appeal to Frank Wells McCabe, Chairman of the Board of Governors, was permission granted to order the pioneering lifesaver. When the proposition was made to Mr. McCabe, his direct question was, "How much does it cost and how many do you need?" The natural assumption being that as man had two kidneys, at least two machines would be needed to replace the malfunctioning organs. Mr. McCabe, a banker, sensed a bargain and the order was placed for the dialyzer on finding that only one was needed. As stated earlier, this was only the fifth machine in the United States. Then came the problem of where to install it. The Hospital was already bursting at the seams, Building K not yet having been completed and bed space was at a premium. A diligent survey found the only room with adequate space to be in the Nursing School. The problem was that the room was occupied by an array of beds and dummies used by the Nursing School to instruct student nurses in the proper procedures for handling patients while changing bed linens. The same mannequins had previously been moved from Pavilion D over strenuous objections by the nursing staff to make way for the new Out Patient Department.

Mrs. Middleworth, recently appointed head of the School, was contacted and a moving description of the lifesaving potential of the machine resulted in her bursting into tears of joy and sympathetic understanding. The dummies were moved forthwith to other quarters. Installation was another imposing hurdle that now confronted the instigator of the purchase. A seemingly endless multiplicity of pipes was required to provide the necessary plumbing for the kidney ma-

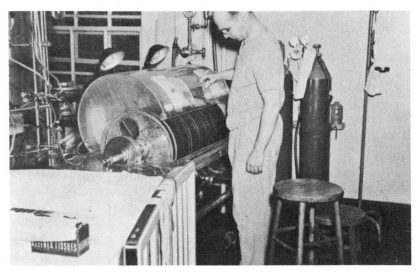

(Fig. 118) Dr. John Garrett with the first hemodialysis equipment.

chine. Unfortunately, the floor of the room was thick, strong concrete. Thundering air hammers and numerous cold chisels finally made the openings and the kidney machine was installed and operating and peace returned to the nurses' residence *(Figure 118)*.

The prevalent lay opinion is that the kidney machine is a precursor pending a kidney implant. However, actually the machine was developed and saving lives years before transplants were attempted.

RESEARCH IN OPEN HEART SURGERY

About the same time a project in the field of heart valve replacement in animals was being carried out in the Theobald Smith Physiology Laboratory and in the Eldridge Campbell Surgical Research Building. The Federal grant from 1948-58 had named G. Rehmi Denton the principal investigator working in conjuntion with Dr. Harold Wiggers, then Chairman of the Department of Physiology.

Plastic heart valves were installed successfully in six dogs in the College laboratory. The experiment was conducted by Dr. G. Rehmi Denton and associates and provided the necessary basis for the later replacement of defective heart valves in patients at Albany Medical Center *(Figure 119)*. Early heart valve replacements had one annoying problem; they clicked. The sound in some instances was sufficiently audible to be heard by the patient and even others. This minor problem was later corrected during the period of research with animals. As related earlier, when the technique was perfected, Dr. Thomas Older, working with Drs. Ralph Alley, Allen Stranahan and Harvey Kausal, was

(Fig. 119)
Dr. G. Rehmi Denton

specially trained in open heart surgery.

KOREAN WAR AND PERSONNEL SHORTAGES

In 1950, the United States was again at war. The war was never officially declared but classified as a police action of the United Nations to resist aggression of the North Koreans against the South Koreans. The United States was the principal supplier of men and material to aid the South Koreans. As a result, Albany Hospital along with others was to experience an acute shortage of nursing personnel. The House Staff was also depleted. In 1951, the Government ordered that no residency was to exceed one year. The Hospital in part countered the shortage of nurses by substituting technicians to perform some of the tasks previously assigned to the nursing staff. This practice has to some extent continued to the present.

At the time of the shortage, Dr. Hale, Hospital Adminsitrator, was issuing periodic information letters to officials and employees of the Hospital. At the inception of the nursing shortage, in quiet tone he requested the doctors not to take nurses from the Hosptial staff to be employed in their private practice offices. As the shortage continued, his request became urgent and the tone more strident. The message was repeated several times and it may be concluded that the initial requests were not fully honored.

The shortage of nursing personnel and residents came at a most inconvenient time. In 1951, Albany Hospital together with the Medical College became one of five medical teaching centers in New York State. The other four were located in New York City, Syracuse, Rochester, and Buffalo. There were at that time, 50 such centers in the United States. In 1954, the Hospital, or rather Medical Center, distributed a pamphlet explaining the concept of a medical center. It explained that a medical center is equipped to diagnose and care for every type of human affliction, and because of the affiliation of the Hospital and Medical College, it was staffed with superior physician teachers who could be called on for consultation in rare or difficult cases. The pamphlet, in an aside, stated that the Medical Center plant was valued at $12,500,000.

The incipient signs of what was to become a national and worldwide affliction became evident in 1953. A growing number of patients began coming to the Hospital with their indispensable television sets in tow. This trend threatened to transform the quiet of a convalescent atmosphere into a Tower of Babel. The strain of infection was too virulent to stamp out so that steps were made to contain it. A firm was contacted to assist in the process. It offered to install television sets in rooms and equip the sets with "pillow-speakers" so that the audio portion of the transmission could be confined to patients who desired the distraction of soap operas and constant array of evening "specials." Now, visitors when concluding their visits make certain that the patient is supplied with sufficient coins to prevent the tube from becoming a "black hole." As a precaution to protect their commercial venture, the entrepeneur insisted that the Hospital forbid the carrying in of private television sets with or by the patients, and thereby the Hospital became a party to electronic wizardry. A patient can now lie in bed and be distracted from his pain and presence in a hospital by seemingly interminable viewing of episodes in fictitious hospitals with fictitious patients and fictitious romances between doctors and nurses.

In 1953, the Medical College was again experiencing a financial crisis. The primary cause of the strain was the cost of maintaining a faculty for third and fourth year students in the College. These are the clinical years. Some thought was given to reducing the College to a two year institution. Had this been done, it is likely that in a few years the College would have closed completely. One of the primary constituents of a medical center is a medical college and, therefore, the Governors of the Hospital made every possible effort to assist the College. To that end, the Hospital gave $120,000 to the College to underwrite part of the expense of the clinical years. In addition, the Hospital requested that all doctors who had offices in the Hospital or Medical College accept a ceiling on the income from their practices. Fees in excess of the ceiling on their income would be given to the College for the support of third and fourth year training programs.

FINANCIAL AID FROM THE CITY
AND TREATMENT OF THE INDIGENT

An almost adversary relationship had been growing between some City administrators and the Hospital for a number of years. While the City had generously donated land to the Hospital for its use, there had developed a bone of contention concerning the amount of payment to the Hospital for patients who were wards of the City. In 1950, welfare payments to the Hospital were $9.00 per day for patients sent there by the city. This was against a cost of $17.03 per day to the Hospital. As the cost is reckoned to the penny, it may be assumed to be stringently accurate. A year later, the payment was negotiated upward to be $11.25 per day. Still short of the $17.03 per day cost which had probably also increased due to inflation. In 1954, the disagreement openly erupted. The Albany County Board of Supervisors requested permission to investigate the finances of the Hospital. The Board of Governors, through Gates B. Aufsesser, replied that the books of the Hospital were open for examination at all times. Patient day costs were now $24.58 and the total cost of operating the Hospital in 1953 was $5,192,988. The loss incurred by the hospitalization of welfare patients was $300,000 and another $110,000 was lost to the maintenance of the free clinics. Annual income to the Hospital from its endowment funds was only $30,000. The compensation to the Hospital for these losses came principally from two sources: increased rates for paying patients and annual fund raising campaigns.

This bone of contention between the Medical Center and the County continued for many more years. In 1965, the Medical Center instituted a suit against the Albany County Commission of Welfare. The purpose of the legal action was to secure payment from the County at the New York State promulgated rate. A year later, the cost dispute was settled by a compromise. That same year, 1966, Medicaid and Medicare legislation became effective on May 1 and July 1, respectively. Both of these programs assured payment to the Medical Center at specified rates. However, like most things, these social reforms were both good news and bad news. The good news was that the Medical Center no longer had to wrangle with the County for rate improvement. The bad news was the complexity of those programs. Record keeping and paper work routines became so extensive that the Medical Center installed a computer to cope with the problem.

To return to the controversy between Albany County and the Medical Center, 498 cases involving treatment of indigents was at issue. The County contended that each claim was to be argued separately. The result, of course, would have been almost endlessly time consuming and expensive litigation. In 1967, the problem was finally resolved through a compromise negotiated by Mayor Erastus Corning II. The Medical Center received $763,300 in settlement for approximately 1,000 claims. It was $236,500 less than the amount sought, but it was the practical solution. While the negotiations were underway and harmony peaked over the horizon, New York State increased the mandated rate to be paid by counties to hospitals for the treatment of welfare cases. Perhaps because of fatigue induced by previous wrangling, little is recorded in the archives concerning the acceptance of the new increase.

Incidentally, the presence of welfare cases did present a benefit to Albany Medical Center because it provided interns and residents a degree of responsibility for those persons; such responsibility was not afforded them by paying patients. When a patient was admitted by his or her own doctor, all decisions concerning treatment were made by the admitting physician; this curtailed or eliminated entirely the needed experience to interns and residents. However, this is not to imply that the indigent received less care in quantity or quality than paying patients. The interns and residents were supervised in all medical decisions by the attending physicians and Chief of Service. More doctors were at that time in training and health insurance programs had severely reduced the welfare case load. One hospital experienced so extreme a shortage of indigent cases that, learning of a person of no financial means and in need of medical care, they transported the person 140 miles. In that instance, a liability in one location was a valued asset in another. While the bard who wrote of, "every cloud having a silver lining," did not have this situation in mind, his theory was borne out.

ALBANY HOSPITAL BECOMES POLIOMYELITIS CENTER

And once again there were comings and goings. The Salk vaccine had not yet been discovered and the coming of hot weather intensified the threat of poliomylitis and increased incidences of the dread disease. Albany Medical Center became the Poliomyelitis Center for its region of New York State.

On the positive side of the medical ledger was the prevention, teatment and cure of tuberculosis. As a result of these advances, it was decided to close the Albany Tuberculosis Sanatorium which was staffed by Albany Hospital. With the decrease in cases of tuberculosis, the Hun Memorial Building could now provide for the treatment of tuberculosis patients. There they could be isolated from other parts of the Medical Center during convalesence. In the instances of chronic tuberculosis, the patients were transferred to other sanatoria in the State. A far point from the time early in the century when tuberculosis patients were kept in tents on the Hospital grounds and not admitted into the buildings. The fear of tuberculosis had not yet been fully eliminated. Even today, all patients must have a chest x-ray to detect possible infection so that if it is present they can be isolated from other patients in the Medical Center. In 1973, the Hun Memorial Tuberculosis Unit was closed because of the decline in the incidence of tuberculosis. The building continued to be used, but as a pulmonary disease facility. Antibiotics made it possible to treat most tuberculosis patients on an ambulatory basis eliminating the months and sometimes years of sanatorium care.

GROWTH OF MEDICAL SCIENCE
REFLECTED IN ALBANY HOSPITAL

Like Alice in Wonderland, it was necessary to run as fast as possible just to stay even with the progress being made in all fields of medicine. New drugs, new surgical procedures, and new equipment were producing more cures and more patients to be treated who heretofore had been incurable.

In 1957, the Hospital employed 1,400 people full time. Dr. John Kiley, who in 1960 became Head of the Division of Renal Diseases, went to Boston to learn how to operate the new dialysis machine *(Figure 120)*. Thirty-four patients were on the machine a year later *(Figure 121)*.

Nineteen fifty-seven saw the first open heart surgery performed at Albany Medical Center. The patient was a five year old boy, Russell Halikas. A team of 14, including three surgeons, attended the operation which required five hours to complete. It was only the second time that such surgey was performed in New York State. A year later in 1958, 48 doctors were on the Attending Staff and 207 had their offices in the Hospital. That year the Hospital was operating at 90 percent capacity and 36 percent of the patients were coming from outside Albany County. The Hospital in keeping with the development of the Medical College now had 23 departments.

Ten years later, in 1967, open heart surgery was successfully performed on the youngest and smallest patient anywhere to that time. The patient was a three-month-old infant, Michael John Dunphy, of Albany. He weighed just nine pounds. Ten doctors attended the operation, which corrected the defective left ventricle to the aorta. Albany Medical Center, through its staff, had accomplished another first, and, most importantly, restored normalcy to another person.

One year prior to that operation, the inception of the cardiac care unit was organized at Albany Medical Center. Compared to that of today, the 1966 unit consisted of a not unusual cluster of four or five beds where cardiac cases could be isolated and attended by a special monitoring system. Two years later, a training program was instituted for nurses who were assigned to the unit. The training consisted primarily of teaching them how to operate the increasingly sophisticated equipment.

Earlier, in 1952, the Cardiovascular Health Center was established by New York State Department of Health at Albany Medical College under the direction of Dr. Joseph T. Doyle, Professor of Medicine *(Figure 122)*. Thomas E. Dewey, then Governor of New York State, became concerned because of the number of associates in his administration who had died of heart attacks. It was at his direction that the

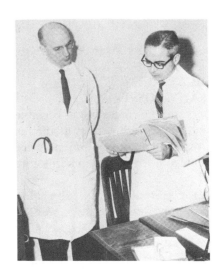

(Fig. 120)
Drs. John Garret (left)
and John Kiley (right).

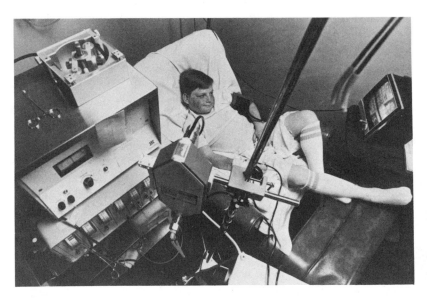

(Fig. 121)
A patient utilizing the current, sophisticated hemodialysis equipment.

(Fig. 122)
Dr. Joseph T. Doyle

State Health Department acted. Each year the Cardiovascular Health Center examined approximately 2,000 State workers of middle age, considered the most likely group to be susceptible to coronary thrombosis and related diseases. This afforded the College a wonderful opportunity to develop case histories and early detection of heart problems. Ironically, Governor Dewey died of a heart attack after retirement in Florida in March, 1971.

As a result of the growth of the Departments of Medicine and Surgery, Albany Medical Center was able to provide more special treatment units in the Hospital. In 1967, the Poison Treatment Center treated 700 cases of accidental poisoning.

That same year, Albany Medical Center received a grant of $914,627 to operate a center for the study of heart disease, cancer, and stroke.

In 1960, the goal of $5,000,000 established earlier in 1957 for expansion had been increased to $10,000,000. To date over $5,000,000 had been realized with $3,255,000 coming from Federal grants and the balance from local pledges.

The recently formed Hematology Laboratory could now perform 40 different tests on a single blood sample and surgical operations were being performed around the clock. The name of Albany Hospital was officially changed to Albany Medical Center Hospital.

THE ETERNAL PARKING PROBLEM

A unique problem not generally associated with medical care was now becoming a concern; if not a paramount concern at least a troublesome concern, that of parking space for automobiles. In earlier days the troublesome problem associated with hospital transportation was centered around where the ambulance horses would be stabled and the bothersome problem of horse manure and the accompanying flies. Students of the Medical College contributed to the parking problem because of the large number who had cars. In 1957, windshield stickers were issued to students so that their cars could be identified. It was suspected that students from other institutions were making use of the Medical College parking area. Could it have been that occasionally a Law or Pharmacy College student was parking amongst the vehicles of future doctors? The traffic and more pressing problem of where to place all the automobiles when their drivers wished them to become temporarily stationary while they were concerned with Hospital business and visits became an increasing problem to Dr. Thomas Hale, Director of Albany Medical Center. In 1961, the problem became more acute. There were, on average, 200 more drivers desirous of parking their vehicles than there were spaces for that purpose. The inconvenience for those seeking to park their cars in Albany Medical College's parking lot is put in proper perspective in light of the following statement.

In 1962, more than 200 cases of open heart surgery were performed — the same number as inadequate parking spaces the year before. However, that same year a solution to the parking problem was provided. Modern technology would prevail over modern problems. In 1963, the Medical Center purchased four and one-half acres on Holland Avenue as an adjunct parking area. This solution sufficed until 1969. That year a multi-story parking garage was constructed adjacent to the medical college. It could house 450 automobiles in comfort and protection from the weather.

ORGAN TRANSPLANTS

In 1969, three kidney transplants were performed, two were successful and one suffered rejection. The transplanting of kidneys soon became so successful that a computer was used to record the availability of the organs and provide identification of the location in which there was the greatest need. Through this arrangement, an Albany man was able to receive a kidney transplant when a kidney of a young girl became available in Toronto, Canada. The kidney was placed in a saline solution, refrigerated, and flown to the helicopter pad at Albany Medical Center where the transplant was performed.

By 1972, the transplant of organs had increased to the point that a public education program was conducted to encourage people to make provision for the use of organs after death. The time interval for removal, matching and implantation was critical. Hundreds of persons throughout the Nation await the critical coincidence of these elements so that they can be restored to a normal life independent of dialysis.

In 1973, a breakthrough was made at Albany Medical Center which greatly facilitated the transplantation of corneas. A procedure was developed so that a salvaged cornea could be preserved by freezing until the transplant could be performed.

That same year, the first patient received relief from pain which could not be alleviated by drugs. A device similar in size to a cardiac pacemaker was implanted in the patient and connected to the first dorsal column of the spine to, in effect, shut off the sensation of pain from being transmitted to the brain.

Development of
Research and Special Units

SPECIAL RESEARCH UNIT OPENED

Many times research must be conducted with direct or frequent observation by the researcher of a patient affected by the subject of the research. As a result, the researcher must work with laboratory animals and without the benefit of hour-by-hour progress of the disease or effect of remedial medication or surgical procedure on an actual case. On March 4, 1965, Albany Medical Center announced the opening of the area's only hospital facility built especially for research in human disease. The eight bed unit, known as the General Clinical Research Center, was initially supported by a United States Health Service grant of $2,170,000. This was the largest grant ever received by the Albany Medical College. Subsequently, additional grants have been made to offset the cost of operation. The operation of the Center is a coopertive effort between the College and Albany Medical Center Hospital.

The primary function of the Research Center is to enable medical and surgical researchers to study human illness under optimum scientific conditions, and to provide them with the most advanced laboratory and other scientific equipment available.

The Research Center permits the doctor-researcher to keep his patient in the hospital as long as necessary to complete the study, without concern for the patient's hospital bill. There is no cost to the patient while he is in the Research Center; costs of hospitalization are absorbed by the Federal grant, and no professional fees may be charged to these patients by their attending physicians.

Dean Wiggers stated that the primary objective of the General Clinical Research Center is "the acquisition of scientific information which will improve the management of human disease and lessen the physical and other problems caused by disease."

He also said the Federal grant to establish the research center "reflected the opinion of the U.S. Public Health Service that such a center would augment the already substantial research activities of the Medical College and increase their fruitfulness."

Located of the fourth floor wing of the K Building, the Research

316

Center consists of three double rooms and two single rooms for patients, a diet kitchen, nursing station, conference room, medicine room, examining room and offices.

It also contains three laboratories, each equipped with the most sophisticated scientific devices. These are a biochemistry laboratory for analysis of the chemical content of body tissues and fluids, a cinefluorography laboratory for high resolution x-ray studies, and a human physiology laboratory which furnishes apparatus for monitoring, mainly by electronic methods, the function of various organs and body systems.

The nearest centers of this kind elsewhere in the State are located in New York City and Rochester. The Albany center was under construction for almost a year prior to its opening.

The first program director of the new center was Dr. John E. Kiley, Professor of Medicine at Albany Medical College, and an experienced researcher. He headed a staff of 20, including a biochemist, ten nuses, two dieticians, and various laboratory technicians.

Only doctors on the faculty of Albany Medical College may admit patients to the Research Center. Before he can admit patients, a faculty member must have his research study plan approved by the Research Center's advisory committee. If his research project is approved by the committee, the physician may then admit patients suffering from illnesses or injuries described in the research plan.

At the inception, the Center's nine research projects were already approved by the advisory committee. These included studies of connective tissue disorders, postoperative metabolic balance, the relationship between vitamin B_6 deficiency and cancer, blood flow in patients with narrowing of the aorta, and bacteriology of duodenal diverticulosis.

Dr. E. Jurgen Plotz, Professor of Obstetrics and Gynecology, was chairman of the advisory committee. Initial members of the committee and the departments they represented were: Dr. John A. Balint, Dr. Thomas L. Hawkins, and Dr. Joseph T. Doyle, Medicine; Dr. Frank C. Ferguson, Pharmacology; Dr. Paul R. Patterson, Pediatics,; and Dr. Samuel R. Powers, Dr. Allan Stranahan, and Dr. Charles Eckert, Surgery.

DEVELOPMENTS IN RESEARCH

During this period, in 1967, Drs. Anthony P. Amarose, Arthur J. Wallingford, Jr., and E. Jurgen Plotz, confirmed earlier research making it possible to predict the sex of an unborn by examination of amniotic fluid. This was the first time that such a prediction could be made in this geographic area.

TRAUMA UNIT—DR. SAMUEL R. POWERS

Synergism is a rather obscure word that is finding its way into the common vocabulary with rapidity. Turning to Webster, synergism is defined as "cooperative action of discrete agencies such that the total effect is greater than the sum of the two effects taken independently, as in the action of mixtures of certain drugs." In 1968, a synergism occurred in Albany Medical Center with the founding of what was to be named the Trauma Unit. The Trauma Unit is the result of the mixture of medical science and scientific technology. The Trauma Unit has saved the lives of nine out of every ten patients treated there when previously eight of ten would not have survived the effects of literally shattering accidents and the after shocks of such injuries. Through the cooperative efforts of the most advanced medical science and the technology similar to that which supports outer space exploration, patients receive constant monitoring of the entire body mechanisms, chemicals to supplement accident induced deficiencies, removal of toxins from the blood and, when necessary, highly complex surgery.

Dr. Samuel R. Powers, Jr., a distinguished Professor of Surgery and Physiology, was the primary contributor to the founding of the Trauma Unit *(Figure 123)*. Dr. Powers stated the goal of the Unit as follows, "in shock-trauma our goal is that if a patient survived the accident that brought him to us, then he should live."

Dr. Powers graduated in 1941 from Swarthmore College having majored in biology. After starting graduate work in biochemistry, he shortly thereafter (a few months) decided instead to study medicine and was admitted to the Class of 1942 at the Columbia Presbyterian Medical College in New York City. During the intervening months, he worked for Harold Urey on the Manhattan Project. It was during his years of medical study that his interest in the effects of trauma were first evidenced and he studied the effects of shock and the effects of morphine of severely traumatized dogs. He published his first paper on the subject and received the degree of D.M.Sc. and M.D. at the same time in 1945. This was followed by work at Johns Hopkins in the laboratory of Richard Bing. There again his interest was in an outgrowth of earlier shock studies. After Johns Hopkins, Dr. Powers became a resident in surgery at Columbia-Presbyterian Hospital.

Dr. Powers had a unique ability—he was ambidextrous. As a child, he had broken an arm and, while the healing took place, he learned to use his uninjured arm. When his arm healed, his mother insisted that he use it to restore its normal dexterity. As a result, he could use either hand with equal efficiency, no small asset to a surgeon.

A result of a social meeting with Dr. Eldridge Campbell, then Head of the Department of Surgery at Albany Medical College, Dr. Powers came to Albany Hospital in 1954. He was offered the opportunity there

(Fig. 123)
Dr. Samuel R. Powers

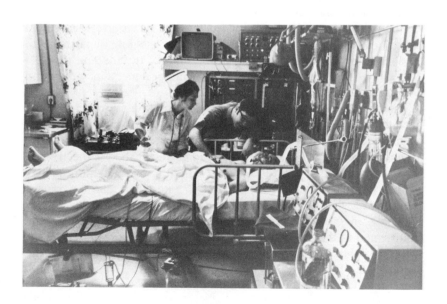

(Fig. 124)
The Trauma Unit

to spend his time one-third in surgery, one-third teaching, and the remaining third in research. Dr. Powers wrote more than one hundred papers on medicine and surgery.

The Trauma Unit consists of one bed and it is surrounded by highly complex equipment which combines sophisticated biomedical engineering, surgical facilities, and basic scientific capabilities *(Figure 124)*. Dr. Powers and his team worked closely with biomedical engineers at Rensselaer Polytechnic Institute in Troy, New York. Scientists from General Electric in Schenectady made substantial scientific contributions to the development of necessary equipment. Since 1963, the Trauma Unit has received grants totalling $2,000,000 from the Federal Government. The devices which monitor the patients are linked to a primary computer known familiarly as "Fat Albert." The speed with which minute changes in the patient's body chemistry, respiratory intake, and blood volume and pressure are detected is beyond the capabilities of any human team. Other members of Dr. Powers' team were Dr. Dhiraj Shah, Dr. Michael E. Valdes, Dr. Thomas M. Saba, and a special group of nurses and technicians trained for service in the Trauma Unit. Dr. Powers was once asked if the shock-trauma unit consisted of three engineers, one computer programmer, three full time nurses, three technicians, and one full time physician. The Doctor replied that it consisted of one full time engineer and two engineering technologist—the rest was as described in the question. However, he prefaced his answer by saying it also included a whole department of physiology with a major interest in the field of trauma and a whole division of biomedical engineering with a major interest in application of instrumentation and computer techniques.

The cost of maintaining this tremendous combination, or mixture, of equipment and personnel has run into the millions of dollars and has been funded by the National Institutes of Health. While saving the life of the one patient who, at the time occupies the one bed of the Trauma Unit, it represents in microcosm the patient care, education and research components of Albany Medical Center. The learning experience provided by the Trauma Unit radiates throughout the Albany Medical Center in its specialized care center and the Albany Medical College and to the entire world of medical sciences.

Effective July 1, 1977, Dr. Powers was appointed Chairman of the Department of Surgery. Dr. Powers died on March 27, 1980, less than three years later, in the midst of a brilliant career.

DR. CHARLES ECKERT

Dr. Charles Eckert was both the predecessor and successor of Dr. Samuel Powers as Chairman of the Department of Surgery of Albany Medical College and Chief of Surgery at Albany Hospital *(Figure 125)*.

(Fig. 125)
Dr. Charles Eckert

Dr. Eckert received his M.D. degree at Washington University, St. Louis, Missouri, in 1939, and his American Board of Surgery diploma in 1945. In 1944, he became Assistant Surgeon at Barnes and St. Louis Children's Hospital where he served until 1956.

In 1956, Dr. Eckert was appointed Chairman of the Department of Surgery at Albany Medical College and Chief of Surgery at Albany Hospital. Dr. Powers had established the Trauma Unit, as related earlier. He was offered a Chief of Surgery position at a prestigious hospital in New York City in 1974. Dr. Eckert was then approaching retirement age and he generously retired earlier than mandatory so that Dr. Powers could be appointed Chairman and Chief of Surgery. After Dr. Powers' untimely death in 1980, Dr. Eckert graciously returned to his former positions until a successor could be selected.

Dr. Eckert was a well trained and excellent surgeon. He willingly gave his time to serve on many committees during his professional career. After retirement Dr. Eckert remained a resident of Albany but spent winters in Florida.

DRS. STEBBENS AND SIMBER
RESEARCH CAUSE OF ANEURYSMS

In 1971, there was another amalgamation of medical and mechanical science at Albany Medical Center. Dr. William E. Stebbens, Professor of Pathology at Albany Medical College, joined with Dr. Thomas E. Simber, an Engineer in Applied Mechanics at Meggs Research Center of Watervliet Arsenal. The combined effort of the two scientists was to determine the cause of aneurysms. An aneurysm results from dialation of an artery due to weakness in the muscular coat. If an aneurysm ruptures, as they occasionally do, sudden death may occur. Working together, Drs. Stebbens and Simber produced evidence that the aneurysm resulted from a vibration in the blood vessel caused by an irregular flow of blood. The vibration produces a stress fracture.

DR. FREDERICK D. McCANDLESS

In 1965, Dr. Frederick D. McCandless initiated a cross-cultural clinical clerkship in British Guiana. The course was an elective for seniors and was of three months duration for which five seniors were accepted. The senior medical student from Albany Medical College served under the direction of three professors from the College.

As initiator of the program, Dr. McCandless was one of the three professors accompanying the students. Dr. McCandless, despite recurrent health problems, underwent the rigors of climate and cultural change in that equatorial nation with the students.*(Figure 126)*.

Dr. McCandless was born in Lexington, Kentucky, but was reared in Great Barrington, Massachusetts. He graduated from Cornell University Medical College in 1945. On graduation, his intention was to be an internist. However, he became interested in neuropsychiatry.

In 1948, he was selected to become Albany Medical College's first Markle Foundation Scholar and was awarded $25,000 in support of training for a medical teaching career. For this purpose, he took two years further training at Albany Medical College and two more years at the Henry Phipps Clinic of Johns Hopkins Hospital, 1950-52. He then returned to Albany Medical Center and the full-time teaching of psychiatry and directed the out-patient psychiatric clinic. He was promoted to Assistant Professor in 1953, Associate Professor in 1955, and Professor of Psychiatry in 1961 and head of the sub-department of Behavioral Science. Dr. McCandless died in 1969.

Two years before Dr. McCandless organized the cross-cultural clinical clerkship in British Guiana, a group of eight doctors from Albany Medical Center went to Algiers to provide medical assistance *(Figure 127)*. During the armed conflict, there was a great shortage of doctors in Algiers, most having left the nation in 1962. The group served for five weeks under the auspices of MEDICO, a branch of CARE. The hospital in the City of Algiers had been severely damaged during the conflict and political and military insecurity still existed within the city. The Hospital Civil de Beni Messous, six miles outside the city, was selected as the site of operation, having been relatively unharmed. The medical service, confined to out-patient work, treated approximately 60 patients each day. Dr. C. Maynard Guest was the director of this unit.

BURN UNIT

A year prior to inauguration of the Truama Center, in 1967, Albany Medical Center inaugurated another important center, the Burn Unit. The Burn Unit was developed under the direction of Dr. W. Brandon

(Fig. 126)
Dr. Frederick D. McCandless

(Fig. 127) The faculty representing Albany Medical Center in Algiers:
(Front row, left to right) Drs. C. Maynard Guest, John L. Berry,
Samuel R. Powers; (Second row, left to right) Drs. Mark K. Wong,
Joseph B. Robinson, Harry M. Judge, Paul M. Clark, John H.P. Holden.

Macomber in the Division of Plastic Surgery. Plastic Surgery is of great importance to the severely burned because of the special treatment required including the repair or replacement of burned tissue. Specially trained nurses and other personnel were essential to this Unit.

The Unit consisted of 8 to 15 beds, depending on need. The most important part of the Burn Unit is the burn care team. That care requires the coordinated effort of doctors from many specialties, highly trained nurses, physical and occupational therapists, nutritionists, social workers, psychiatrists, and researchers. Continuous training and education programs are necessary to support this program. The effect of the Burn Unit extends beyond its perimeter. An eductional program is conducted for the families of the victims to help them to be supportive to the patient during treatment in the Unit and for home care after the patient is discharged.

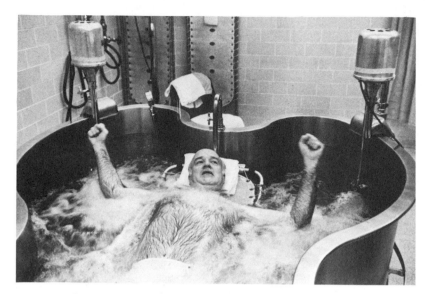

(Fig. 128)
A patient using the Burn Unit's hydrotherapy tank.

(Fig. 129)
An accident victim is transported from Potsdam, N.Y.
to the Albany Medical Center's Burn Unit via the unit's helicopter.

The rooms used by the Unit are specially equipped with unique beds and frames to afford the least discomfort to the patient. The large volume of supplies necessary is readily on hand. The Unit is equipped with a nurse call system to afford easy communication between burn team members in all parts of the Unit. Filtered air is supplied to patient areas at a greater pressure than other areas. This prevents the chance for cross contamination between patients.

One of the unique features of the Burn Unit is the tub room *(Figure 128)*. It contains a specially built stainless steel hydrotherapy tank where initial assessment and washing of patients is performed. Here most of the patients have their wounds cleaned (debrided) daily.

To prevent infection, one of the greatest dangers to the burn victim, special attention is given to maintaining a bacteriologically clean environment. Staff and visitors are all gowned to minimize the risk of contaminating the patient. In 1978, 104 patients were admitted to the Burn Unit; of this number less than 20 percent succumbed. In view of the fact that these are persons with severe, excruciating burns, the recovery and survival rate is remarkable.

As would be expected, this is a costly Unit for the Hospital to maintain. The average daily rate in 1978 was $420, but individual cases can exceed this average by hundreds of dollars. Two cases illustrate this. Case No. 1 extended for fourteen days—the cost, $17,000. Case No. 2 required 42 days of treatment—the cost, $44,000.

Much of the cost for equipment and nursing was paid for through the support of Firefighters of Orange, Ulster and Sullivan Counties. New York Telephone Company had also generously contributed to the support of the Burn Unit. A special helicopter pad is located in the Hospital parking lot *(Figure 129)*. The use of helicopter transportation directly to the Hospital provides rapid transporation of a burn victim from the scene of the accident or from a hospital that does not have the special facilities required for treatment.

Since the inception of the use of helicopters as a means of transporting emergency cases to Albany Medical Center, the helicopter pad has had increasing use. Today, the arrival of a helicopter bearing a patient for emergency care or organs for transplant, while not an everyday happening, is not an unusual event.

NUCLEAR MEDICINE AT ALBANY MEDICAL CENTER

Following is a report by Dr. Robert B. Chodos, who formerly directed the Program of Nuclear Medicine.

The development of nuclear medicine as a distinct entity at the Albany Medical Center recapitulates the historical development of Nuclear Medicine as a medical specialty which, in 1971, culminated in the establishment by the American Board of Medical Specialties of a

Conjoint Board of Nuclear Medicine.

Radioactive isotopes were initially used for research at Albany Medical College and Albany Medical Center Hospital by various basic science and clinical investigators. In the early 1950's a radioisotope laboratory was established in the outpatient area of the Albany Medical Center Hospital adjacent to the West Lobby. A "hot" laboratory was subsequently constructed in the basement of the College and, in the late 1960's, the radioisotope laboratory was reestablished in an area contiguous to the Radiology Department in the basement area of Albany Medical Center Hospital. During this period and through most of the 1960's, radioisotopes were employed clinically for diagnosis and treatment of thyroid and hematological disease by Doctors Donald Baxter, John McClintock, Robert Wadlund, John Garrett, Robert O'Koniewski and William Conklin. With the acquisition of a single probe automatic scanner diagnostic imaging of the brain, thyroid, lungs, liver/spleen, and bones became feasible.

In 1966, a decision was made by Doctor John F. Roach, Chair of the Radiology Department, and Doctor Stuart Bondurant, Chair of the Department of Medicine, to expand the facilities and to develop a more extensive nuclear medicine program at Albany Medical Center. With the support of Doctor Thomas Hawkins, President of The Albany Medical Center Hospital and Dean Harold Wiggers of the Albany Medical College, Doctor Robert B. Chodos was appointed in 1969 as Head of the Nuclear Medicine Division in the Department of Radiology.

With the appointment of Dr. Chodos, Albany Medical Center Hospital and the Albany Medical College made a commitment to the development of a far more extensive nuclear medicine program than had existed up to that time. Additional space was literally carved out in the Radiology department area, additional physicians and nuclear medicine technologists were employed, and state-of-the-art imaging equipment was obtained. An important collaborative relationship was established with the Albany Veterans Administration Hospital with Doctor Chodos as Chief of the Nuclear Medicine Service at that institution. A similar commitment of space, personnel and equipment was made by the Veterans Administration Hospital. In 1971 Doctor Samuel S. Ciccio joined the Nuclear Medicine program and was appointed Chief of the Nuclear Medicine Service at the Veterans Administration Hospital and Physician in the Nuclear Medicine Division at Albany Medical Center Hospital, while Doctor Chodos continued as Head of the Nuclear Medicine Division and a participant in the Veterans Administration Hospital program. The collaborative program between the two institutions continued and in 1974 an approved Nuclear Medicine Residency program was established with

Doctor Chodos as Program Director.

A most significant development occurred in 1975 with the relocation of the Nuclear Medicine program in the former operating room area (K-7) at Albany Medical Center Hospital. This provided excellent space for the continued development of the program. With this additional space a well-equipped radioisotope laboratory was completed and new imaging equipment was added to meet the clinical service demands of the institution. It is interesting to note here that with the physical expansion of the program from 1969 to 1980, the patient case load also increased from 2244 in 1970 to 4004 in 1980.

With the appointment of Doctor Glenn Robeson as Chair of the Department of Radiology, computer equipment was obtained in 1980 along with additional imaging units. These provided the essential equipment for quantitative dynamic functional nuclear cardiology studies, as well as imaging and functional studies of the brain, lungs, kidneys, and other body organs and systems.

In 1981 Doctor Chodos became Assistant Dean for Student Affairs at Albany Medical College and Doctor Bruce Line was appointed Head of the Nuclear Medicine Section at Albany Medical Center Hospital. Under his direction, and with the reorganization and expansion of the entire Radiology Department by Doctor Robeson, the Nuclear Medicine Section is employing computer technology extensively in the administration, clinical and research applications of radioactive materials in medicine.

Thus, nuclear medicine at Albany Medical Center has developed extensively from its origin as a small laboratory in the 1950's with single probe, well counter and scanner to a modern facility in the 1980's with multiple imaging units and computers, with the ability to provide essential studies for the diagnostic evaluation and treatment of patients at this Center *(Figure 130)*. This progress parallels the history of nuclear medicine as an established medical discipline, from research radioisotope laboratory to an established clinical service based on the remarkable development of sophisticated electronic equipment, new radiopharmaceuticals and, most significantly, the introduction of rapidly developing computer technologies in medicine.

During the period included in this history of nuclear medicine at the Albany Medical Center there have been many additional physicians, physicists, biochemists, health physicists, electronic engineers and technologists who have participated in and contributed significantly to the training of professionals and to quality patient care at Albany Medical College, Albany Medical Center Hospital and the Albany Veterans Administration Hospital. The number is too large to permit individual listing in this brief history.

In conclusion it would seem appropriate to comment on the

(Fig. 130) A recent view of the Neuro-radiology Unit.

significance of the developments in nuclear medicine. These represent a microcosm in the field of life sciences. The history of nuclear medicine is relatively brief. The discovery of the X-ray by Roentgen in 1895 was followed by the first radioactive "indicator" experiments by Hevesy in 1913. Dr. Herman Blumgart first used a radioactive substance in man, employing radon to study blood circulation in man in the late 1920's. The Curies identified artificial radioactivity in 1935. Hertz at the Massachusetts General Hospital and the Lawrences at the Donner Laboratory in Berkeley initiated more extensive studies and treatment with radioactive isotopes in the late 1930's. With the development of the atomic bomb and the public announcement of the Manhattan Project in 1945, radioactive isotopes became far more available for both research and clinical use. In the thirty odd years since 1950, there has been rapid and extensive development which has brought nuclear medicine to its present level as a representative of a high-technology field contributing significantly to the health and welfare of man.

Nuclear medicine reflects the inter-reactions of many disciplines, of inter-disciplinary teamwork that is the hallmark for discovery and progress, be it in physical or social sciences. Progress will continue in nuclear medicine as it is now occurring in ultrasound, in computerized axial tomography, and in nuclear magnetic resonance technology, to name only a few growing high-technology areas. It is truly remarkable to contemplate that most of these developments have occurred over a period of less than fifty years.

It is appropriate to note here that rapidly changing applications of state-of-the-art equipment and computer technology will produce more information than scientists will be able to comprehend or use in the healing arts. This reality should contribute to a constant state of humility and awe in the training of the professional and in the education of the physician and the patient.

NORTH END CLINIC

In a sense, free or public clinics have existed from the first time a doctor treated a patient knowing full well that the patient could not pay the fee. With the development of social conscience, formal clinics were formed in most cities throughout the Nation. The old South End dispensary was the first in Albany that was not physically located in the Hospital. It treated the indigent and accepted as payment whatever they could afford. It was, as related elsewhere, moved to occupy a part of Albany Hospital.

In 1969, the Albany Medical College proposed a Health Center be founded in the North End (Arbor Hill section) of Albany *(Figure 131)*. The Center was to care for all ages and to include the medical fields of pediatrics, adult medicine, obstetrics, mental health, dentistry, eye examinations, home care and other "health related" services. The major goal of the center was the achievement of better health for all the people of the North End. No one was turned away because of inability to pay.

This was another step that Albany Medical College took to become

Courtesy of Whitney M. Young Jr. Community Health Center

(Fig. 131) Whitney M. Young Jr. Community Health Center.

an integral part of the community and a step away from the "ivory tower" concept.

The College discussed the plans with officials of the United States Health Service. The College was encouraged to submit grant applications to permit the program to begin. The hope was that through the cooperative efforts of the College, citizens' organizations, institutions, and professional people, health care could begin in 1970.

The realization of the plan is detailed in a summary report issued in 1976. As of September of its sixth year of operation, the Whitney M. Young Jr. Community Health Center had 16,359 active registrants. An active registrant is a person who has come to the Center for services at least once during the past 18 months. The ages of the registrants ranged from infants to persons over 65 years.

CARDIAC RESEARCH

Heart disease had been long recognized as one of the leading causes of death and for many years was the subject of intensive research. In 1971, Albany Medical Center received $4,000,000 to perform research toward the prevention of arteriosclerosis from the Federal Government. This was one of 29 similar grants made at the time concentrating on the prevention and cure of heart disease.

Albany Medical Center, prior to the grant, had been performing cardiac research and the development of new surgical procedures for the correction of heart disease. In 1971, Dr. Stuart Bondurant, then Professor of Medicine and Physician-in-Chief and Dr. Joseph T. Doyle, Head of the sub-department of Cardiology, had used a procedure whereby a helium filled balloon is inserted into the aorta to assist the heart function after a heart attack.

Beginning in 1968, EKG records were stored on microfilm so that in an emergency the retrieval of earlier cardiograms could be made in minutes: minutes that were vital to the decision for treatment of the patient.

At the time of the $4,000,000 grant, Albany Medical Center had been conducting research in arteriosclerosis. Dr. Kyu Taik Lee, Professor of Pathology and Director of Animal Facilities of Albany Medical College, had been conducting research with Dr. Wilbur Thomas, Chairman of the Department of Pathology, on pigs whose hearts are much like the human organ both in size and physiology *(Figure 132).* By feeding the pigs a high cholesterol diet, Dr. Lee and his associates were able to induce myocardial infarctions and the causative relationship between diet and the infarction. By 1981, 15 doctors and 35 technicians were participating in the research *(Figure 133).*

When searching through archives, there are numerous photographs of stricken "porkers" lying on their backs, mouths agape and eyes

(Fig. 132)
Some of the senior staff of the 1960 Department of Pathology:
(Front row, left to right) Drs. A.S. Daoud, A.A. Stein, W.A. Thomas,
E. Morrison; (Top row, left to right) Drs. F. Goodall, R.F. Scott,
F. Florentin, K.T. Lee, K.S. Chang.

(Fig. 133)
Dr. Jack N.P. Davies

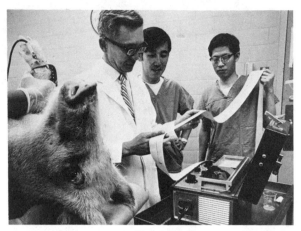

(Fig. 134)
Dr. Kyu Taik Lee and his associates monitoring a research animal's heart rate.

dulled *(Figure 134).* In attendance are researchers monitoring each pig. In the March 3, 1976 issue of the *New York Times,* there was a picture of a man holding a tiny pig under his arm. The accompanying article identified the man as Heroski Omi, the breeder of comparatively tiny pigs which at maturity weighed only sixty pounds. It was reported that Albany Medical College expressed an immediate interest in purchasing some of the tiny pigs to replace the 400 pounders that they were then using. It is interesting to speculate why Mr. Omi, through selective breeding, sought a smaller pig when agriculture experts were awarding blue ribbons to the largest. The answer may lay in the fact that Mr. Omi, before becoming a farmer, had been a jockey. He was well aware that bigger is not necessarily better. At one time, some 44 pigs were in residence at the animal laboratory with 60 to 80 lodged elsewhere. The miniturization of the pigs must have been a relief to those in charge. In the early 1900s, when pigs were maintained by the Hospital for the mundane purpose of providing bacon, chops and ham, the object was; the bigger the better. Times change and so has the purpose of maintaining pigs by the Albany Medical Center. One can only hope that today's pig realizes that he or she is now serving a higher purpose in life and death.

Dr. Lee has discovered that when pigs are changed from a diet of large amounts of milk proteins to soybean proteins, cholesterol level goes down. Dr. Lee advocates a diet which includes fish, chicken, vegetables and rice and less red meat and fats. One may assume that bacon is to be avoided.

MORE RESEARCH INNOVATIONS

Research and new methods of treatment were going along a variety of paths. In 1970, two rooms were especially equipped for the treatment of bone marrow disorders in children. The rooms, which cost $39,000 to equip, required an exacting system of ventilation to prevent the entrance of viruses into the rooms atmosphere. In one year 11 operations were performed using these rooms, saving the patients from almost certain death.

On October 5, 1971, Laser equipment costing $300,000 was purchased by the Hospital. The laser enabled painless operations on the retina. At the time of purchase, 120 patients were awaiting operations.

SOME EVENTS OF THE 1970's

In 1979, news of an unusual event occupied daily space in the local newspapers for several days. The situation came about when a Mrs. Ruby Mitchell, a gypsy queen, suffered congestive heart failure while in Albany. Congestive heart failure is not an unusual ailment. What was unusual was the behavior of Mrs. Mitchell's followers. They insisted on staying as close as possible to their queen. Shortly after Mrs. Mitchell's arrival, her followers had "taken over" the foyer of the Hospital. Her room was crowded to such a degree that doctors and nurses had difficulty in getting to the patient. A camp complete with cooking fires was established by the gypsies in nearby Memorial Park. As a final measure, the Hospital opened the yet not completed Pavilion C-2 for the use of Mrs. Mitchell's devoted followers.

Another group prevalent at the time noted for long hair and casual attire, but unrelated to the gypsies, seized on the opportunity for free lodging. They felt that the facilities afforded the gypsies should be made available to them without discrimination. Happily, Mrs. Mitchell recovered and she and her contingent proceeded on their journey. The relief to the Hospital administration with the recovery of Mrs. Mitchell was unsurpassed.

Another "happening" was the source of attention in the local newspapers. In 1974, W.C. Heinz, author of M.A.S.H., spent several days in the Albany Hospital Emergency Room. The reason was not a medical emergency. It was academic. He was getting background information for his next book entitled "Emergency." Had Mr. Heinz been present in the Emergency Room on the night of the fateful crash of Mohawk Flight 405, there may not have been room for him to stand. Nineteen of the survivors of the horrible crash were taken to Albany Medical Center as rapidly as ambulances could transport them. Eleven other survivors were rushed to St. Peter's Hospital.

Harking back to the day when Dr. March had to personally transport cadavers for dissection, in 1974 the College found itself running short of material. The problem was eliminated by assigning four students to a cadaver instead of two. The source for cadavers was largely unclaimed bodies. Thereby, Dean Wiggers was spared long journeys to Boston in a one-horse shay and the company of a silent companion on the return trip.

Cadavers were not the only shortage in 1974. President Nixon, contrary to the will of Congress, impounded $200,000,000 intended for funding medical colleges throughout the Nation. This may have deferred research which was performed later—too late for some.

When the Flexner Report was issued, the odds would have been long that in 1974 Albany Medical College would celebrate its 125th anniversary. The celebration may not have been the convivial occasion associated with anniversaries, but it was one for reflection on accomplishments of long and recent past. Just the year before, in 1973, the list is impressive. Eighteen kidney transplants were performed, 101 patients had coronary artery bypasses, 11,074 linear accelerator treatments for cancers were administered, 797 patients had cardiac catherizations, there were 547 neurological operations, and 1,169 babies were delivered.

Albany Medical Center continued to reach out with help. Health care information was recorded on 39 subjects, enabling the public to dial a phone number and receive pre-recorded health information free of charge.

Expansion of Albany Medical College for the 1970's

Classes for first, second, and third years at the Medical College were each increased by 10 students in 1969. The cost of medical education was estimated at $12,000 per student per year. To close the gap between cost of education and tuition, New York State granted the College $2,400 for every graduate regardless of his or her state of residence, and an additional $1,500 for each student enrolled who was from New York State. In part to handle the increased enrollment, 33 new members were added to the faculty. In 1970, 75 students graduated and 310 students were enrolled in the College, 2,300 having applied for admission. In 1971, the enrollment increased to 320 with a goal of 400 in the future. In 1972, 110 first year students were enrolled. This number was to remain constant through 1974. An interesting development took place in 1974 when 31 females were included in the class of 110 first year students. Of the 95 graduates in 1974, 10 were female. The following year, 1975, 28 females were admitted to the freshman class, evidence that the 31 in 1974 was not by chance. As recently as 1962, only seven females had been admitted to the freshman class.

THE SKULL

Some interesting insights into the times are provided by the Medical College Yearbook entitled *Skull*. The first publication of the yearbook was in 1910 and publication has continued through the present with one long interruption, 1917 through 1946. If time had permitted, a thorough review of those publications would provide very substantial sidelights to this history. For example, a handbook sponsored by *Skull* for incoming freshmen in 1970 provides an indication of the concerns of the students in 1970 in contrast to those of before the turn of the century and for many years thereafter. The first item discussed in the handbook was parking facilities. The second was availability of dormitory rooms and outside apartment rentals. First the car, then the owner. A subsequent item concerned student employment. Just four years earlier, in 1966, freshman students were not permitted to take any extra curricular employment. However, as recently as 1966, tuition was

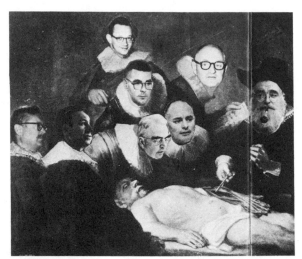

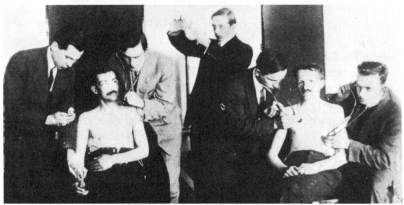

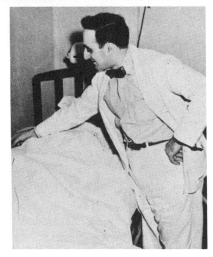

*(Figs. 135-138) A selection of the visual humor
from issues of* Skull, *the Albany Medical College yearbook.*

$1,000 per year and satisfactory food and lodging could be obtained for from $732 to $980 per year. It is no doubt coincidental that the last two items in the handbook concerned, first a discussion of health insurance available to students at $52.50 per year. The second item told of Albany Medical Center's rugby team. The implication might be drawn that first get health insurance and then, and only then, join the rugby team. A medical student has little time to indulge in levity or the pranks associated with undergraduate years. However, that their sense of humor is not lost is evidenced by many of the photos posed and arranged for publication in *Skull*. No group escapes *Skull's* editors as evidenced by *Figures 135* through *138*.

In 1972, Albany Medical College completed its largest physical expansion with the addition of the Medical Education Building. Construction had begun in 1969. The Federal government contributed $4,100,000; New York State $4,000,000; and $2,400,000 was sought from private sources. The building was the College's most costly project in its 131 years. The Medical Education Building is actually a complex of buildings. As it is located behind the Neil Hellman Medical Research Building, it is not visible from New Scotland Avenue — the entrance to the Medical College. The Medical Education Building includes a much needed library, additional classrooms and other modern educational facilities.

One wing of the Medical Education Building provides three small amphitheaters, each having a seating capacity of 122. In addition, there is a large amphitheater dedicated to Dean Wiggers, which seats 266 (Figure 139). The lecture rooms are connected by closed circuit television.

GROWTH OF THE COLLEGE LIBRARY

The Albany Medical College Library has had a varied and at times precarious history. In 1849, ten years after the College was founded, we find that its Library contains "at the present time to upwards of 2,000 volumes." In 1928-29, we read that "the bound volumes number 3,500, periodicals 40 and reprints 1,200."

The 1974-75 Catalog describes the Library as possessing 61,000 volumes and receiving 1,100 medical journals. It is obvious that for the Library of Albany Medical College, there was not a steady progression of growth from 1849 to 1975.

What, then, is the history of the Library at Albany Medical College? How was it begun? Who took care of the collection? Why are there only 61,000 volumes in the Library's collection one hundred and thirty-six years after the College was founded?

Let us examine the records.

The Albany Medical College circular of 1838 advised students to

(Fig. 139) Dean Wiggers speaking in the amphitheater named after him.

provide themselves with the following standard works:

in *Chemistry*—Turner's Elements; Beck's Manual; Brand's Manual or Thompson's Chemistry.

Anatomy and Physiology—Horner's Special, Pathological and Practical Anatomy; Bell's, Cloquet's, Paxton's, Wistar's and Meckel's Anatomy; Dunglison's, Boshock's and Magendie's Physiology.

Theory and Practice of Medicine—Good's Study; Gregory's, M'Intosh's, Eberle's, DeWees's and Cullen's Practice; Dunglison's Hygiene and Therapeutics.

Surgery—Liston's Surgery; Cooper's Surgical Dictionary; Samuel Cooper's Surgery; and Sir Astley Cooper's Lectures.

Obstetrics—DeWee's System; Ryan's Manual, Velpeau's Midwifery.

Materia Medica—Edwards and Varasseur's Manual; Eberle's Therapeutic; Murray's Materia Medica; and the United States Dispensatory.

Medical Jurisprudence—Chitty's, Beck's and Ryan's Medical Jurisprudence; and Ray on Insanity.

This advice was repeated, with some variations in the book titles listed, in 1839. Not until the circular of 1844 does one find a Library mentioned as follows:

A Library, containing all the standard elementary works is appropriated to the use of students. No additional fee is charged for the use of the Library. As this collection is intended to furnish books for reference and for reading, rather than for text books, students are advised to provide themselves with at least one good textbook in each department.

A notice in the 1849 circular provides the further information "that a Library has also been accumulated from funds set apart for the purchase of books, and by the donations of friends to the Institution. From these, about three hundred volumes have been set apart for the sole use of the students during the continuance of the course of lectures. No fee is charged for the use of it, to those who have matriculated. Students, however, are advised. . ." and here another list of recommended titles appears for the student to purchase. The "also" in the quotation above is added because the description of the Library follows that of the Museum which contains "an extensive collection of Minerals, with numerous and increasing specimens on Comparative Anatomy. The whole is at all times open to students for purposes of study and descriptive catalogues are on hand for convenient reference."

From the drawings of Philip Hooker's architectural plans for the Lancaster School, which was the first home of the College, we know that a Library was located in the rear of the first floor, occupying approximately one-sixth of its floor space. Whether the College used all or some of that ample space for its Library and Museum is not known.

The Albany Medical College Catalogs indicate librarians as one of the officers of the faculty for the years 1841-1870. The positions were held successively by:

T. Romeyn Beck, M.D.	1841-1854
Thomas Hun, M.D.	1856-1858
Howard Townsend, M.D.	1859-1866
Jacob S. Mosher, M.D.	1867-1870

Librarians are not mentioned in the Albany Medical College Catalogs after that date until 1935-36.

In subsequent circulars, the number of volumes cited increases, reaching 5,000 volumes by the circular of 1853 and then remains at that plateau until the circular of 1889-90. In the circular of 1891-92, the Library is enumerated as part of the building and by 1893-94, the Library is no longer mentioned. Not until the catalog of 1920-21 does a paragraph on the Library reappear with an explanation of its absence.

> In 1893 the Medical School presented its library to the State of New York to form the nucleus of a large medical library which should be forever open to the students of the medical schools and in general to physicians throughout the State. The medical library is now unusually well housed and equipped in the new Education Building where every assistance and convenience is afforded to students. The entire library has 500,000 bound volumes and takes 8,800 current periodicals. The medical library possesses over 25,000 bound volumes and receives 500 current periodicals. In addition to this library, each department has its own small working library of books and journals for ready reference.

In subsequent Albany Medical College Catalogs, the date of the gift is given as 1890.

At the time that the Albany Medical College Library collection was given, the New York State Library was located in the State Capitol, only one short block away from the College. Thus faculty and students were not greatly inconvenienced. The nucleus medical collection was later destroyed in a fire that occurred in the Capitol in 1911.

When one follows another thread of the library's history, one finds that the Medical Society of the County of Albany elected a physician to be librarian as early as 1820, when Dr. Platt Williams was so elected. A Committee on the subject of the library reported to the Society's Annual Meeting in January 1821 with a recommendation for the purchase of journals in the amount of $21.25 and books in the amount of $21.12½. These recommendations were approved as well as the following regulations:

> *That all persons who have paid the annual tax be entitled to use of the library.*
> *Second. No more than a single volume or pamphlet to be taken by a person at the same time.*
> *Third. Members not residents within the city shall be allowed to retain a book or pamphlet six weeks, and all others a fortnight.*
> *Fourth. A fine of two cents per day shall be paid for every day that a book is detained beyond the above time.*
> *Fifth. All damage done to books or pamphlets shall be assessed by the Librarian, and the amount collected from the person who held the book during the time it received the injury.*

Rules were a part of libraries, then as now!

What is not clear is where the books and journals of the Medical Society were housed, initially. Librarians continued to be elected and provided detailed reports on the growth and some of the losses sustained by the collection. By 1840, there were 65 bound volumes (journals and books) and 48 or 49 numbers and pamphlets. In 1851, a Medical Reading Room was set up in Mr. E.H. Pease's store on State Street.

The 1865 annual meeting of the Medical Society which incidentially was also attended by "gentlemen of the class of the Albany Medical College" carries the announcement "that the Library had been donated to the Albany Medical College, and, consequently, the Soiety had neither library nor librarian."

It is curious that the Albany Medical College circulars of that period do not reflect the increase in volumes provided by this gift.

From 1893, (or 1890) then, Albany Medical College had no library of its own, except for small departmental collections. Just before the move to the College's current location, the Alumni Notes in the 1926 *Albany Medical Annals* includes a paragraph entitled "Library" in which "it is hoped that memorial gifts may be secured for equipment and furnishings of the Trustees' Room and Library in the new building. In both, certain of the memorabilia in this old school should be preserved." Library and memorabilia continue to be mentioned until in the catalog of 1928-29 the first description of the new Albany Medical College Library appears:

> *In the new school building a large library room, located on the main floor, is open every week day and evening for general reading and special assignments. The bound volumes number 3,500, periodicals*

40 and reprints 1,200. By means of a "courier service" the school library has available the resources of the State Medical Library.

Three thousand five hundred volumes and 40 journals in 1929 provide an adequate explanation for the low statistics in 1975.

But a library must not be judged by numbers of volumes. A library collection must serve a purpose and support the programs of the parent institution. It had already become apparent to Dean Thomas Ordway that the College in its new uptown location could no longer depend totally on the New York State Library's Medical Section. Responsibility for the library described in the 1928-29 catalog was added to the already crowded schedule of a faculty member who assisted the Dean with the organization of Regional Medicine. It was also Dean Ordway who appointed in 1933, the first Advisory Committee on library-museum activities at Albany Medical College. The first members were: Dr. W.M. Baldwin, Dr. L.W. Gorham (Chairman), Dr. V.C. Jacobson, Dr. E.C. Kelly. The Dean and Dr. Randles, Secretary, were ex-officio members.

Dr. Ordway entrusted the management of the library, initially on a part time basis to Marion Frances Dondale, who had been a member of the Anatomy Department since 1923 and whose major activities in 1932-33 centered on assisting the Dean with the operation of the Department for Regional Extension. The College catalog of 1935-36 carries a greatly expanded section on the library, and mentions for the first time the existence of a librarian; not only that, but the librarian and her assistant are listed in the same catalog as offering an elective course on "Medical Literature and Use of the Library."

A description of the library at that time appears in a 1941 report:

> In 1935 the library of the Albany Medical College consisted of a main reading room and a small combined library and museum room on the first floor of the school building. It contained approximately 2,000 books and bound volumes of medical journals and about 200 volumes of unbound journals. Some 52 medical journals were received regularly. The reading room was open from nine to five each week day and from nine to twelve on Saturday. Since 1933 a librarian had been in charge, nominally for full time, but her duties were not limited to the library and she was often called upon to help with work in other departments. Frequently, therefore, the library was unattended.

From that same report, we glean that a library committee under the chairmanship of Dr. Gorham studied the needs of the library and made recommendations which included the setting up of a small budget.

By 1937, the total number of volumes increased by gift and by purchase to 3,200 and the number of journal subscriptions had doubled to just over 100 titles.

Back issues which until then had been sent to the New York State Medical Library now were retained in the College and a program of binding journals was begun in 1937. The committee could find no binder approved by the American Library Association and the Library Binding Institute, in Albany. The firm, in Syracuse, to whom the task was then entrusted remains the library's proficient binder to this day.

The rapid improvement is delightfully expressed in the letter from Miss Dondale that accompanies the annual report on the library for 1935-36.

> Dear Dr. Gorham:
>
> *This report sounds very inadequate and not particularly interesting, but it is difficult to make a report which might not seem childishly enthusiastic to the Executive Faculty. It has been a wonderful year. It was only two years ago that I used to sit here at 5 o'clock and see Cecil and Romanis and Mitchiner and Williams go out night after night to one or two men, and nothing else — and not much else on the shelves worth taking out. And this year they have borrowed 2,200 books and 1,800 periodicals. Cecil and Romanis and Mitchiner have gathered dust, while Lewis, White, Joslin, Fishberg, Cope, Homans, Kanavel, Curtis, and a great many others have been taken out every night. At least ten of this year's graduates borrowed something every night. It has been worth all the effort that we have all put into it to see the growing interest in books and reading outside of prescribed textbooks. It has been good to see, too, the beginning of a feeling of pride in the library. It may be good for us in the future that they are beginning to think that we have a better collection of books than the state!*
>
> Sincerely,
> Marion Dondale

It was fortunate for the College that a new Dean, Dr. Robert J. Cunningham, arrived in 1937 from Vanderbilt University who had assisted his first wife in establishing not only a library there but also a medical classification scheme for its books. Dr. Cunningham, with assistance from Dr. Arthur W. Wright as Chairman of the Library Advisory Committee, greatly encouraged the growth of the fledgling Albany Medical College Library.

Under Marion Dondale, who, despite the lack of formal training in librarianship, became a first rate medical librarian, the quality of the collection was well maintained. She recognized the importance of possessing major abstracts and indices and saw to it that funds were found, for instance, for the *Excerpta Medica* Series from their inception. She recognized that the College could "never" catch up with the collection of the New York State Medical Library and wisely concentrated on acquiring back runs of basic clinical journals, rather than subscribing to the German "Archivs"; Pfluger's, Virchow's; Naunyn-Schmiedeberg's and others. With the help of the capable assistant she acquired in 1942, Helen A. Fraser, she built the foundation for the College's journal collection through the Medical Library Association's Exchange Program. Miss Dondale became a pillar of that Association in various capacities, culminating in serving as its President in 1953-54. Her sudden death, soon after the completion of her term as MLA President came as a shock for the Albany Medical College community, as well as her colleagues across the Nation. Miss Fraser carried on as Acting Librarian.

Samuel Davis became the new librarian in Fall 1955, continued the expansion of the library's collection with the assistance of Helen A. Fraser, as his Associate Librarian and Lucy Norton, as Assistant Librarian. In 1956, Anita Flores took Miss Norton's place to become the library's first full-time cataloger.

When Helen Fraser assumed the leadership of the library in 1958, she soon realized that the Library of the Surgeon General's Office, newly renamed the National Library of Medicine, was creating procedures for bibliographic control and indexing, that would become standard for all medical libraries in the United States. The decision was therefore made to recatalog the entire collection (still only approximately 10,000 books) from the Cunningham classification to that of the National Library of Medicine classification scheme. Budget increases were very small and much reliance was still placed on gifts from faculty, the Friends of the Medical Library, and graduating students. Many journal titles were obtained from the exchange of the New York State Journal of Medicine or through the MLA Exchange program. Since Helen Fraser was a diligent correspondent, she soon built up an excellent relationship with her counterparts throughout the United States and abroad; thus, her success rate in receiving needed items from the Exchange list was very high. That the Albany Medical College collection has solid runs in basic medical journals going back to the first half of the 19th century is entirely due to Helen Fraser's activities.

During this period of the library's renaissance another person assisted in its welfare. This was Dr. Emerson Crosby Kelly, a 1926 graduate of the College and a member of the Surgery Department faculty *(Figure 140)*. Throughout his medical career he had an interest in medical bibliography, history of medicine and the collecting of rare books; indeed these interests overtook his career in surgery toward the latter part of his life and he devoted his services fulltime to the Albany Medical College Library from 1963 until 1975 when his health no longer permitted his daily attendance.

Emerson C. Kelly served on the Library Committee from its inception in 1933; he quickly assumed the role of becoming the College's unofficial historian, by carefully collecting all documents and memorabilia pertaining to both the Albany Medical College, the Albany Hospital and its School of Nursing. He organized the original papers of Alden March, M.D., co-founder of the College, he set up the archives and systematically added to them throughout his life. Dr. Kelly's rare book collection was initially housed in a specially constructed sliding

(Fig. 140)
Dr. Emerson Crosby Kelly

glass door map cabinet, designed in 1931 by McLaughlin-Stevens of Mohawk, New York; it now forms the nucleus of the library's rare book holdings in the third floor History of Medicine Room named for him.

When Miss Fraser resigned her position late in 1963, it was Emerson C. Kelly who became Director of the library until in 1965 when Ursula H. Anker, who had joined the staff as full-time librarian in 1964, was given the responsibility of managing the library. Dr. Kelly stayed on as Bibliographer/Historian and elder Statesman. His advice was sought on subjects ranging from surgical procedures to remote facts in the History of Medicine. He continued to maintain the archives, the library's exchange programs, and organized a history of medicine club.

By 1964, the collection had grown to 42,000 volumes (books and bound journals) and 625 journal titles received. Besides the librarian, the cataloger, and Dr. Kelly, the staff consisted of a full-time serials/reference assistant, a part-time circulation assistant and a part-time page. During evening hours, medical students kept the library open until 10 p.m. *(Figure 141)*. Dr. Kelly kept the library open on Saturday mornings and on Sundays it was closed.

From the two small rooms on the first floor of the Medical College, by now known as the J Building, the library's reading room now extended along the entire north side of the first floor. In addition, with the assistance of a generous bequest from Dr. John A. Sampson, Professor of Gynecology at Albany Medical College, 1912-1946, a large area in the basement of the K Building was furnished with stacks and the entire retrospective journal collection moved into it. A large room in the same basement became a work room for the library, where the cataloger had her desk, the archives and rare books were housed and all gifts and exchange packing as well as bindery preparations took place. Older books were housed under the eves of the Hospital, above the operating rooms.

Dr. Robert S. Alexander tells of the need for more adequate library space relating the following mini crisis that occurred when the library was to be further reduced for increased faculty use.

> When Dr. Harold Wiggers became Dean in 1953, Albany Medical College had a very small full-time faculty crowded into an inadequate physical plant. The initial attack on the space problem was to draw up plans for enlarging the old Theobald Smith Building, but this project generated little enthusiasm. Then in the late '50's federal construction funds became available and sights were raised to focus on a much more ambitious expansion which was to eventually rise as the MS or Hellman Building. Enlargement of the faculty, however, could not be delayed until this new structure was completed. Dean Wiggers searched every nook and cranny of the existing buildings trying to find spots that could be temporarily assigned to new staff.

> During this era of striving to upgrade the institution, the college library had been a perpetual thorn in the Dean's side. A pathetically inadequate collection, and a cramped reading room supplemented by a small catacomb of stack space in the basement, created a wall of

(Fig. 141) Albany Medical College Library as it appeared in the 1940s.

antagonism between the library and the rest of the institution. No one had anything good to say about the library, while those interested in serious literature searches soon learned to by-pass the college library and take advantage of the excellent state medical library. The most charitable appraisal could identify only one unquestioned asset in the library: a magnificent old fireplace that graced the west wall of the reading room. Under these circumstances, the only substantial use of the library reading room was as a study hall by the nursing students who lacked such a facility in the School of Nursing. To the Dean, this vision of the library crowded with nursing students was a source of particular rancor, since it was a glaring example of the seemingly endless series of services which the hard-pressed medical college was donating to the hospital.

It was a fateful Monday morning when I drove into work and parked in my assigned spot in front of the Theobald Smith Building in direct view of the old library across the way. As I entered the building, I could hear my phone ringing and made haste to unlock my office and answer the telephone. The message was as curt as it was urgent: "Dr. Alexander, will you please come to the library immediately!" The scene that I beheld when I stepped into the library remains vivid to this day, though difficult to describe in words. A couple of workmen were noisily chiselling notches in the floor and poking holes in the false ceiling so as to erect a neat row of studs with the obvious purpose of walling off a sizeable chunk of the west end of the reading room, including that magnificent old fireplace. They were doing their best to ignore the gaggle of library staff who were fluttering around their heels and wringing their hands while bewailing this tragic turn of events. A handful of bewildered students were watching these strange proceedings from a safer distance. When I directed a question to the senior workman, he grabbed a work order from his tool box and thrust it under my nose with the gruff observation: "I think you will recognize that signature." It was signed by "Harold C. Wiggers." On calling the Dean's office we learned that Dr. Wiggers would be at Miami Beach for the week attending a meeting. Turning to the Chief of Maintenance, we were assured that postponing the work until the Dean returned was out of the quesiton, since before he left he had explicitly directed that top priority be given to carving this new office out of the library since its intended occupant was due to arrive in town in another week.

It became apparent that only Dean Wiggers had the authority to halt the desecration of the library. After a brief huddle with the library staff, it was agreed that proper protocol called for asking the help of our newly appointed Chairman of the Library Committee, Dr. Eckert. A call to Dr. Eckert's office fortunately caught him just returning from rounds and with no surgery scheduled that day. He shortly joined the swelling crowd in the library and quickly agreed that the Dean should be asked to delay the project until the whole problem could be reviewed, whereupon he left to place a call to Miami. About ten minutes later I received a telephone report from Dr. Eckert that the Dean had been adamant that the work simply had to go forward because there was no other space in the insitution to provide for the new appointee. As I was hanging up the phone, frustration gave way to compulsion and I regrabbed the phone and dialed Dr. Eckert's office to obtain from his secretary the telephone number of the call that she had placed to Miami.

The phone was answered by that always cheery voice of Ginny Wiggers who responded to my request by saying "He's just left for his meeting; let me see if I can cach him." In the background I could then hear her hailing him down the corridor and in a couple of minutes Dr. Wiggers was on the phone. I proceeded to go over what I am sure must have been the identical ground that Dr. Eckert had already been over with him. Initially Dr. Wiggers remained firm in his insistence that there was no possible alternate solution to the problem, but after several more minutes of discussion he began to yield. This was not an indication that my arguments were in any way more persuasive than those of Dr. Eckert, but the Dean was becoming impatient in the realization that he was going to have difficulty in getting to his meeting until he yielded to our request. His final statement was that he would give the matter "serious consideration." Within an hour, word came through that the Dean had called the Head of Maintenance and instructed him to postpone further construction of the new office until he returned.

For the remainder of that week, while the Dean was conducting his business in Miami, those naked studs marching across the library reading room were dramatic evidence of the crisis that the library confronted. Faculty and students who did not stumble upon the evidence themselves heard the story from others and came down to the library to survey the situation. Faculty and student opinions congealed to a rare degree of unanimity in defense of what they regarded as their inalienable rights. His first day back, the Dean's calendar was crammed with appointments with individuals wishing to express their outrage over the library situation.

The most extraordinary and significant part of this tale was the Dean's reaction to this mutinous rebellion. He seemed neither irate nor indignant that his decision had been challenged. As he sat and listened patiently to the protests of his many visitors, he appeared surprisingly receptive to their arguments. It was many months later that I caught the Dean in a moment of candor and heard a full explanation of his side of the story. At the outset of his deanship, he was committed to the proposition that the library was a vitally important component of any educational institution, but in struggling to meet the problems of the library under severe constraints of space and funds, he seemed to be almost alone in trying to improve the library. Academic departments were constantly vying for a bigger share of the pie, with the library dismissed as a source of endless annoyance without a friend in the world. In electing to invade library space to solve the critical needs for additional staff offices, the Dean had set aside his personal values and acquiesced to what he deemed to be the value judgment of the majority of the institution. For Dean Wiggers it was a most heart warming transformation to learn that the faculty and students of Albany Medical College had suddenly discovered the importance of their library.

> *Henceforth, there was a remarkable change in institutional policy towards its library. The studs were removed and the scars in the ceiling and floor patched. The urgency of providing the institution with an adequate library moved to a high rank on the priority list. A task force was shortly set up to investigate the possibility of purchasing the old Fort Orange Legion Post, a building that formerly stood near what is now the exit ramp from the parking garage, as the nucleus of a new medical library. That project was set aside in favor of acquiring the Dudley Observatory property on South Lake Avenue, a major purpose for which was originally projected as a library site. The final culmination of these endeavors in the design and construction of our present library is not only a tribute to the generosity of Henry Schaffer. It is also a testimony to the leadership of Dean Wiggers who once learned, while attending meetings in Miami, that he was not alone in thinking that a good library was of fundamental importance in the development of a leading medical college.*

SCHAFFER LIBRARY OF HEALTH SCIENCES

Library space needs, already cited in 1941, now reached a critical stage. Fortunately, in 1965, the Medical Library Assistance Act was passed by Congress, which signaled an era of expansion for medical libraries everywhere in the United States. Grant money became available for expansion of collections and services, for remodeling of library facilities and for construction of new libraries. Planning for a new library was begun; the initial program for transforming the entire J Building into the library was suspended by planning an entirely new building in the area bounded by three existing Medical Center Buildings: the Mosher Pavilion of the Hospital, the original Medical College (J Building), and the recently completed Medical Science Building.

While the library was successful in obtaining a three year grant from the National Library of Medicine during 1967-69, for acquisition of books, journals, equipment, furnishings and for rebinding older journals, the library's request for construction funds was approved, but not funded. Since the building of the new library was part of a larger construction project (a medical education building and a group of lecture halls) and since grant monies were obtained for these buildings, the Board of Trustees of the College also approved the construction of the library. The Schaffer Library of Health Sciences is a portion of the Medical Science Building complex. It is five stories high and is an ultimate representation of university library design *(Figure 142)*. Private funds were sought and were mostly supplied by an intensive drive by the Alumni Association and gift from Mr. and Mrs. Henry Schaffer for whom the new library was named, on its completion in 1972 *(Figure 143)*. The first floor of the library was dedicated to Miss Mary E. Carroll at the request of the Alumni Association which had donated generously to the construction of the library. A local firm of architects was chosen for the project and the librarian worked closely with the senior architect, Henry Blatner and his associate, James Cohen, from initial planning of the library to its final furnishing and dedication.

In its new space of five floors and a half basement, the library collection and staff offices could at last be brought under one roof from eight separate locations, one of them half a mile distant, in the basement of the Junior College of Albany Library where "10 years" of the Medical College's journal collection was placed in open storage from 1967 until 1972! Eighty percent of the moving was accomplished in two days in July 1972 when teams of faculty, students, technicians, and library staff used all available equipment that had wheels, to bring the collection and office furniture to its new location.

The 1970's not only brought expansion of physical facilities but also expansion of services, the collection, equipment and new technology; all of these also required an increase in staff.

Already in 1966 the first full-time clerical assistant was added to the library staff and faculty status was given to the professional librarians. By 1975, there were twenty full-time employed library staff of whom six were qualified librarians. During the academic year the library was open until midnight on weekdays, and open for eight hours each on Saturdays and Sundays. A further expansion took place in 1978 when a branch library of the College library was established in the adjacent Capital District Psychiatric Center. The library's collection in psychiatry, psychology and related subjects was moved to the branch library and a bibliographer/librarian placed in charge of additional staff to maintain services for almost as many hours as at the Schaffer Library of Health Sciences.

A further National Library of Medicine Grant assisted in dividing the library's card catalog from a completely interfiled dictionary catalog into a three way divided catalog, giving access by name (author, editor, etc.), title and subjects. At the same time the subject headings were changed from Library of Congress to National Library of Medicine headings to which users had become accustomed through their use of INDEX MEDICUS. This change was accomplished in 1972 concurrently with the move into the new library building.

A third National Library of Medicine Grant was obtained for two years (1977-78) to make fully operational a multi-media self-instructional center on the fifth floor of the library and to establish an outreach program for multi-media services to area hospitals. A separate area for the use of films, slides, tapes, etc. was planned for the new library from its inception. However, when the library was built, only the space could be provided for this purpose and the provision of equipment and programs had to wait for several years. A generous gift from an alumnus

(Fig. 142)
The Mary E. Carroll Reading Room of the Schaffer Library of Health Sciences.

(Fig. 143)
Mr. Henry Schaffer

had enabled the library to recruit the first multi-media librarian in 1973, initially on a part-time basis. Departments of the College, especially those of Ophthalmology, Pathology and Postgraduate Medicine donated equipment and programs to the emerging Multi-Media Center and this provided the needed foundation to obtain the two year grant. Today the Multi-Media Center of the library is avidly used by students and instructors, has its own dedicated staff and service desk and provides needed programs to allied health instructors in the greater Albany area.

In this period the library began to align itself with other emerging information technologies.

The Albany Medical College library was one of nine charter members in the first on-line Biomedical Communication Network of the Nation when it began operation in 1968. This was the SUNY (State University of New York) Biomedical Communication Network developed at the SUNY Upstate Medical Center Library in Syracuse. SUNY/BCN provided access to INDEX MEDICUS on-line and enabled a librarian to generate a bibliography of references on a given topic in a few minutes. This was a great improvement for users of the library for whom such bibliographies were formerly provided by manual searches of INDEX MEDICUS, often requiring two day's working hours of a librarian, and later by submitting requests to the MEDLARS section of the National Library of Medicine where such a search would be "batch processed" and returned to the requestor in four to six weeks. For clinical purposes, the on-line in-house searches were a forward leap that has steadily expanded in depth of coverage and variety of on-line data bases. Schaffer Library of Health Sciences can now, in the 1980's, access a variety of biomedical, technical, social-behavioral and physical-science data bases through three data base vendors. Librarians at Albany Medical College supply from 250 to 300 bibliographic searches per month to the library's clientele.

Other technical improvements in the library were the addition of a Western Union telewide communication terminal (TWX) in 1970 to speed inter-library loan lending and borrowing and joining the national cataloging service begun by the Ohio College Library Center (OCLC), in 1979. OCLC, now a freestanding corporation whose acronym stands for On-Line Computer Library Center, not only provides automated cataloging services to member libraries, but is gradually adding subsystems for other library operations. Their inter-library loan subsystem, serials and acquisitions sub-system are already operational and Albany Medical College makes use of the first. Circulation will be added soon. For the Albany Medical College libraries, the on-line cataloging has speeded the processing of books and multi-media programs, eliminated repetitive typing tasks and will provide the future possibility of eliminating the card catalog altogether, and make possible the total reliance on an on-line catalog.

The combination of advanced technology, rising costs of informational material and above all the greater demands made by a larger and more sophisticated clientele have led to a proliferation of coordinated and cooperative services through library networks, beginning in the mid-1960's.

SUNY/BCN and OCLC have already been described. In New York State the Reference and Research Library Resources Councils were established which brought academic, public and special libraries into cooperating systems. On the National level the Medical Library Assistance Act established eleven Regional Medical Libraries (RML). Albany Medical College entered into active membership of both networks. Within the Capital District Library Council (CDLC), Albany Medical College's libraries have become net lenders (i.e. more is loaned to other CDLC libraries than is borrowed from them). Since 1976, as part of the RML program, Albany Medical College has assumed a primary responsibility to health institutions and educational facilities in the seventeen counties comprising Health Service Area V of New York State. Responsibilities include provision of interlibrary loan service, consultation services, regional conservation of biomedical information resources (journals) and are supported by a subcontract with the RML for this region, the New York Academy of Medicine in New York City.

That the Albany Medical College library was able to take its place effectively in network operations, despite the deficiencies in collection strengths engendered by the long gap of being without a library, was due to support povided by the College's administration, by the efficiency of a dedicated library staff and by the unfailing encouragement from a steady advisory body.

Since 1933, the Library Advisory committee has assisted the librarian and the library staff in bringing about the expansion and improvements in library services for the Albany Medical Center community; for the library has not only served the College, since then, but also the Albany Medical Center Hospital and its School of Nursing. Credit is especially due to the members of the faculty who chaired the Library Advisory Committee with great dedication. Dr. L.W. Gorham (1933-37), Dr. Arthur W. Wright (1937-56), Dr. Emerson C. Kelly (1957-59), Dr. Charles Eckert (1960-64), Dr. Robert S. Alexander (1964-70), Dr. Robert D. Reinecke (1970-77), Dr. Ian H. Porter (1977-   ).

Paralleling its parent institution, the library is facing a period of consolidation and curtailment in the beginning of the 1980's. Introduction of new technology has made it possible to maintain services to the user in spite of slight staff cutbacks. Maintenance of the quality of the collection is a problem not only faced by Albany Medical College, but many other academic institutions. Thus, the importance of attracting gifts, endowments or steady dedicated contributions is as acute now as it was when the present library was reestablished in 1935. The Friends of the Library who loyally supported it from 1941 to 1959, were replaced by a new group, the Fellows of the Society of the Schaffer Library of Health Sciences beginning in 1976. That there have been many generous donors throughout this period can be ascertained by examining the plaques in the library that either name the donors or the person honored by a group of donors. Thus, through the generosity of the Albany Medical College Alumni Association, the first floor of the Schaffer Library of Health Sciences is named the Mary E. Carroll Reading Room for the Registrar of the College from 1937-64, who in 1982 still serves as Secretary of the Alumni Association. The History of Medicine Room was named for Emerson Crosby Kelly, M.D. The dedication of the History of Medicine Room in honor of Dr. Kelly took place in 1972. Dr. Kelly had retired from practice in 1965 and had been Director of the library from 1963 to 1965. Until his death in 1977, he continued as historian for the Albany Medical Center. The Center and future historians remain indebted to him for his diligent accumulating and filing of material associated with Albany Medical Center. The fourth floor of the library was named for Arthur W. Wright, M.D., Cyrus Strong Merrill Professor of Pathology from 1934-59, and a long term chairman of the Library Committee.

Other plaques proclaim donations to the library building and its furnishings or significant gifts to the collection. The latter are also itemized in the library's card catalog.

The Library Newsletter which was begun in 1972 publicly chronicles significant events of the last ten years. The librarian's annual report provides further details which will ultimately aid future historians in continuing the chronicle of Albany Medical College's library.

NEIL HELLMAN GIFTS

Mr. Neil Hellman, a lifetime resident of Albany, had generously contributed $2,075,000 to the College *(Figure 144)*. Of this amount, $1,575,000 was given to Albany Medical Center for research and education and was without restriction. The balance, $500,000 was for the purchase of a computer linked brain scan laboratory. This would provide a computer assisted axial tomograph able to distinguish between normal brain tissue, a brain tumor, blood clots, and parts of the brain deprived of blood supply. The $2,075,000 was the largest gift ever made to the affiliated institutions. On June 22, 1975, at 2:30 p.m., the Medical Science Building was dedicated and renamed the Neil Hellman Medical Research Building *(Figure 145)*. The dedication was a gala occasion. Dr. Michael E. DeBakey, the world renowned cardiovascular surgeon was the principal speaker. Dr. DeBakey and associates had performed the first aortocoronary bypass in 1964.

A tour of the building was included in the program and the public was invited. The guests were entertained by Mr. and Mrs. Neil Hellman with a buffet luncheon.

1970-1975, BANNER YEARS

Nineteen seventy-five was a year to be remembered for many reasons. A 2½ year old boy's foot was severed from his leg in an accident involving a power mower. The boy and the severed foot were promptly taken to Albany Medical Center. Dr. Richard L. Jacobs, Professor and Chairman of Orthopedic Surgery; Dr. Allastair M. Karmody, Assistant Professor of Surgery; and Dr. James G. Hoehn, Clinical Instructor in Surgery, restored the severed foot. The operation required five hours to perform but it was successful. The restoration of severed limbs had been performed elsewhere but the procedure was new to the world of surgery and regarded as a spectacular accomplishment. This case was the first attempted at Albany Medical Center.

The Trauma Room had now been in existence for nine years. The death rate there was reduced from 80 percent during its early period to just 10 percent in 1975. During those nine years, 300 patients had been treated there and 75 percent had been saved.

Under the direction of Dr. Robert W. Sponzo, a breast cancer clinic was established, having been funded with $1,200,000 by the Federal Government. The purpose of the clinic was to reduce the morbidity and mortality from breast cancer, the incidence of which had increased dramatically in recent years.

The arbitrary selection of the year 1975 to conclude this history of the Medical College ends on sweet and sour notes. The sweet notes were sounded by the expansion of facilities, an increase in research efforts, the growth within the departments, and increased enrollment. All of these advances resulted in a general revitalization of the College. The sour note was the oncoming of financial problems for the College. Federal support of medical colleges and research was being reduced and in some areas, support was totally eliminated. Inflation was driving the cost of operation upward and tuition would rise to unimagined heights. But this was nothing unique in the history of Albany Medical College. The little ship might slip into another deep trough of the tempestuous ocean of financial distress, but it would, as in the past, rise to the next crest.

To conclude the history of the Hospital portion of Albany Medical Center, a return in time is made to 1968. That year the Board of Governors authorized borrowing $26,000,000 for the construction of what is known as Building C and for other improvements to the

(Fig. 144)
Mr. Neil Hellman

(Fig. 145) The Neil Hellman Medical Research Building.

Medical Center. Two years later, in 1970, construction was begun on Building C which was to cost $22,500,000 on completion in 1973. It incorporated the most modern hospital design and concluded a 25 year development program of the Hospital facilities begun in 1948. The total cost of the 25 year expansion program was in excess of $40,000,000. The timing of the expansion program was excellent because in 1973, the Federal Government sharply curtailed its financial assistance to medical development. The curtailment would continue and aid from Federal sources became more stringent. It is questionable if the private sector will be willing or able to take up the slack caused by reduction and near elimination of Federal funds. The Albany Medical Center Foundation would henceforth be required to provide funds for new equipment and development of the Medical Center.

As science finds solutions to age old problems in the process new problems are unearthed or created. In 1967, Dr. Thomas Hale, then Executive Vice President of the Hospital, expressed his anxiety in that year's annual report. Dr. Hale wrote of the problems concerning transplant of vital organs and the development of life sustaining devices. His concern was with the ethics, morality and cost to society of these great developments. In another vein, he appreciated the government support of health services but he recognized the growing intervention of the government, whether Federal or State.

On July 1, 1970, abortions became legal in New York State. In just six months of legalization, 890 abortions were performed at Albany Medical Center. More than 50 percent of the abortions were performed on unmarried women. In the three months preceding January 1971, abortions at Albany Medical Center exceeded the number of births performed there. Later that year, births regained dominance in numbers over abortions. The Hosptal was in effect the instrument of the legislation, but a difference of opinion on the ethics or morality of such operations was to descend on the Hospital and the Nation.

The tremendous developments of the recent decades placed an additional burden on the Hospital. Besides making room to house more equipment and patients for the newly found treatments, the Hospital required more personnel to administer its growing population. Volunteered money and supplies had in the past provided a bulwark of support for the Hospital. Since World War II volunteered services had begun to perform growing support for the Hospital. In 1970, volunteers provided 42,483 hours of donated help, the equivalent of 21 full-time employees. A year later, the total grew to 51,675 hours or 1,292 man weeks. In earlier days, the Hospital was in part sustained by gifts of food and material; now the Hospital was being sustained by gifts of hours.

Amidst the trials of reduction and elimination of financial support, the annual reports from the Medical Center continued to offer new hope for the seriously sick. In 1971, the Medical Center obtained a Medical Linear Accelerator for the treatment of cancer, the growing use of radiation for treatment of leukemia together with bone marrow transplants. An arthritis laboratory was established. A year later, 41 kidney transplants were performed. Forty-two coronary bypass operations were performed with a success rate of 95 percent. Hip joint replacement was inaugurated and 100 patients were operated on.

Drs. March, Armsby, Vander Veer, Ordway, and the many, many others who marched in step with them must be thanked.

Board
Chairmen and Presidents

It is appropriate that a portion of the history of Albany Medical Center be devoted exclusively to the Presidents of the Board of Governors of the Hospital and the Chairmen of the Board of Trustees of the College. Many of them have been identified throughout the history of the Medical Center when the history focused on issues in which those people performed a significant and often pivotal act. Of course, each was supported by the members of their respective Boards and the Board members themselves were vitally important to the success of the Medical Center. To be elected to a Board of Governors or Trustees is always an honor because the appointment is in itself recognition of the ability of the individual and a demonstration of confidence in his or her judgment and integrity.

Board members of business institutions receive some remuneration for their service, but those who serve in that capacity for charitable or non-profit institutions receive nothing other than the satisfaction of rendering a service. And as conflicting demands are frequently placed before a Board, the members are unable to please all and must suffer the criticism of the dissatisfied.

To those interested in medical education and the history of medical schools and hospitals, it is apparent that doctors have rarely made progress without the guidance from boards of governors and trustees. The doctors' attention is properly directed in scientific channels. The major decisions to be made in building and maintaining the schools and hospitals are of a completely different nature. These decisions are generally of long range and of a financial nature. At all times, they must be made above any partisanship and based on an overview of the issue.

Albany Medical Center continues to be fortunate to attract to its Boards men who have been capable of meeting the crises as they occur such as financial problems, decision to expand when the need occurs, or to resolve sometimes strongly held differences within the faculty. Something which happens in the best of families.

Appendix B lists the names of the Presidents of the Board of Trustees and Governors and the years in which they served in those offices.

358

(Fig. 146)
Mr. Edmund Niles Huyck

Such listing is scant recognition for the services they have rendered, but it is at least an acknowledgement.

In a few instances, short biographical sketches of those Presidents are included herein. The completeness of the biographies or the omission of some is forced by the constraints of space and time but principally by the unavailability of information.

In 1920, Mr. Edmund Niles Huyck was elected President of the Board of Trustees of the College *(Figure 146)*. Mr. Huyck's complete support for Dr. Ordway during a tempestuous period was a vital factor in the College's survival. With the faculty problem resolved, Mr. Huyck recognized the need for a modern, adequate building to house the School. As owner of Huyck Mills, Mr. Huyck was knowledgeable about building costs and what was possible to construct with the funds available. The auditorium, completed in 1928, was dedicated to Mr. Huyck. It is now part of the Medical Center complex which has grown around it. Its continued usefulness and durability gives testimony to his good judgment and that of those from whom he sought advice.

During the period when Mr. Huyck was President of the Board of Trustees of the College, Mr. Frederick W. Kelley was Presdient of the Board of Governors of the Hospital, serving from 1919 to 1932. During his administration, many additions were made to the Albany Hospital as well as construction of the Nurses' Home. Mr. Kelley maintained a close relationship with Doctors Ordway and Elting and in many ways the expansion of the Hospital during the period may be attributed to that close association. The accomplishments during that period laid much of the groundwork for the emergence of today's Albany Medical

Center. Mr. Kelley was also President of the North American and Portland Cement Companies.

After Mr. Kelley's death in 1932, Mr. John A. Manning became president of the Board of Governors, serving until 1937. Mr. Manning devoted uncountable hours to the Hospital and no detail missed his attention. It was not unusual for him to sample food which was to be served to patients. If the quality or tastiness did not meet his standards, the kitchen was so informed. If the soup was weak, in unequivocal terms he would declare that it tasted "like dishwater." As a consequence, the food became excellent. Mr. Manning's family had been in the paper making industry for several generations. On the death of his father, he reluctantly assumed control of the John A. Manning Paper Company and found it to be an interesting challenge. Later, he founded the John A. Manning Sand Paper Company which merged with the Behr Company to found the Behr-Manning Co., also manufacturers of abrasives.

While President of the Board of Governors, Mr. Manning enlisted the expertise of members of his Company to help solve problems which the Hospital encountered. Mr. Everitt Jones of Behr-Manning was appointed Director of the Hospital succeeding Dr. John Copeland.

Mr. Lewis Greenleaf, then Vice President of the John Manning Corporation, succeeded Mr. Huyck as Presdient of the Board of Trustees of the Medical College. During the five years of his Chairmanship, it was the mutual agreement of both Boards (Trustees and Governors) that Dr. Ordway, the Dean of the College and Dr. Elting, Chief of Surgery, should resign. As told earlier, both of these men were skilled physicians and received deserved recognition throughout their careers. Both had served the College and Hospital with complete devotion. But Mr. Greenleaf made the hard and not unanimously accepted decision.

Mr. Alfred Renshaw was elected President of the Board of Governors of the Hospital and Chairman of the Board of Trustees of the College in 1946. Mr. Renshaw was a seriously ill man during the later period of his administration and his unremitting effort to raise funds for the needed expansion of the institution may have further shortened his life. Despite suffering reactivation of pulmonary problems, he continued to serve until his retirement in 1954. He carried through with Dr. Cunningham, perhaps, the most dynamic period of growth of both institutions and the birth of the Medical Center.

Mr. James Fairfield Adams succeeded his friend Alfred Renshaw and served as Chairman of the Board of Trustees of the College until 1964 *(Figure 147)*. He had been a Trustee of the Medical College and the Dudley Observatory since 1932 and was a member of the Board of Governors of the Hosptial for 26 years. In addition, his list of service included that of a board member of Union University, Vassar College,

(Fig. 147)
Mr. James Fairfield Adams

(Fig. 148)
Judge Francis Bergen

Russell Sage School of Nursing, and the Westminister Presbyterian Church and a director of many corporate boards. After retiring as President of Manning Paper Company in 1953, having succeeded Mr. Manning in 1938, he devoted virtually all of his time to the Medical College. He and Dean Wiggers were tireless in their efforts to build alumni support. Both recognized the necessity of an active alumni association in the further development of the College. Mr. Adams was sympathetic to the needs of the faculty and was always willing to entertain their recommendations. It was during his administration that the Medical Science Building, now the Neil Hellman Medical Research Building, was built.

Judge Francis Bergen succeeded Mr. Adams as Chairman of the Board of Trustees in 1964 *(Figure 148)*. Judge Bergen was a leading jurist, having been on the Board of New York State Supreme Court and presiding judge of the State Court of Appeals. He served as Chairman carrying on the program of Mr. Adams and Dean Wiggers to maintain the high academic standard of the College both in the faculty and students. Judge Bergen retired in 1970.

Mr. Frank Wells McCabe was President of the Board of Governors from 1948 to 1952 *(Figure 149)*. He continued to serve on both Boards until he was elected Chairman of the Board of Trustees in 1970, where he served until 1974. Mr. McCabe used his time well, at the same time that he was serving the Medical Center in those capacities, he was also conducting a variety of business interests. Mr. McCabe was born in 1902 and educated at Taft School and Yale University. After service in

(Fig. 149)
Members of the Board of Governors: (Standing, left to right)
Col. Ralph Wagner, Mr. George Pfaff, Mr. Arnold Cogswell;
(Seated, left to right) Mr. Frank Wells McCabe, Mr. Gates Aufsesser.

(Fig. 150)
Mr. Woods McCahill

World War II he became President of the National Commercial Bank and Trust Company in 1955. The Bank flourished under his administration. In 1973, he became Chairman of the Board of Directors of the Bank. Mr. McCabe together with Dr. Thomas Hale, Director of the Hospital, directed vast improvements in the Hospital, raising funds for that purpose and for important additions to the faculty. After retirement, Mr. McCabe continued to serve the Medical Center as a stimulating adviser and helper.

Mr. Andrew Fisher succeeded Mr. McCabe as Chairman of the Board of Trustees serving from 1974 to 1977. Mr. Fisher had retired as Vice President of the *New York Times*. He devoted much of his time and vast business experience, but after three years, because of business reasons, he relinquished the chair to Mr. Woods McCahill.

Mr. Woods McCahill became Chairman of the Board of Trustees of Albany Medical College in 1977 *(Figure 150)*. He was faced with a period during which Government financial aid was withdrawn from medical colleges. He stood firmly behind the newly appointed Dean Friedlander to meet and overcome the financial crisis. Mr. McCahill was a graduate of Harvard University and Harvard Law School. During his professional career, he was a prominent legal council in the General Electric Company. Despite the reoccurence of health problems, which had necessitated his retirement from General Electric, he accepted his responsibility as Chairman of the Board of Trustees with unstinting effort.

Colonel Ralph Wagner was President of the Board of Governors from June 1, 1955 through June 20, 1963 *(Figure 149)*. He was also a Trustee of Albany Medical College and Albany College of Pharmacy. An alumnus of the University of Nebraska, Harvard Engineering School, and retired Colonel of the Air Force, he was able to give much time to the Hospital in spite of many other business interests, including General Commercial Manager of Niagara Mohawk Power and Light Company. It was during his years as President that the groundwork was laid for the building of the new "K" wing at a cost of over five million dollars. This building would add 230 beds to the enlarging Medical Center. In addition, during his administration plans were made for the seven story dormitory to house 144 house officers and the five story medical science buiding with laboratory facilities for research.

Mr. Arnold Cogswell was President of the Board of Governors for nine years, 1963-72 *(Figure 149)*. He, like many of his predecessors, had other obligations, but managed to spend much of his time concerned with the affairs of the Hospital. He could usually be found in the Directors Office working with Thomas Hale, M.D., who was Director of the Hospital from 1946 to 1968, and later with his successor Thomas L. Hawkins, M.D. Mr. Cogswell, like his predecessors, ran a "tight ship" and it was a common experience when one was seeking finances for laboratory equipment to be told that the Hospital had a reserve of only $500. During this period, the Hospital was financing a building program of twenty million dollars. By some ununderstandable means, Arnold Cogswell was able to manage this expansion with the $500 reserve. The Cogswell family has a long tradition of service to the community and many of its institutions. A point of interest is that Arnold's grandfather, Mason Cogswell, had been a curator early in the history of Albany Medical College. So it was in the tradition of community service that Arnold Cogswell served as President of the Board of Governors of the Hospital so long and so well.

Mr. George Pfaff succeeded Arnold Cogswell as President of the Board of Governors of the Hospital in 1972 *(Figure 149)*. Mr. Pfaff, like Mr. Huyck, had been President of the Huyck Corporation. It is interesting to note that two Presidents of both Huyck Corporation and Manning Paper Company served as Presidents of the Boards of Albany Medical Center.

When Mr. Pfaff became President there existed the need for financial support so that the Medical Center could maintain the great medical advances of the preceeding years. During this period, "C" Building was opened providing the new 16 room operating complex; the Neil Hellman Intensive Care Unit became operative, as did the Burn Unit and many other innovations to the Hospital. All of this had to be maintained at high standards during a period of growing inflation and reduced Federal support throughout the Nation.

At the same time that he dealt with the financial problems he undertook the task of educating the general public to the problems facing the maintenance of a medical center. The responsiblity of maintaining a medical school, a nursing school, sub-departments staffed by specialists, and continuing expensive research, placed a tremendous financial strain on the Medical Center. Mr. Pfaff enthusiastically met the challenge. He retired in 1975.

Mr. Gates Aufsesser served the Albany Medical Center in varying capacities for twenty years *(Figure 149)*. He first became a member of the Board of Governors of the Hospital in 1948; a year prior to his retirement as President of Mohawk Brush Company where he had been President since 1911. He became President of the Board of Governors, serving in that post from 1952 to 1955. Concurrent with his membership on the Board of Governors, he was a member of the Board of Trustees of the College from 1950 to 1958. Mr. Aufsesser was a man of charming personality and he accomplished much with his pleasant, persuasive manner. The meetings over which he presided were sometimes day-long sessions, but never boring. He had the ability to stimulate his associates to even greater participation in the affairs of the Hospital and Medical College. Mr. Aufsesser, born in 1888, died in 1982, and maintained his interest in the Medical Center even after his 90th year.

Carrying on in the tradition of service to the Medical Center, his son-in-law, Richard Sonneborn, was elected President of the Board of Governors of the Hospital in 1976.

Epilogue

It is awesome to think of the future. In the not too distant past, a medical student studied a medical text written by one author. That book would encompass all of the knowledge of that particular subject known to medicine. One man could master the entire subject matter. Present day texts are contributed to by as many as 50 co-authors, so vast has the science grown. Each specialty grows as the entire field of medicine grows. Like the single cell, specialties grow, divide, and the divisions themselves subdivide creating a growing complexity of knowledge for new medical treatment, surgical procedures and therapy.

Severed limbs are restored, organs transplanted, and defective hearts restored to normalcy. Malignancy is no longer the certain harbinger of death. Ultra medicine now almost defies the capability of the human mind. Computer science has entered the field of medicine because only through the computer can the maze of discovered medical science be applied and analyzed. First the brain could be examined to detect tissue abnormality before surgery was performed, if necessary. Now the entire body can be similarly examined with marvelous machines.

However, therein lies danger. The danger is great of doctors losing interest and the ability in the time-proven technique of physical examination and sympathetic understanding of the patient. No machine can restore confidence of recovery to the patient as well as the trusted physician.

Doctors can err in diagnosis and machines can fail in analysis. It is the synergism of doctor and machine, the human and mechanical, that offers realization of the great future which is launched from the great past of medical science.

All that is new is not de facto good, and everything of the past must not be disregarded. If the physicians of 1700 A.D. had studied the biblical story of Job written 400 B.C., they would have found therein the cure for scurvy, the curse of early day mariners. When Job was denied the fruits of his orchards, his limbs became swollen and he suffered other symptoms of scurvy, "my skin is black upon me, my bones are burned with heat." When Job could again enjoy fresh fruit, his recovery was quick. Medical science must continually look forward to the future, probing for the unreachable final frontiers of knowledge but it must also remember and look back to the past.

Historians have graphically described the ravages of tuberculosis, syphilis, vitamin deficiencies, plague, smallpox, leprosy, and many other diseases. What will historians write of the present in the oncoming 21st century? Will they tell of the ravages of obesity, diabetes, arteriosclerosis, hypercholesterolemia, collagen disease, cancer, or death from radiation? For most of these afflications, we now have the knowledge of prevention, control, and even cure. But it was centuries before ships outfitting for long voyages laid in a stock of limes or homely sauerkraut for the prevention of scurvy.

The future is splendid to contemplate but we live in the present. It is through the complete application of the knowledge of the present that we can make the "now" splendid.

Unless there is a sudden turnabout by the Federal Government in its funding for research, the support of education, and student loans, Albany Medical College and its sister institutions face hard days. Albany Medical College has frequently been beset by similar threats and survived and grew. Ways will be found to overcome today's threats.

Alden March, the founder, set four major responsibilities for the College. They were:

1. To improve patient care;
2. To improve student instruction;
3. To improve postgraduate education;
4. To establish research facilities.

His successors followed his precepts, sometimes concentrating on one more than another of these goals. In 1915, Dean Thomas Ordway reaffirmed them and revitalized the College. There is no reason to assume that fervor will diminish in the future. The flame that Dr. Alden March ignited in 1839 still burns brightly in 1982 to illuminate the true course.

*　　*　　*　　*

Following is a listing of some of the significant events since 1975. So that this book can go to press sometime near schedule, each is mentioned in just a line or two of copy. A later historian will hopefully elaborate, giving each the attention it richly deserves and including the many others that have been missed.

1976
—A course in Biomedical Electronics is initiated at Albany Medical College.

—Union University joined Albany Medical College in a six year Medical Education Program.

—Brain scanner is installed.

—Department of Family Practice is established.

1977

—A Division of Pediatric Cardiology and a Pediatric Coronary Catherization Laboratory is installed.

—Dr. Gordon I. Kaye is appointed Professor and Chairman of the Department of Anatomy.

1978

—A Division of Ultrasound is established.

—Woods McCahill is named Chairman of the Board of Directors.

—Special operating rooms are established for one-day surgery cases.

1979

—Department of Health, Education and Welfare contributed $150,000 to continue the eight bed research center.

—Computerized EKG technology made its debut in Albany Medical Center.

—Dr.Friedlander became Dean of Albany Medical College.

1980

—Entire body scanner is installed at Albany Medical Center.

—Dr. Julio Sosa develops a new heart catherization method.

—$100,000 is received from Robert Wood Foundation to reorganize the medical clinic.

—Hospital Group Medical Practice group is established.

—Albany Medical Center is established as regional hemodialysis center.

1981

—Tuition is substantially increased for medical students.

—Dr. John A. Balint is appointed Chairman of the Department of Medicine.

—WAMC ceases to be operated by AMC.

—Largest bequest received to date from an AMC graduate: Dr. Robert Brockway Lamb, AMC 1891.

—Dr. Michael Vanko becomes President and Director of Albany Medical Center Hospital.

—Dr. Samuel S. Ciccio, Vice President for Academic Affairs, Dr. Douglas L. Johnson, Vice President and Treasurer and Mrs. Amber B. Jones, Vice President for Planning, join administrative staff of the College.

1982

— Simon Portee, AMC fourth year student, wins $1,500 Joseph B. Robinson, M.D. Medical Scholarship for 1982.

— Dr. Gerald Austin is elected President of the Alumni Association.

— Dr. Rosalyn S. Yalow delivers the Theobald Smith Lecture.

— Dr. G. Timothy Johnson addresses the graduates of 1982.

— The Clark Foundation awards Albany Medical College and Rensselear Polytechnic Institute a career physician program grant to aid minority students.

— Mathew Bender IV is named Chairman of Albany Medical College Board of Trustees.

— AMC receives $400,000 in grants to fund cancer research on drug resistant tumors.

— Dr. James Cerilli is appointed Chairman of the Department of Surgery.

— Extensive review of four year medical education curriculum is begun.

— Albany Medical College researchers examine sponges from Columbia space shuttle.

— Dr. C. Rollins Hanlon keynotes dinner in honor of Dr. Charles Eckert, retiring surgeon.

— Dr. Louis Sokoloff presents 50th Salmon Lecture at Albany Medical College.

— Albany Medical Center, Inc. is established as administrative link of Albany Medical Center Hospital and Albany Medical College.

January 1983

— J. Richard Gaintner, M.D. is appointed as first President and Chief Executive Officer of Albany Medical Center, Inc.

* * * * *

Union University includes the following institutions:
Union College, founded 1795
Albany Medical College, founded 1839
Albany Law School, founded 1851
Dudley Observatory, founded 1852
Albany College of Pharmacy, founded 1881

* * * * *

Sesquicentennial Celebrations
1988-1989

It is fitting to end on a note for the future. As this book goes to press, Dean Robert L. Friedlander has appointed a prestigious committee to plan the sesquicentennial celebrations of Albany Medical College. The committee includes members of the community who have responsibility for the history and cultural education of Albany and New York State, as well as those who have close ties with Albany

Medical College.

In his invitation to members of this Committee, Dean Friedlander said: "In its years of operation, the Albany Medical College has compiled a list of accomplishments deserving of recognition. We plan to use the occasion of our sesquicentennial year to make more public our heritage. We wish to plan a series of activities to highlight the past, present and potential contributions of the College particularly as these relate to the northeastern region of New York State." The author is a member of the committee and will assist with planning the celebrations.

APPENDIX A:

A

LECTURE

ON THE EXPEDIENCY OF ESTABLISHING A

Medical College

AND HOSPITAL

IN THE CITY OF ALBANY:

DELIVERED JANUARY 11th, 1830; INTRODUCTORY TO A COURSE ON

Anatomy and Operative Surgery.

BY ALDEN MARCH, M. D.
Professor of Anatomy and Physiology in the Vermont
Academy of Medicine, &c.

ALBANY.
Printed by L. G. Hoffman, 44 Dean-street.
371........
1830.

June 10, 1921

To the Alumni and Other Friends of
The Albany Medical College:

The words of Dr. Alden March, written in 1830,
expressed so well the importance of establishing
a medical school in Albany, that we have felt, in
inviting your active cooperation at the present
time in maintaining and improving the Albany
Medical College, that the reprinting of Dr. March's
address would be particularly appropriate on this
centenary of his first course of demonstrations
and lectures in Anatomy; representing as it does
the one-hundredth anniversary of the teaching of
medicine in Albany.

(Signed)

Edmund N. Huyck	Francis C. Pratt
Alden Chester	Willis R. Whitney
Robert Olcott	Frederick W. Kelley
Luther H. Tucker	Ellis J. Staley
Amasa J. Parker	Gerrit Y. Lansing
Frederick Townsend	Benjamin W. Arnold
Charles Gibson	William Barnett
Charles A. Richmond	Henry M. Sage
George Alexander	A. Page Smith
Edgar S. Barney	Walter H. Conley
Franklin H. Giddings	James R. Watt
Charles B. McMurray	Edward Easton, Jr.

Trustees, Albany Medical College,
Medical Department, Union University

Albany, January 12th, 1830

Dear Sir:

A number of gentlemen, who were present at the delivery of your introductory address, conceiving the objects contemplated by you, too important to the cause of humanity and the interests of science, not to have your views made more public than the nature of the circumstances under which they were offered, could be supposed to admit, have conferred on us the honor of presenting to you their grateful acknowledgments, and requesting a copy of the address for publication.

We are, sir, with sentiments of respect,

Your obed't servants,

L. WELLINGTON
A. F. LAWYER
O. CROSBY, JUN.

To Professor Alden March, M. D.   Committee

––––––––––––

Albany, January 12th, 1830

Gentlemen:

In replying to your complimentary note received this morning requesting a copy of my introductory address for publication, permit me, through you, to tender my thanks to the gentlemen assembled, for this favorable expression of their approbation.

This familiar lecture was not designed for the public eye; and although, owing to the multiplicity of my avocations, it affords but a hasty and imperfect sketch of my views upon this important theme, yet I cannot refuse complying with your polite request, hoping thereby to advance in some degree, the interest of the cause already auspiciously commenced.

I have the honor to be, gentlemen,

Very respectfully, your obed't servant,

ALDEN MARCH.

L. WELLINGTON, M. D.
A. F. LAWYER, M. D.
DOCT. O. CROSBY, JUN.
            Committee

374

Lecture

Gentlemen:

The return of another season has called together the teacher and the pupil; and with this laudable meeting are associated some of the strongest interests of the community.

We are assembled for the purpose of communicating and receiving instruction in the science and the art of medicine,— the science and the art of restoring and preserving the health and the life of man. The value of our pursuits, therefore, can be estimated only by the value of life itself, and of that which alone endears it to its possessor,— health.

The enlightened and judicious practitioner of medicine is justly ranked among the benefactors of mankind. In proportion as his time and talents are employed in acquiring an accurate and extended knowledge of his profession, in the same proportion will he become useful to his fellow citizens, and be entitled to their approbation and support. He should not be devoted to the mere sordid accumulation of wealth. A more noble, generous and humane motive should hold the first place in his sentiments and actions. Prevent and relieve human misery, should be his motto, engraven in indelible characters on the tablet of his heart. No real benefit can result from the services, or acts of one man rendered to another who is languishing under pain and disease, unless the one has more knowledge of disease and of remedies than the other. The question then arises, how are we to become possessed of a proper knowledge of the science of medicine, thereby to render an essential service to the sick. It is evident that, as an incipient step, a preparatory education is required; a knowledge at least of the useful branches of general science, if not of the classical languages and literature.

The means of obtaining this preliminary education are abundant, and brought within the reach of almost every student of medicine. Our country is supplied with numerous and well regulated colleges of arts, academies and schools for private instruction. In such institutions is to be laid the basis, upon which the superstructure of a medical education is to be erected. Though I must here confess with much regret, that by far too many young men enter upon the study of our profession, without a due regard to a preparatory education. True it is, that men have reached the highest eminence in our profession, without having been graduates in arts. John Hunter, Sir Astley Cooper and John Abernethy are striking examples of the eminence of character to which a man may arrive, by the force of native talent and genius. We might also specify with pride, individuals among our own countrymen. But is this any proof that the same men would not have shone more conspicuously in the literary and scientific world, if they had enjoyed all the advantages of a good early education?

Formerly the science of medicine was not taught as thoroughly and as systematically as it is at present. Within my recollection, the time was, when we had but few schools of medicine in this country, and when but a small proportion of the whole number of young men who were studying medicine, attended lectures at any public medical school. Without the advantages of a public medical school, or the same advantages enjoyed by private instruction, no man ever was, or can be well qualified to practice in the various branches of our profession. Without having an opportunity of being instructed in practical anatomy, and without founding upon this knowledge, correct principles of surgery, the surgeon, at least, was constantly liable to mis-judge and to commit the grossest errors.

To illustrate and to enforce this assertion, I shall here relate an anecdote of a surgical case that occurred in the western part of this state as recently as during the late war,— perhaps about fifteen years since. As the story was related to me, it appears that a man in the vicinity of Sacketts-Harbor was affected with a tumor, situated in the ham. It had been of some months standing when a physician was called to attend the case. He took the swelling to be a common phlegmonous abscess — accordingly ordered a succession of poultices, and to his great surprise, after persevering for a considerable length of time, he found no more symptoms of a spontaneous discharge from the tumor than at first. Being at this time rather at a loss to know what the contents of the tumor were, he determined on thrusting his lancet into it at once; which, however, was no sooner done, than the surgeon and patient were both deluged in blood! By this time we infer that the physician, or surgeon, if he is thought entitled to the latter appellation, was fully and awfully apprised of the dangerous nature of the disease. In this place we must do him the justice to say that he had sufficient presence of mind to command the hemorrhage, by passing a fillet or ligature around the thigh, with which he succeeded in compressing the femoral artery. In this dilemma, it seemed to be the only object of the physician, to save the life of the patient if possible; though it is presumed from what followed, that he did not even as much as dream that the limb could also be preserved, a useful member to his patient. Accordingly a neighboring physician was sent for, to meet with him in consultation, and to determine on the proper course of treatment. The result of the consultation was, to amputate the limb above the situation of the diseased part. But neither the attending, nor the consulting physician had the necessary instruments for operating. However, to turn necessity to the best account, they sent to a house-joiner, and obtained a sash-saw; and to a shoe-maker, and procured a shoe knife; and with these, together with a few other domestic instruments, picked up, or prepared on the spur of the occasion, they proceeded to operate, and save the life of the patient; though, we presume, the loss of the limb was entirely overlooked, when they reflected on the wonderful surgical feat they had performed. At the present day, a surgeon would be held responsible for a man's limb, thus unnecessarily sacrificed to sheer ignorance, as it inevitably appears that this must have been. Had they known that the femoral artery could be taken up, and that the hemorrhage could be thus arrested, and the limb preserved, in all probability the patient might have been a living and perfect monument to reflect honor upon their skill, instead of being a mutilated object, to reflect disgrace upon these individuals not only, but through them, upon the whole profession.

Since the facilities for obtaining medical and surgical knowledge are diffused throughout the civilized world, mistakes of this kind very rarely occur to physicians of the present day. And if any one thing has contributed more than another, to disseminate medical and surgical knowledge among the common ranks of our profession, it is the circumstance that medical instruction is now within the reach, and is carried almost to the very doors of all who may seek it.

Numerous as are our medical schools, and as much rivalry as there appears to be among them, still I conceive no evil to the profession generally, nor to the community has thence arisen. It is alleged by some that we have medical schools enough, and more than enough and that by establishing new ones, we incur the risk of impairing the value and utility of those that already exist. If this argument be true now, why was it not equally so, in application to the same subject, fifteen or twenty years ago, when there were but about half the number of medical institutions in this country, that there are at the present time? And suppose, as most likely will be the case, the population of the United States to increase in the same geometrical ratio that it has for the last twenty years, should we then say the present number of colleges of arts, of academies, and of common schools, or even of medical colleges are sufficient for the demands of this vast increase of population? Surely facilities for acquiring literary and scientific information must accumulate and extend in proportion to the increase and demands of the population.

In connection with these sentiments, I propose to make a few remarks upon the subject of establishing a hospital and medical college in the city of Albany.

Before I enter upon the subject, I trust my audience will gratify me with their patience, while I briefly state the origin and progress of this private course of medical instruction.

I came to this place in the autumn of 1820, and in November 1821, I commenced a course of demonstrations and lectures in anatomy, to a class of 14 students; and from that time to the present, which is the commencement of my ninth course of lectures in this place, there has been a gradual increase in the number of the pupils, so that last year our class exceeded thirty in number. I shall not obtrude upon my audience, a recital of the many difficulties that were constantly rising up at the commencement of my career in this place, as I advanced step by step. Suffice it to say that it was an undertaking which required nerve and sinew, (if I may be allowed the technical phraseology) to carry the project into effect. My efforts however, have been pretty uniformly crowned with success. I have had but little assistance in the line of instructing, except such as has been rendered by my distinguished colleague Dr. Tully. Our exertions were united in this infant establishment for the purpose of aiding the growth of a well established medical institution in the city of Albany. As it respects myself, I have no doubt but my humble merits have been duly appreciated; and it is with feelings of sincere regret, participated, I doubt not, by my auditors, that I notice the absence of Dr. Tully, whose eminent attainments in literature and science, and unbounded qualifications in our profession, have caused his removal from this city to an honorable situation in an institution, where from a longer acquaintance, his talents and acquirements are better known, and of course more highly valued. But however deserving the subject of these remarks may be, the present is not the time nor the place for eulogizing the living.

I shall now proceed to notice the several circumstances that require deliberate consideration, before we adopt any measures towards establishing a medical college in the city of Albany.

Firstly — It will be necessary for us to show that the location of this city is good, possessing many advantages, and but few disadvantages.

Secondly — That an institution of this kind is required in this place, and that it will be useful to the public.

Thirdly — That the object is practicable.

We shall prove by a reference to other medical institutions, both in the city and country, of the management of the concerns, of which, we claim to be familiar, that a place of this size, unites the advantages of both a large city and the country; and that it commands some advantages that neither enjoy individually.

In the first place, this city is sufficiently large to afford ample employment in the practice of medicine, for the several professors in the intervals of the regular courses of lectures.

Again, it is large enough to give us most, if not all the advantages of a hospital, including a sufficiency of subjects.

I am well aware that the above points are strongly urged by the supporters of the schools of our large cities, as being all important, and I will readily allow that the first has the highest claims for regard, in selecting a location for a medical school. No one can fully conceive the inconveniences of having a school located in a place too small to afford employment to the professors in the intervals of the lectures, except those who have suffered from the evil. It is not confined to an individual, but its influence is extended to the very vitals of the school. For what confidence can the public have in the stability of an institution where there are frequent changes in its professors? If the question be asked,— cannot this be obviated and still keep up the reputation of the school? I answer, that it can in one way, and in one way only. I shall state it, though objections can be raised even to this. The only way of permanently retaining able professors, is to give them a salary that would support them and their families handsomely, without their attending to any other duties than those which are directly connected with their professorship. But even though the institution had the means to meet these heavy salaries, yet a strong objection would very soon grow out of this plan. These professors, though able men, would soon become mere theorists, if not visionary speculators. They could not be sound, practical men, which seems to be at least important, if not absolutely necessary, in most of the branches of our profession.

Men, that are capable of filling a place in a public medical school, can generally command a respectable business in private practice. This they could not, nor ought not to relinquish, unless the pay of the professorship was a sufficient inducement. We make the assertion then, that a moderate income from a school in this place, would be better for those practitioners who might be engaged in it, than twice the amount, and even much more, received from a country institution, where the practitioner would be under the necessity of abandoning his friends and practice, for the time being at least, to a very great disadvantage.

There are other objections to being an itinerant lecturer; but as some of them, to say the least, relate to the affairs of domestic life, I shall not notice them in this place.

With respect to the advantages of a hospital, it may be stated that we have a population of upwards of twenty thousand, as estimated by good judges, and of this number a pretty large proportion, in comparison with the population of many other places, are foreigners, destitute and friendless. A large number of this class of people too, are liable to all the diseases "which flesh is heir to;" and as they are dependent upon public charity for relief, there seems to be a kind of moral obligation on their part, to repay the public by affording a clinical school in medicine to the young and inexperienced part of the medical profession.

Nor are the advantages of a hospital confined to the young practitioner and medical student alone. It affords an opportunity for the grey headed practitioner to keep up with the improvements of the day, and in instructing others, to instruct himself. It is universally conceded, that no man can qualify himself so well, in any branch of science or literature, as by teaching others. Here it is that he is compelled to become master of his subject; and his talents, and strongest energies are called into action.

Neither is the benefit confined to the teacher and the pupil. The physician, or physicians, who are in habits of intimacy with the teacher are also benefited in a great degree, by a practical school of medicine, such as is afforded by a well regulated hospital. Nor does the advantage cease here.— The public comes in for its share of the benefit.

It is to be distinctly understood then, that by getting up a public institution of this kind, its benefits are not to be confined to the poor, nor to the physicians and surgeons who might be employed in it.

One of the advantages, that is expected to extend to the public by establishing a hospital and medical college in this place, is, the probability of elevating the character of the profession in this city, not only, but in a good degree its influence must extend to our neighboring physicians.

We hope and trust, therefore, that our citizens will view the project under consideration, in a far more extended light, than that of a mere public charity, designed solely for the relief of the poor.— And as far as the subject has been discussed among the friends of charitable institutions, and among those interested for the advancement of medical science, and also among those who take a deep interest in all general improvements in the city, it seems to have been uniformly favorably received.

The advantages, or perhaps I ought to say the only advantage which a country institution has over one located in the city, is the extremely low rate at which students are enabled to attend the lectures, and which principally regards the price of board and tuition. Now both of these items can be made reasonable in the city of Albany,— and with respect to the first, I am prepared to say, that any number of medical students can procure good wholesome board and lodgings in this city, for two dollars a week, though they may go as much beyond this sum as they please. Upon this subject, I speak with the utmost confidence, as we have had for several years past, quite a number of students from our office, boarded and lodged for the sum that I have named.— Then again, our lecture fee need be but a trifle more than that of a respectable country school. So that the extra charges on these two items, ought not to exceed the sum of twenty or twenty-five dollars for each course of lectures.

I shall, now, notice the sources from which it is expected that from eighty to one hundred students may be collected, within two or three years at farthest.

We can determine this point, with almost a certainty, by referring to the following statistical table.

Whole No. of Students attending the Vermont Academy of Medicine in the years	No. from the State of New York	Whole No. of Students attending the Berkshire Medical Institution in the years	No. from the State of New York
1823-126	41	1823- 84	18
1824-124	50	1824- 94	23
1825-101	42	1825-112	30
1826-103	34	1826-104	34
1827-100	33	1827-106	27
1828- 94	38	1828-100	13

Total No. from N. Y. 238   Total No. from N. Y. 145

It will be perceived by the above statement, that there has been an average annual number, for the last six years, of nearly sixty-four students from this state, who have attended at the schools in Vermont and Massachusetts.

We shall now refer to the catalogues of the Fairfield school, for the last two years, to ascertain how many students have attended from this and several of the counties in its vicinity. On examination, we find that the number of students from the counties of Albany, Saratoga, Rensselaer, Montgomery, Washington, Columbia, Schoharie, and Schenectady in 1827-1828, amount to twenty-four, and that from the same counties in 1828-1829 amount to twenty-three. Now, these twenty-three or four, added to the average number for the last six years, attending at the other two schools, as above stated, and also about twenty in Albany and its immediate vicinity, who have been in the habit for a number of years of attending a private course in this place, and who have not attended a public course in the same season, will give us something more than one hundred.

In making this statement, it will be perceived, that we have not calculated upon any that may now attend from year to year at New York, Philadelphia, New Haven, or Boston Schools, nor upon any that might be induced to come into the state from Connecticut, Massachusetts, or Vermont.

I may here observe, that medical students cannot be induced, or coerced by legislative enactment, to attend medical lectures at any other institution, than that of their own choice. This assertion is proved, by the fact that there were but seven students who belong north and west of the city of Hudson who attended medical lectures in the State School in the city of New York the last season. This would seem to support the opinion of a distinguished individual, who has said, that, " It should be borne in mind, that a monopoly of learning, or knowledge, cannot be created by legislative enactment." " The fostering care with which the arm of power confers and sustains exclusive privileges in science, neither stimulates the exertions, increases the capacity, nor elevates the views of character of those who may enjoy them."

"A monopoly of the business of teaching, may indeed be effected; but should it even be conceded, that this would produce higher attainments in literature in the few, it cannot effect a more general diffusion of knowledge throughout the public mind, or, be productive of so much general benefit."

As it respects the argument of some, who say there are two classes of medical schools in this country, viz. the city, and the country institutions, and if one were to be located in this city, it would be ranked among the former, and that the expenses of attending a course of lectures in this place, would be about the same that they are in the city of New York or Philadelphia, we conceive it to be groundless.— One moment's reflection will set this matter in its true light. If it is, or has been an object for me, or for any other practitioner of this place to leave our business, and lecture in a country institution at the rate of ten dollars for each student, it must be obvious that we could quite as well afford to lecture in this place for the same sum, and in the meantime attend to our regular and stated practice among our private patients. I, for one, would prefer giving a course of lectures in this place, and attending to my private practice during the time for five hundred dollars, to going to a country institution and receiving twice the sum for the same services:—and at the end of three years, I have no doubt that I should be the gainer in a pecuniary point of view, as well as in reputation.

Let us suppose there were six professors, who should compose a faculty in a medical school at this place with a fee of ten dollars each,— board and lodging to be obtained for two dollars a week, as it can be in this city,— and the course to consist of sixteen weeks:— the expense of board and lodging would be thirty-two dollars, and the fee for all the tickets sixty dollars, making a total of ninety-two dollars. Adding a few dollars for contingencies, might make the whole, in round numbers, about one hundred dollars. Certainly, this is far from being an exorbitant sum for a complete course of medical lectures.

Perhaps it may not be entirely impertinent here, to allude to the facilities which this city affords for traveling in all directions, and in every mode of conveyance, and in which it probably is not surpassed by any place in the Union. A considerable number of medical students now pass annually through this city, on their way to their respective institutions while on the other hand, in reaching some of the interior colleges, they often experience serious delays and inconveniences, and are sometimes, for a part of the distance, even obliged to resort to the expense of a private conveyance.

We have, thus far, proceeded upon matters of fact; and if we may now be allowed the liberty of reasoning exclusively upon the subject, I think it can be made out conclusively, that a medical institution is required in this place,— that it would be supported, and that it would be useful to the public. In entering upon these points, it will be perceived that we embrace our second proposition.

It evidently is the true policy of the state, to retain its circulating wealth, as far as is practicable, in its own territory. Money that is carried out of the state and expended, by the medical students, rarely, if ever returns. The expenses of a full course of lectures at the Castleton or Pittsfield Schools, cannot vary but little from eighty dollars and this, multiplied by sixty-four, the average number of students going from this state for the last six years, will give us the sum of five thousand, one hundred and twenty dollars annually. A medical institution is farther called for in this place, because it will best accommodate the students who now go to Vermont and Massachusetts for their education.

Besides the benefits of a medical college, even with regard to the diffusion of useful knowledge, will by no means be exclusively confined to the profession for which it is more particularly established. The science of medicine is so comprehensive that it might almost be defined the science of nature. Anatomy, Physiology, Zoology, Botany, Mineralogy, Chymistry, are interesting to every lover of knowledge; and some of these branches cannot be thoroughly studied in the present day, except in medical schools. The science of medical jurisprudence also, is as important to the practitioner at the bar, as to the physician.

These are matters in which the public is interested; and if we were, now, merely to allude to local interest, we should barely remark, that it requires not the least argument to convince any one of the importance of the acquisition of an institution like this to the city of Albany.

If a professor is in pretty good practice, as there is no doubt but he might be, were he a practical man, it requires no enormous salary from the professorship, to induce him to engage in it. One hundred students, or even seventy-five, at ten or twelve dollars each would amount to a very considerable sum. We repeat, therefore, that a school can be supported in this place, with as much certainty as perhaps in any other in the Union.

In showing that the object, under consideration is practicable, we shall be under the necessity of referring to some of the arguments that have already been brought forward in support of other positions.

If we were to consider this point in detail, it would be necessary for us to take it up in the regular order in which we should proceed, were we now actually to engage in the undertaking.

And in the first place, it is necessary that the subject should be well digested, and a kind of plan sketched out by some one who is familiar with it in all its bearings. The first step, then, will be for us to make a judicious selection of a number of gentlemen for a board of trustees or corporation.

In the next place it devolves upon those more immediately concerned, whether of the number selected for the corporation, or others to make all the interest possible with the medical public, particularly in this vicinity. Nor should it be confined to medical men only. Every liberal and enlightened citizen should be well informed upon the subject, and his influence brought to bear and co-operate with the physicians.

It is preposterous to suppose, that all the learning and talent of the immense population of this country, is, or can be concentrated in one or two sets of medical teachers as has been argued by the friends of a monopoly.

After it is made out that we have selected a good location for our medical institution, that it possesses all the advantages heretofore enumerated, that the wants of the public now call for it, and that all preliminary measures respecting its organization have been completed, the important question remains, can we obtain a charter that will secure to us, all the rights, privileges, and immunities, usually enjoyed by similar institutions? The brief answer to this question is that the entire success of the measure, depends upon the zeal and assiduity with which the subject is pursued by those who are interested.

If any one is doubtful as to the practicability of effecting so great an undertaking as that before us, we would call his attention to what has been accomplished by individual enterprise and perseverance.. If it should be desired, we can confine our notice of the success of personal exertion, to men in our own profession.

If we cast our eyes upon the historic page of medical science in Europe, we shall there notice the brilliant achievements of individual effort. The elder Monro by his splendid talents and industry, happily established the celebrated medical school of Edinburgh: the success, if not the origin of the London school of medicine, is to be attributed to the zeal and perseverance of the Hunters: and Boerhaave may be considered the father of the great university of Leyden.

More might be said concerning the vast achievements of men abroad. But leaving Trans-Atlantic talent and enterprise, let us examine the origin of some of the medical institutions in our own country. Dr. John Warren of Boston, conceived and furnished a plan for a medical school connected with Harvard college, and owing to his talents and exertions, the several professorships were filled, and the institution soon put into successful operation. We may also notice the amazing labours of the late Dr. Nathan Smith in founding, and actually representing in his own person the whole corps of professorships, for twelve successive years in the medical department of Dartmouth college. He was also eminently instrumental in raising the character of several other medical institutions in New-England. Again, Dr. Wm. Shippen of Philadelphia is entitled to the honor of founding the most distinguished medical institution in America. He gave his first course of lectures on Anatomy and Midwifery, to a class of ten students.

We might carry this subject still farther, and notice the more modern medical institutions, and their living founders; but I trust enough has already been shown, to prove what has been, and what can be accomplished by the exertions of individuals. If in reply to this statement it is said that these men, or most of them, were possessed of pre-eminent talents, learning, and genius, and that their ability to accomplish great undertakings was far above that of ordinary men, we will cheerfully grant it to be true.— But let the efforts of twelve or fifteen men of medium talents and acquirements be concentrated, let there be a perfect co-operation in their power and influence, and we will see how much the sum of their forces will exceed that of any individual, however distinguished.

Gentlemen:— I cannot conclude, without expressing the (I trust well-grounded) hope, that the efforts now making by the friends of knowledge and benevolence, will be continued, and rewarded with success, that ere long, our city will be able to boast of a well conducted Medical College and Hospital, institutions favorable alike to the interests of Science and of Humanity.

It has been suggested that it might be expedient to connect with the Hospital, an Asylum for the Insane, which seems at present to be quite a desideratum in this part of the state.

APPENDIX B: OFFICIALS OF UNION UNIVERSITY, ALBANY MEDICAL COLLEGE and ALBANY HOSPITAL

Chancellors of Union University

1871-1884	Eliphalet Nott Potter
1884-1888	Judson S. Landon ad interim
1888-1894	Harrison S. Webster
1894-1907	Andrew Van Vranken Raymond
1909-1928	Charles Alexander Richmond
1928-1933	Frank Parker Day
	Edward Ellery (Acting President)
1934-1945	Dixon Ryan Fox
	Benjamin Whitaker (Acting President)
1946-1965	Carter Davidson
	Meade Brunet (Acting President)
1965-1974	Harold C. Martin
1974-1978	Thomas N. Bonner
	Norman P. Auburn (Acting President)
1979-	John S. Morris

Deans of Albany Medical College

1839-1869	Alden March, M.D.*
1869-1874	James McNaughton, M.D.*
1874-1875	James H. Armsby, M.D.*
1875-1896	Thomas Hun, M.D.
1896-1903	Albert Vander Veer, M.D.
1903-1914	Samuel B. Ward, M.D.
1914-1937	Thomas Ordway, M.D.
1937-1951	Robert S. Cunningham, M.D., Ph.D., Sc.D.
1951-1953	James Campbell, M.D.
1953-1974	Harold C. Wiggers, Ph.D, Sc.D.
1974-1979	Stuart Bondurant, M.D.
1979-	Robert L. Friedlander, M.D.

*Then designated as President of the Faculty

Chairmen of the Board of Trustees of the Albany Medical College

1839-1843	Jared L. Rathbone
1846-1850	Daniel D. Barnard
1851-1875	Ira Harris
1876-1888	Amasa J. Parker
1889-1898	Joseph W. Russell
1899-1903	William L. Learned
1904-1919	Simon W. Rosendale
1920-1930	Edmund N. Huyck
1931-1945	Lewis S. Greenleaf
1946-1953	Alfred Renshaw
1953-1964	James F. Adams
1964-1970	Francis Bergen
1970-1974	Frank Wells McCabe
1974-1977	Andrew Fisher
1977-1982	Woods McCahill
1982-	Matthew Bender, IV

Presidents of the Hospital

1851-1855	John C. Spencer
1855-1860	Ezra P. Prentice
1860-1874	Thomas W. Olcott
1874-1877	Robert H. Pruyn
1877-1888	Rufus W. Peckham
1888-1889	Archibald McClure
1889-1892	Thomas McCredie
1892-1893	Andrew Mather
1893-1896	Joseph W. Russell
1896-1904	James McCredie
1904-1919	J. Townsend Lansing
1920-1927	Charles Gibson
1927-1932	Frederick W. Kelley
1932-1937	John A. Manning
1938-1946	Alfred Renshaw
1948-1952	Frank Wells McCabe
1952-1955	Gates B. Aufsesser
1955-1963	Ralph P. Wagner
1963-1972	Arnold Cogswell
1972-1976	George O. Pfaff
1976-1980	Richard F. Sonneborn
1980-	Thomas D. O'Connor

Directors of the Hospital

1851-1857	Richard Bygate
1857-1861	Jacob D. Eaton
1861-1865	Richard Bygate
1865-1867	Charles Bartram
1867-1868	Ira W. Palmer
1868-1872	James Alexander
1872-1875	Isaac De Touche, M.D.
1875-1878	Mrs. James Alexander
1878-1893	Mr. S.B. Cavert
1893-1896	John A. Stephenson
1896-1898	Miss S. Snyder
1898-1899	William B. Wemple
1899-1906	John L. Godley
1906-1907	Simon F. Cox, M.D.
1907-1920	Harold C. Goodwin, M.D.
1920-1925	W.D. Rockefeller
1925-1926	Robert H. Dodds
1926-1935	John G. Copeland, M.D.
1935-1942	Everett W. Jones
1942-1946	Robert S. Cunningham, M.D.
1946-1968	Thomas Hale, M.D.
1968-1981	Thomas L. Hawkins, Jr., M.D.
1981-	Michael Vanko, Ph.D.

393

APPENDIX C: ALBANY MEDICAL COLLEGE
1982 - 1983

394

APPENDIX D: ALBANY MEDICAL CENTER HOSPITAL
June 1982

APPENDIX E: CHAIRMEN OF DEPARTMENTS AND DIVISIONS

When Dr. Ordway was appointed Dean of Albany Medical College in 1915, he organized the faculty on the basis of departments. Each department chairman at that time, and since then, also held the title of "Professor" in addition to "Chairman." Similarly, when during the 1940's, divisions were established as distinct parts of the departments, those heading the divisions were titled "Chairman" and also "Professor." In this appendix when the title "Chairman" is used, the title of "Professor" is to be assumed. It is omitted in the interest of brevity.

Prior to Dr. Ordway's administration, those who headed a specific area of medical education were identified as "Professors." Those persons are identified in this appendix with that title. One might assume it to be the equivalent of Chairman in the later period.

In a few instances, individual service to the College spanned the two periods—before the department structuring and during the department structuring. They are identified for the first period served with the title "Professor," and for the second period with the title "Chairman."

Abraham, Rajender, Ph.D.
Director, Institute of Experimental Pathology and Toxicology, 1981-

Alexander, Robert S., Ph.D., Sc.D.
Department Chairman, Physiology, 1955-1972

Alley, Ralph D., M.D.
Division Chairman, Thoracic Surgery, 1973

Archambault, LaSalle, M.D.
Professor, Neurology, 1913-1915
Department Chairman, Neurology, 1915-1929
Consultant, Neurology, 1929-1930

Armsby, James H., M.D.
Professor, Anatomy and Physiology, 1838-1839
Professor, Anatomy, 1840-1869
Curator of Museum, 1846-1869
Professor, Principles and Practice of Surgery, 1870-1875

Balch, Lewis, M.D.
Professor, Anatomy, 1876-1887
Professor, Anatomy and Medical Jurisprudence, 1887-1889
Professor, Medical Jurisprudence, 1889-1890
Professor, Medical Jurisprudence and Hygiene, 1895-1899

Baldwin, Wesley Manning, M.D., A.M.
Department Chairman, Anatomy, 1915-1936

Balint, John A., M.B., B.Ch.
Division Chairman, Gastroenterology, 1963-1980
Department Chairman, Medicine, 1981-
Robert E. Lamb Professor of Medicine

Ball, Stanley M., M.D.
Acting Department Chairman, Neurology, 1968-1969

Barker, George F., M.D.
Acting Professor, Chemistry, 1862-1863

Barrera, Eugene S., M.D.
Department Chairman, Neurology and Psychiatry, 1944-1951

Barron, Kevin D., M.D.
Department Chairman, Neurology, 1969-

Bartholomew, Lee E., M.D.
Division Chairman, Rheumatology, 1971-

Baxter, Donald H., M.D.
Acting Department Chairman, Radiation Therapy, 1981-

Beck, Lewis C., M.D.
Professor, Chemistry and Therapeutics, 1840-1841
Professor, Chemistry and Pharmacy, 1841-1853

Beck, T. Romeyn, M.D.
Professor, Materia Medica, 1842-1853

Bedford, Gunning S., M.D.
Professor, Obstetrics, 1839-1840

Beebe, Richard T., M.D., Sc.D.
Department Chairman, Medicine, 1948-1967
Robert E. Lamb Professor of Medicine
Distinguished Professor, 1968

Bennett, Alan H., M.D.
Division Chairman, Urology, 1979-

Bernstein, Harry Saul, M.D.
Professor, Pathology and Bacteriology, 1911-1913

Bigelow, John Milton, M.D.
Professor, Materia Medica, 1870-1873
Professor, Materia Medica and Therapeutics, 1873, 1876-1882
Professor, Materia Medica and Therapeutics, Diseases of the Throat and Clinical
  Laryngoscopy, 1882-1888
Professor, Materia Medica and Therapeutics, Diseases of the Throat and Nose, 1888-1895
Professor, Diseases of the Nose and Throat, 1895-1899

Blackwell, James H., M.D.
Department Chairman, Military Science and Tactics, 1931-1934

Blumer, George, M.D.
Professor, Pathology and Bacteriology, 1901-1903

Bondurant, Stuart, M.D.
Department Chairman, Medicine, 1967-1974
Robert E. Lamb Professor of Medicine

Bourke, Robert S., M.D.
Division Chairman, Neurosurgery, 1975-
Acting Department Chairman, Surgery, 1979-1981

Boyd, James Peter, Jr., M.D.
Professor, Diseases of Women and Children, 1876
Professor, Obstetrics, Gynecology and Diseases of Children, 1886-1911
Professor, Obstetrics and Diseases of Children, 1911-1913

Brandow, Edward C., Jr., M.D.
Acting Division Chairman, Otalaryngology, 1972-1974

Brown, Curtland C., M.D.
Division Chairman, Rheumatology, 1960-1970

Bryan, Ray W., M.D.
Department Chairman, Military Science and Tactics, 1926-1931

Caliguiri, Lawrence A., M.D.
Department Chairman, Microbiology, 1972-1976
Department Chairman, Microbiology and Immunology, 1976-1980

Cameron, D. Ewen, M.B., Ch.B., M.D.
Department Chairman, Neurology and Psychiatry, 1938-1944

Campbell, Crawford J., M.D.
Division Chairman, Orthopedic Surgery, 1954-1974

Campbell, Eldridge, M.D.
Department Chairman, Surgery, 1946-1956
Division Chairman, Neurosurgery, 1955-1956

Carr, Ezra S., M.D.
Professor, Chemistry and Pharmacy, 1853-1857

Carroll, Robert E., M.D., M.P.H.
Acting Department Chairman, Preventive and Community Medicine, 1967-1968
Department Chairman, Preventive and Community Medicine, 1967-1980

Cerilli, G. James, M.D.
Department Chairman, Surgery, 1982-

Clymer, Meredith, M.D.
Professor, Diseases of Nervous System and the Mind, 1870-1873

Converse, J.G., M.D.
Department Chairman, Anesthesiology, 1953-1956

Coulston, Frederick, Ph.D.
Director, Institute of Experimental Pathology and Toxicology, 1962-1980
Director, Institute of Comparative and Human Toxicology, 1976-1977

Covert, Scott V., Ph.D.
Department Chairman, Microbiology, 1956-1972

Cowden, Ronald R., Ph.D.
Department Chairman, Anatomy, 1972-1975

Craig, Joseph Davis, M.D.
Curator of Museum, 1887-1891
Curator of Museum and Demonstrator of Anatomy, 1891-1901
Curator of Museum and Professor of Anatomy, 1901-1914

Cunningham, Robert S., M.D., Sc.D.
Department Chairman, Anatomy, 1937-1946

Cunningham, Thomas J., M.D.
Acting Division Chairman, Oncology, 1976-1977

Curtis, Frederick Colton, M.D.
Professor, Dermatology, 1884-1914

Davies, Samuel, M.L.S.
Librarian, 1955-1958

Dean, Amos, Esq.
Professor, Medical Jurisprudence, 1839-1859

Degnan, Mark, M.D., D.P.H.
Division Chairman, Medical Genetics, 1975-1980

DeLeo, Bernard C., M.D.
Department Chairman, Anesthesiology, 1979-

Demis, D. Joseph, Ph.D., M.D.
Division Chairman, Dermatology, 1967-1970

Dondale, Marion Francis,
Librarian, 1928-1955

Donhauser, J. Lewi, M.D.
Department Chairman, Surgery, 1937-1946

Doyle, Joseph T., M.D.
Division Chairman, Cardiology, 1960-

Dresbach, Melvin, M.D.
Department Chairman, Physiology, 1918-1935
Department Chairman, Physiology and Pharmacology, 1935-1936

Eckert, Charles, M.D.
Department Chairman, Surgery, 1956-1974
Distinguished Professor,
Acting Department Chairman, Surgery, 1981-1982

Elting, Arthur Wells, M.D.
Professor, Practice of Surgery and of Clinical Surgery, 1910-1915
Department Chairman, Surgery, 1915-1937

Emmons, Ebenezer, M.D.
  Professor, Chemistry and Natural History, 1838-1839
  Professor, Materia Medica and Natural History, 1840-1843
  Professor, Obstetrics and Natural History, 1843-1853

Faust, Otto A., M.D.
  Department Chairman, Pediatrics, 1941-1950

Ferguson, Frank C., Jr., M.D.
  Department Chairman, Pharmacology, 1953-1973

Fillippone, John F., M.D.
  Division Chairman, Cardiology, 1950-1960
  Division Chairman, Associate Physicians, 1973-1975

Fraser, Helen A., M.L.S.
  Librarian, 1958-1963

Frawley, Thomas F., M.D.
  Division Chairman, Endocrinology, 1952-1963

Friedlander, Walter J., M.D.
  Division Chairman, Electroencephalography, 1963-1966

Fruehan, Alice E., M.D.
  Department Chairman, Family Practice, 1977-

Furth, Eugene D., M.D.
  Acting Department Chairman, Medicine, 1974-1975

Gabriele, Thomas, M.S.E.E.
  Division Director, Computer Science, 1976-1980

Ghiulamila, Radu I., M.D.
  Department Chairman, Physical Medicine and Rehabilitation, 1976-

Glenn, Joseph E., Ph.D.
  Acting Department Chairman, Biochemistry, 1974-1976
  Department Chairman, Biochemistry, 1977-1978

Goffin, Floyd B., M.D.
  Division Chairman, Otolaryngology, 1965-1972

Goldstein, Jerome C., M.D.
  Division Chairman, Otolaryngology, 1974-

Goodman, A. David, M.D.
  Division Chairman, Endocrinology, 1964-

Goodwin, Edward S., M.D.
  Acting Department Chairman, Pediatrics, 1951-1953

Gordinier, Hermon Camp, M.D., A.M.
  Professor, Physiology, 1895-1913
  Department Chairman, Medicine, 1915-1931

Gordon, Myron, M.D.
  Department Chairman, Obstetrics and Gynecology, 1981-

Gorham, L. Wittington, M.D.
  Department Chairman, Medicine, 1937-1948
  Division Chairman, Oncology, 1948-1951

Graham, George S., M.D.
  Department Chairman, Pathology, 1917-1921

Graves, Robert W., M.D.
  Department Chairman, Neurology, 1951-1957

Gray, John F., M.D., LL.D.
  Professor, Psychological Medicine, 1876-1886

Green, David, M.D., B.S.
  Acting Department Chairman, Neurology, 1967-1968

Greenberg, Martin H., M.D.
  Division Chairman, Newborn Services, 1972-1974

Greene, Henry, M.D.
  Professor, Obstetrics and Diseases of Women and Children, 1838-1839

Gruber, Charles M., Ph.D.
Department Chairman, Physiology, 1915-1918

Hailes, William, Jr., M.D.
Professor, Histology and Pathological Anatomy, 1876-1886
Professor, Histology and Pathological Anatomy and Clinical Surgery, 1886-1889
Professor, Pathological Anatomy, Histology, and Fractures and Dislocations, 1889-1897
Professor, Pathological Anatomy, Embryology, Histology, and Fractures and Dislocations, 1896-1901
Professor, Pathological Anatomy, Histology, and Fractures and Dislocations, 1908-1912

Harris, George W.
Department Chairman, Military Science and Tactics, 1934-1935

Harris, Ira, LL.D.
Professor, Medical Jurisprudence, 1870-1874

Haskins, Henry R., M.D.
Professor, Surgical and Descriptive Anatomy, 1869-1874
Professor, Anatomy, 1874-1876

Henriques, Edgar S., M.D.
Department Chairman, Obstetrics and Gynecology, 1979-1981

Hesser, Frederick H., M.D.
Department Chairman, Neurology, 1957-1967

Hesslin, John E., M.D.
Division Chairman, Urology, 1955-1956

Hilleboe, Herman E., M.D.
Department Chairman, Preventive and Community Medicine, 1948-1953

Himwich, Harold E., M.D.
Department Chairman, Physiology and Pharmacology, 1936 -1946

Hines, Orlando T., M.D.
Acting Division Chairman, Renal Diseases, 1978-1979

Holt, William L., Jr., M.D.
Department Chairman, Psychiatry, 1951-1968

Horton, John, M.B., B.Ch.
Division Chairman, Oncology, 1972-1976

Howard, William P., M.D.
Department Chairman, Radiology, 1941-1950

Hun, Edward R., M.D.
Professor, Diseases of the Nervous System, 1876-1880

Hun, Henry, M.D.
Professor, Diseases of the Nervous System, 1885-1887
Professor, Diseases of the Nervous System, and Psychological Medicine, 1887-1889
Professor, Diseases of the Chest and of the Nervous System, 1889-1890
Professor, Diseases of the Nervous System, 1891-1913

Hun, Thomas, M.D.
Professor, Institutes of Medicine, 1839-1853
Professor, Institutes of Medicine and Materia Medica, 1853-1855
Professor, Institutes of Medicine, 1855-1859

Jacobs, Richard L., M.D.
Division Chairman, Orthopedic Surgery, 1974-

Jacobson, Victor C., M.D.
Department Chairman, Pathology, 1921-1934
Cyrus Strong Merrill Professor of Pathology, 1929-1934

Jensen, Wallace N., M.D.
Department Chairman, Medicine, 1976-1980
Robert E. Lamb Professor of Medicine

Johnson, J. Garth, M.D.
Department Chairman, Preventive and Community Medicine, 1953-1967

Johnston, John F., M.D.
Department Chairman, Military Science and Tactics, 1923-1925

Kaye, Gordon I., Ph.D.
Department Chairman, Anatomy, 1976-

Kellert, Ellis, M.D.
Professor, Bacteriology and Pathology, 1913-1915
Department Chairman, Pathology, 1915-1917

Kelly, Emerson C., M.D.
Director, Library, 1963-1965

Kiley, John E., M.D.
Division Chairman, Renal Diseases, 1960-1978

King, Theodore M., M.D., Ph.D.
Department Chairman, Obstetrics and Gynecology, 1968-1972

Knobloch, Hilda, M.D., D.P.H.
Division Chairman, Developmental Disabilities, 1979-1980

Knudson, Arthur, A.B.
Professor, Biochemistry (Sub-Department), 1915-1929
Department Chairman, Biological Chemistry, 1929-1931
Department Chairman, Biochemistry, 1931-1952

Kouyoumgian, Joseph, M.D.
Acting Division Chairman, Otolaryngology, 1963-1965

Kraft, Alan M., M.D.
Department Chairman, Psychiatry, 1968

Laffin, Robert J., Ph.D.
Acting Department Chairman, Microbiology and Immunology, 1981-

Landmesser, Charles M., M.D.
Department Chairman, Anesthesiology, 1956-1967
Acting Department Chairman, Anesthesiology, 1967-1968

Lansing, John V., M.D.
Professor, Materia Medica, 1867-1870
Professor, Physiology and Clinical Medicine, 1870-1873
Professor, Principles and Practice of Medicine and Clinical Medicine, 1873-1876

Lende, Richard A., M.D.
Division Chairman, Neurosurgery, 1964-1974

Ludlum, Robert B., M.D., Ph.D.
Department Chairman, Pharmacology and Experimental Therapeutics, 1976-1980

Lumpkin, Lee R., M.D.
Division Chairman, Dermatology, 1972-1980

MacDonald, Willis Goss, M.D., LL.D.
Professor, Abdominal and Clinical Surgery, 1901-1912

MacFarlane, Andrew, M.D.
Professor, Physical Diagnosis and Medical Jurisprudence, 1906-1914

MacLachlan, David M., M.D.
Professor, Materia Medica, 1838-1839
Professor, Materia Medica and Therapeutics, 1839-1840
Professor, Diseases of Women and Children, 1840-1842

Macomber, W. Brandon, M.D.
Division Chairman, Plastic Surgery, 1955-1971
Acting Division Chairman, Plastic Surgery, 1971-1977

March, Alden, M.D.
Professor, Surgery, 1838-1869

March, Henry, M.D.
Curator of Museum, 1877-1884

Maxon, Frank C., Jr., M.D.
Division Chairman, Pulmonary Diseases, 1955-1978

McCafferty, William B., M.D.
Department Chairman, Anesthesiology, 1973-1978

McCandless, Frederick D., M.D.
Division Chairman, Behavioral Sciences, 1959-1970

McGoldrick, M. Donald, M.B., B.Ch.
Division Chairman, Renal Diseases, 1978-

McNaughton, James, M.D.
Professor, Theory and Practice of Medicine, 1840-1874

McShane, Richard H., M.D.
Division Chairman, Plastic Surgery, 1978-

Merrill, Cyrus Strong, M.D.
Professor, Ophthamology, 1876-1881
Professor, Ophthamology and Otology, 1881-1913

Meuwissen, Hilaire J., M.D.
Division Chairman, Clinical Immunology and Infectious Diseases, 1979-1980

Miller, James E., M.D.
Department Chairman, Ophthamology, 1963-1969

Miller, John K., M.D.
Division Chairman, Infectious Diseases, 1961-1969

Milner, William A., M.D.
Division Chairman, Urology, 1956-1968

Montgomery, William L., B.A.
Division Director, Computer Science, 1981-

Morrow, Samuel Roseburgh, M.D.
Professor, Anatomy and Orthopedic Surgery, 1889-1896
Professor, Anatomy and Orthopedic and Operative Surgery, 1896-1902
Professor, Practice of Surgery and of Orthopedic Surgery, 1902-1915

Mosher, Jacob S., M.D., Ph.D.
Professor, Chemistry and Medical Jurisprudence, 1864-1870
Professor, Medical Jurisprudence and Hygiene, 1876-1882
Professor, Pathology, Practice of Clinical Medicine and Hygiene, 1882-1883

Mott, Walter C., M.D.
Division Chairman, Ophthamology, 1955-1961

Muntz, John A., Ph.D.
Department Chairman, Biochemistry, 1955-1974

Nardacci, Anthony W., M.D.
Acting Division Chairman, Dermatology, 1971-1972

Nelson, Louis R., M.D.
Acting Division Chairman, Neurosurgery, 1974-1975

Nesbitt, Robert E.L., Jr., M.D.
Department Chairman, Obstetrics, 1956-1958
Department Chairman, Obstetrics and Gynecology, 1958-1962

Neuman, Leo Haendel, M.D.
Professor, Gastro-Enteric Diseases and Clinical Theory and Practice of Medicine, 1906-1914

Offutt, Harry D., M.D.
Department Chairman, Military Science and Tactics, 1925-1926

Olson, Kenneth B., M.D.
Division Chairman, Oncology, 1951-1972

Ordway, Thomas, M.D., A.M.
Professor, Pathology and Bacteriology, 1909-1912
Department Chairman, Medicine, 1931-1937

Patterson, Paul R., M.D.
Department Chairman, Pediatrics, 1953-1957

Paul, Boris J., M.D.
Acting Department Chairman, Physical Medicine and Rehabilitation, 1967-1968
Department Chairman, Physical Medicine and Rehabilitation, 1967-1975

Pearce, Richard Mills, M.D.
Professor, Pathology and Bacteriology, 1903-1908

Pearl, Manuel J., M.D.
Acting Department Chairman, Obstetrics and Gynecology, 1967-1968

Peaslee, Edmund R., M.D.
Professor, Diseases of Women, 1870-1873

Perkins, Maurice, M.D.
Professor, Chemistry and Toxicology, 1870-1876
Professor, Chemical Philosophy and Organic Chemistry, 1876-1901

Plotz, E. Jurgen, M.D.
Department Chairman, Obstetrics and Gynecology, 1962-1967

Poggi, John A., M.D.
Acting Division Chairman, Pulmonary Diseases, 1978-

Poland, Ursula H. (Anker), M.L.S.
Librarian, 1965-

Policoff, Leonard D., M.D.
Department Chairman, Physical Medicine and Rehabilitation, 1954-1967

Pollara, Bernard, M.D., Ph.D.
Division Chairman, Clinical Immunology, 1972-1979
Department Chairman, Pediatrics, 1979-

Porter, Charles H., M.D.
Professor, Chemistry and Pharmacy, 1857-1859
Professor, Chemistry and Medical Jurisprudence, 1859-1864

Porter, Ian H., M.B.
Department Chairman, Pediatrics, 1967-1979
Division Chairman, Medical Genetics, 1964-

Powers, Samuel R., M.D.
Department Chairman, Surgery, 1974-1979

Procita, Leonard, Ph.D.
Acting Department Chairman, Pharmacology, 1973—1976

Propp, Simon, M.D.
Division Chairman, Hematology, 1951-1970

Quackenbush, John V.P., M.D.
Professor, Obstetrics and Diseases of Women and Children, 1855-1856
Professor, Midwifery and Diseases of Women and Children, 1856-1859
Professor, Obstetrics and Diseases of Women and Children, 1859-1870
Professor, Diseases of Women and Children, 1876

Raymond, Robert W., M.D.
Division Chairman, Allergy, 1965-

Reese, David M., M.D.
Professor, Theory and Practice of Medicine, 1839-1840

Reichert, Leo E., Jr., Ph.D.
Department Chairman, Biochemistry, 1979-

Reinecke, Robert D., M.D.
Department Chairman, Ophthamology, 1970-1981

Remp, Donald G., Ph.D.
Acting Department Chairman, Biochemistry, 1952-1953

Risemberg, Herman M., M.D.
Division Chairman, Newborn Services, 1975-1980

Roach, John F., M.D.
Department Chairman, Radiology, 1950-1978

Robeson, Glenn H., M.D.
Department Chairman, Radiology, 1979-

Rogers, John B., Jr., M.D.
Division Chairman, Gastroenterology, 1981

Root, Arthur Gurnsey, M.D.
Professor, Diseases of the Throat and Nose, 1906-1914

Rosenblum, Ira, Ph.D.
Administrative Director, Institute of Comparative and Human Toxicology, 1976-1977

Ruedeman, Rudolph, M.D.
Division Chairman, Dermatology, 1955-1963

Russo, Joseph J., M.D.
Division Chairman, Dermatology, 1963-1967
Acting Division Chairman, Dermatology, 1971-1972

Saba, Thomas M., Ph.D.
Department Chairman, Physiology, 1972-
Harold C. Wiggers Professor

Sampson, John Albertson, M.D., A.M.
Professor, Gynecology, 1911-1915
Department Chairman, Gynecology, 1915-1932
Department Chairman, Obstetrics and Gynecology, 1932-1937

Schaffer, Charles A., A.B.
Director, Biomedical Electronics, 1967-

Scharfman, William B., M.D.
Acting Division Chairman, Hematology, 1976-1977
Division Chairman, Hematology, 1977-

Schmidt, Kurt F., M.D.
Department Chairman, Anesthesiology, 1968-1973

Schwind, Joseph L., Ph.D.
Acting Department Chairman, Anatomy, 1936-1937

Seymour, William P., M.D.
Professor, Obstetrics and Diseases of Women and Children, 1870-1876

Shaher, Reda, M.D., B.Ch.
Division Chairman, Pediatric Cardiology, 1968-1975

Shapiro, David E.
Director, Medical Illustration, 1980

Shapiro, Stephen M., M.S.
Division Director, Medical Illustrations and Media Services, 1978-1980

Singer, Harold, M.D.
Division Chairman, Ambulatory Pediatrics, 1977-1980

Smith, William B., Jr., D.D.S.
Division Chairman, Dentistry, 1955-

Smith, Richard S., M.D.
Department Chairman, Ophthamology, 1981-

Stevens, George T., M.D.
Professor, Ophthamology and Orthopedic Surgery, 1870-1873
Professor, Physiology and Opthamology, 1873-1875
Professor, Opthamology, 1875-1876

Stranahan, Allan, M.D.
Division Chairman, Thoracic Surgery, 1953-1973

Swartz, Donald P., M.D.
Department Chairman, Obstetrics and Gynecology, 1972-1979

Swinburne, John, M.D.
Professor, Fractures and Dislocations and Clinical Surgery, 1876-1880

Tartaglia, Anthony P., M.D.
Division Chairman, Hematology, 1970-1975

Thomas, Wilbur A., M.D.
Department Chairman, Pathology, 1959-
Cyrus Strong Merrill Professor of Pathology

Thompson, Howard K., M.D.
Division Chairman, General Internal Medicine, 1978-

Tillotson, James R., M.D.
Division Chairman, Infectious Diseases, 1970-

Townsend, Franklin, Jr., M.D.
Professor, Physiology, 1881-1891

Townsend, Howard, M.D.
Professor, Obstetrics, 1853-1855
Professor, Materia Medica, 1855-1859
Professor, Materia Medica and Physiology, 1859-1867

Tricky, David L., M.B., B.S.
Acting Department Chairman, Anesthesiology, 1978-1979

Tucker, Willis G., M.D.
Professor, Inorganic and Analytical Chemistry, 1876-1882
Professor, Inorganic and Analytical Chemistry and Medical Jurisprudence, 1882-1887
Professor, Inorganic and Analytical Chemistry and Toxicology, 1887-1901
Professor, Chemistry and Toxicology, 1901-1914

Urizar, Rodrigo E., M.D.
Division Chairman, Renal Diseases (Pediatric Department), 1972-1980

Vander Poel, S. Oakley, M.D., LL.D.
Professor, General Pathology and Clinical Medicine, 1867-1870
Professor, Theory and Practice of Clinical Medicine, 1876-1878
Professor, Pathology and Practice of Clinical Medicine, 1878-1882

Vander Poel, S.O., Jr., M.D.
Adjunct Professor of Pathology and Practice of Clinical Medicine, 1880-1884

Vander Veer, Albert, M.D.
Professor, General and Special Anatomy, 1869-1873
Professor, Principles and Practice of Surgery and Clinical Surgery, 1883-1889
Professor, Didactic, Abdominal and Clinical Surgery, 1889-1901
Professor, Surgery, 1901-1913

Vander Veer, Edgar Albert, M.D.
Professor, Abdominal and Clinical Surgery, 1910-1914

Van Heuven, Wichard A.J., M.D.
Acting Department Chairman, Ophthalmology, 1969-1970

Van Rensselaer, Howard, M.D.
Professor, Materia Medica and Therapeutics, 1897-1913

Vedder, Danica K., M.D.
Acting Division Chairman, Infectious Diseases, 1969-1970

Volk, Benjamin M., M.D.
Division Chairman, Otolaryngology, 1955-1962

Wallingford, Arthur J., M.D.
Department Chairman, Gynecology and Obstetrics, 1937-1956
Department Chairman, Gynecology, 1956-1958

Ward, Samuel Baldwin, M.D.
Professor, Surgical Pathology and Operative Surgery, 1876-1880
Professor, Surgical Pathology and Operative Surgery and Clinical Surgery, 1880-1883
Professor, Pathology, Practice, Clinical Medicine and Hygiene, 1883-1889
Professor, Theory and Practice of Medicine and Hygiene, 1889-1913

White, John J., M.D.
Division Chairman, Pediatric Surgery, 1977-

Whitfield, Robert D., M.D.
Division Chairman, Neurosurgery, 1956-1964

Wiggers, Harold C., Ph.D., Sc.D.
Department Chairman, Physiology and Pharmacology, 1947-1953

Wolfe, Jack M., Ph.D., Sc.D.
Department Chairman, Anatomy, 1946-1972

Woodruff, Marvin W., M.D.
Division Chairman, Urology, 1968-1978

Woolsey, Frank M., Jr., M.D.
Department Chairman, Postgraduate Medicine, 1960-1980

405

Wright, Arthur W., M.D.
   Department Chairman, Pathology and Bacteriology, 1934-1953
   Department Chairman, Pathology and Microbiology, 1955-1956
   Department Chairman, Pathology, 1956-1959
   Cyrus Strong Merrill Professor of Pathology, 1934-1959

Ziegler, Lloyd H., M.D.
   Department Chairman, Neuropsychiatry, 1930-1932
   Department Chairman, Neurology and Psychiatry, 1932-1938

APPENDIX F: ALBANY MEDICAL COLLEGE GRADUATES 1839 - 1982, M.D. DEGREES

Class of 1839:

Jared Bassett
Gilbert H. Brownell
Henry Cartier
Alfred Cook
Anderson S. Dean
Almon Brundage Edmonds
Nahum P. Monroe
John V. Newman
Marcus T. Peake
William H. Snyder, Jr.
Rial Strickland
Phineas Barman Strong
John Vought

Class of 1840:

David S. Beardsley
Thomas C. Durant
Daniel V. Folts
Henry Gibson
John Hallam
Amos P. Jones
Robert Kells
Morgan Lewis
Ezra May
Joseph Oliver Morin
Henry D. Ranney
Francis N. Sill
Stetson E. Southworth
Amos Wescott
William A. Wescott
Samuel W. Wilson
David C. Winfield

Class of 1841:

David Atwater
John Henry Beech
William H. Biggam
Alfred P. Blakeslee
Israel I. Buckbee
James B. Cook
Willard G. Davis
Morgan L. Finch
Sebastian F. Fonda
Levi Cornell Frisby
Charles Goodale
Mel D. Thompkins Hamlin
Odenanthus Hill
David W. Hiscox
Alson D. Hull
George F. Huntington
Erasmus Darwin Jones
Daniel McNeil
Marvin M. Marsh
Charles Miller
Samuel Moore
Moreau Moyse

Bryan Fitch Ransom
Benjamin Franklin Sherman
Henry Waterhouse Sprague
Richard F. Stevens
Isaac L. Tobey
Magloire Turcot
Philip M. Wheaton
David Chase Woodman
William S. Young

Class of 1842:

Welcome A. Babcock
Charles H. Baker
Myron Blair
Levi Bronson, Jr.
Casper Van Wie Burton
John S. Cameron
Lewis Charette
John W. Corson
Stephen G. DeLaMater
Edward Duffy
Ira B. Geer
William Gow
James McIntyre
Henry O. Mayo
Francis B. Parmele
Joseph N. Poulin
John VanPelt Quackenbush
Tabor B. Reynolds
Erasmus D. Root
Jacob M. Schermerhorn
John Wilkinson Sleight
Addison P. Strong
Richard F. Thompson
Edward Willard Trotter
David Walker
Ira R. Wells
Samuel J. Wright
Ira Zeh

Class of 1843:

Lewis Armstrong
J. McMurray Austin
D. Bryan Baker
Uriah G. Bigelow
John Campbell
Hallam C. Champlin
Ennis Church
William A. Clark
Rockwell Cowles
Abraham W. Crowell
George N. Dox
Henry B. Fay
Nicholas N. Lawyer
Thomas Millspaugh
James K. Murphy
James D. Niver

Andrew VanAntwerp, Jr.
D.P. Van Vleck
Humphrey C. Watson
Nicholas VanRensselaer Witbeck

Class of 1844:

Wilson T. Bassett
Joseph B. Brown
Peter A. Brumagin
Benjamin E. Bushnell
Silas James Chesebrough
Jacob A. Crounse
Horace B. Day
Charles B. Gunn
Edwards Hall
Rensselaer Jewett
Daniel Lewis
Rowley Morris
Walter Mott
Julius Dayton Munn
John F. Norbury
Rensselaer Ottman
William S. Parkhill
Henry Camp Potter
James Rawson
James Riggs
Isaac M. Schermerhorn
Albert E. Sullard
John N. Talyor
Sterry A. Weaver

Class of 1845:

Almon N. Allen
William Bassett
Abraham C. Burke
John Calhoun
Augustus Campbell
Denman Clark
Luther Cochran
Albert H. Corliss
Edward Diefendorf
Jacob A. Dockstader
Lyman C. Felch
William H. Gidney
F.M. Hammond
Joseph W. Harmon
Hiram Hubbs
Abraham H. McKown
William H. Miller
Solomon W. Moyer
James A. Russell
Thomas Smith
Harlow A. Van Deusen
Alfred Wands
Henry R. White

Class of 1846:

Henry A. Almy
John D. Arnold
Henry G. Bates
Diodorus Beals
Jeptha Bingham
David E. Bostwick
Daniel D. Bucklin
Eldridge G. Buswell
Izrahiah Whitmore Chesebrough
George W. Chittenden
Conrad J. Crounse
John Dennison
Henry D. Didama
John J. Flint
Eliakim Reed Ford, II
Charles J. Fox
Samuel Huntington Freeman
Stephen V.R. Goodrich
Frederick S. Greene
Samuel S. Guy
Martin C. Hall
Forrest H. Harwood
Charles House
Abisha Shumway Hudson
Milton Jerome
James Keeler, Jr.
Christopher Kiersted
Sylvester Lewis
Allan Cameron Livingston
George Lorillord
Robert S. McMurdy
Robert Morris, Jr.
Henry M. Neff
David W. Patrick
Rensselaer Platner
James H. Read
Charles H. Roberts
Francis H. Simpson
Joseph H. Smith
John Swinburne
Howard Towsend
Abram Van Woert
Ransom H. Vedder
John S. Weidman

Class of 1847:

Frederick Chollet Adams
Thomas S. Avery
Hiram Barber
Charles R. Cook
John J. Dewey
George T. Foster
David Frasier
John S. Herrick
J.H. Holmes
David H. Holsapple
Abijah Thurstin Hudson
Henry Huntington
Almon Hubbell Koon
Seth W. Langdon

Hezekiah Leonardson
George P. Livingston
Henry B. McHarg
Julius F. Miner
Orville H. Mott
Peter Onderdonk
David Pangburn
Gilbert Richmond
Carman C. Saunders
Benjamin A. Sheldon
Frederick A. Smith
John P. Wallace
John Wesley Warner
Felix Weidman
James Warren Wilkie
David Wiltse

Class of 1848:

Elihu Butts
Garretson L. Carhart
Edward H. Clarke
Thomas Spencer Dawes
Samuel Dodge
Joseph S. Dolson
Samuel B. Foster
Austin W. Holden
Lyman B.W. Johnson
Samuel H. Kelley
John A. Lidell
Alexander W. McNaughton
Delos H. Mann
Francis Gillet Mosher
Charles C. Murphy
Jonathan Nichols
George W. Reynolds
DeWitt Clinton Rice
Henry M.T. Smith
Sylvester David Willard
Randall Leroy Williams

Class of 1849:

Arlington Boyce
George W. Conklin
Simeon Curtiss
Daniel G. Dodge
John Duffin
William Dryden Fitch
Abram Groesbeck
Thomas C. Howes
Samuel Ingraham
Stephen C. Johnson
James Duane Jones
Edward McCamus
Henry M. Neff
Oliver B. Nelson
Adelman North
Allen F. Patch
James H. Scoon
Rensselaer R. Sherman
Samuel Mosley Smith
Paul Todd Taber

George M. Teeple
Samuel Oakley Van Der Poel
William C. Way
Allyn Wheeler
Lathrop A. Willis
Cornelius S. Younglove

Class of 1850:

George W. Avery
James Leonard Babcock
George Beakley
Frank S. Burgess
Alvin Cooper
Ira M. DeLaMater
Henry C. Foote
E. Willard Harker
William Frederick Holcomb
William N. Hubbs
Jay Kling
Bradley S. McCabe
Henry K. McLean
Charles D. Marsh
Thomas Harmon Neeley
John O. Niles
Willoughby O'Donohue
James Henry Salisbury
Levi Shafer
William B. Sims
James H. Smiley
Alfred TenEyck
Edward Tupper
Richard S. Valentine
Alonzo G. Westervelt

Class of 1851:

Ephraim R. Aiken
Renaldo M. Bingham
William T. Burton
Francis Leroy Chapin
Simeon Crounse
Theodore Davenport
Charles W. Gebhard
Augustus H. Gidney
Louis C. Greene
Henry T. Hawley
William A. Hawley, Jr.
Samuel L. Hooker
Joseph Keeny
Levi Moore
Marvin R. Peck
Gustavus W. Pope, Jr.
John H. Reynolds
Lauren Ford Rose
Rufus J. Rowe
Peter Edward Sickler
Edward D. Sill
Perrin A. Skiff
Solomon S. Stanley
Staats Winne

Class of 1852:

Orson Barnes
George D. Bassett
Charles G. Bryant
James E. Casey
James William Cox
William H. Craig
Thomas Lawyer
John E. Losee
John W. Mower
Philip W. Mull
George Henry Noble
James G. Parshall
Lucius G. Robinson
William H. Runkle
Andrew Fenwick Safley
Zebulon W. Scriven
Henry Slack
Alfred S. Spearman
Henry T. Spencer
Asa Sternberg
Francis J. Stevens
David VanDyke
Palmer Way
Charles T. Webb
Joseph Langford Wever
John Perry Witbeck
Isaac Newton Wyckoff
David Yates

Class of 1853:

James H. Allen
Gabriel D. Ayres
James Spencer Bailey
William Howard Bailey
Stephen P. Barnard
Henry B. Barstow
John Haswell Becker
George E. Benson
Delos W. Braman
William B. Brown
George E. Bullard
Matthew H. Burton
William F. Cady
Henry S. Case
James Cromwell
Hercule Dansereau
Alexander A. Edmeston
Hiram Augustus Edmonds
Thomas Jefferson Gardiner
William R. Griswold
Reuben H. Hammond
Ferdinand VanDeVeer Hayden
Frederick T. Henderson
John H. Hill
John H. Hoysradt
Ezra D. Huntley
Ianthus G. Johnson
Roger Keyes
Charles H. Lord

Asa D. McIntyre
H.C. McMahon
Henry March
Frank E. Martindale
Emery A. Merrifield
James A. Mowris
Isaac J. Moxley
Barent A. Mynderse
Dwight W. Rector
Herman M. Reynolds
Edmund C. Rogers
W. Scott Schermerhorn
Marinus Seaman
Darius H. Seelye
Alexander Shiland
Newton C. Spann
Charles Platt Staats
Peter L. Stanley
John I. Swart
Robert Leroy Telfair
Levi P. Wagner
Henry Van Wert
Levi Weed
James M. Wheat
George D. Whedon

Class of 1854:

O.C. Alexander
Solomon W. Austin
James Irwin Baker
George B. Barrus
Adoniram Judson Billings
Henry L. Bullions
William C.P. Butman
Jonathan Cass
Heman C. Chaffee
Samuel Chapman, Jr.
Edwin R. Chase
Levi R. Church
Peleg A. Clarke
Robert Lafayette Cumming
Charles H. Darrow
Estis Howe Davis
John C. Dixon
James H. Eaton
Peter Faling
T.B. Flagler
Lyman Force
A.W. Giddings
William Hamilton
Samuel T. Hance
Thomas Helme
G.H. Hubbard
Richard E. Hudson
Amos S. Jones
Douglas S. Landon
John D. Lewis
Milford Marshall
William Murphy
John T. Neal
Byron E. Osborn

Richard R. Owen
Henry Palmer
Nathaniel B. Rice
William C. Rogers
Charles H. Smith
Henry F. Smith
G.O. Spence
Dudley Carlton Spencer
Henry T. Spencer
Horatio Spencer
Richard Sutphen, Jr.
Granville S. Thomas
Sylvester M. VanAlstyne
Sumner C. Webb
Marshall Whiteside
Henry B. Whiton
William H. Woodruff
R.S. Wright

Class of 1855:

John S. Adams
David F. Alsdorf
Henry E. Babcock
Thomas Jefferson Barton
Adoniram Judson Billings
Harmon A. Buck
Reuben B. Burton
Elias W. Capron
Robert G. Carr
Thomas H. Chambers
Robert Orr Craig
Hiram C. Cutler
Hamilton DeGraw
David Fogg Drew
William H. Dutton
Alexander Ennis
Solomon S. Forbes
Daniel Gillis
Joseph C. Greene
S. Henry Harrington
Josiah Hasbrouck
Jerome B. Holcomb
Daniel Josephus Hostetler
John W. Hurst
Charles K. Irwin
Henry B. Johnson
L. Melancthon Johnson
James Elias Jones
Thomas J. King
John William Knight
William F. Lauderdale
Benjamin Lemon
John Low
John D. McConnell
LeRoy McLean
Henry D. Mann
Thomas L. Morgan
Marion Nash
Nelson Neeley
George H. Newcomb
John L. Nihill

Gilbert E. Palen
Warren W. Palmer
Daniel Pardee
Moses B. Pardee
Charles A. Peters
Charles Richards
William H. Rulison
Edwin F. Silcox
Julius Augustus Skilton
John A. McP. Smith
Arie B. Snell
Andrew Stafford
Charles Storck
Lewis W. Sutherland
Stephen B. Valentine
Solomon VanEtten
C. Halsey Vaughn
Hamilton M. Weedon
Peter S. Weidman
Jared P. Wheeler
J. Ralsey White
Stephen Wright
Daniel S. Young

Class of 1856:

William E. Allen
William Arthur, Jr.
Charles E. Bates
George M. Beakes
Samuel T. Beardslee
Isaac S. Becker
Henry J. Bennett
Truman S. Brinkerhoff
Alfred H. Brundage
John Cipperly
Jerome R. Collins
Jeremiah A. Cross
Lemuel Cross
Albert C. Dedrick
Henry H. DuBois
Henry M. Edsall
Obadiah T. Ellison
E. Lee Ensign
Edward A. Everitt
John Flickinger
Edward J. Frissell
Pierson J. Galloway
Benjamin P. Grinnell
John J. Harris
John B. Hartwell
L.B. Healey
Charles E. Heath
Lewis W. Hodgkins
Harvey A. Horton
Delos W. Hunt
Urban Jansen
Hammond Johnson
James A. Johnson
J. Russell Little
Hiram W. Lobdell
Thomas Lockrow

John MacAllister
Henry McKennan
Henry G. McNaughton
Alvarado Middleditch
John N. Miller
Robert V.K. Montfort
Charles M. Mosher
Wolcott W. Paige
Rufus Palmer
Castanus B. Park, Jr.
P. Gould Parker
Charles M. Pierce
Charles S. Richardson
Samuel A. Richardson
Aaron W. Riker
Charles W. Robinson
J. Henry Robinson
Edward B. Root
Robert H. Sabin
Arnold Strothotte
George B. Todd
John H. VanBuren
Samuel D. VanScoy
Henry Van Tuyl
Henry Van Wert
Jacob Vreeland
Fleming Webster
John P. Wheeler
George A. Wilkins

Class of 1857:

William G. Allenn
James D. Benton
Charles H. Carpenter
Matthew R. Carson
George H. Chadwick
Adam H. Cochrane
Lewis Coon
Samuel Crawford
George S. Dearborn
D. Estaing Dickerson
John Dirker
George Carpenter Douglass
Thomas B. Drake
Robert E. Ensign
Aaron Gustavus Goss
John Grant
Lansing Griffin
Zina G. Harrington
Newton C. Harris
Charles N. Hewitt
Edward P. Howe
Dana E. Kelsey
John Denison Kenyon
Franklin Kidder
William B. LaBaw
William S. Layman
Robert Loughran
Hamlin B. Maben
S.J. McDougall
Charles Mead

John Jacob Myers
Isaac Bonaparte Payne
John Elias Prichard
George Wilder Sargent
Benjamin F. Smith
Horace Snyder
Charles L. Spencer
Henry Sperbeck
Charles H. Spring
John H. Stevens
Ephraim P. Stubblefield
Lorenzo Traver
Thomas Spencer Virgil
Henry D. Wells
W. Antul Whedon
Hugh McGregor Willson
Ira Woodward
John Yauney

Class of 1858:

Washington Akin
N. Roundes Barnes
Edgar C. Bass
E. Collins Blaisdell
Elisha C. Bowen
Elias B. Boyce
James R. Brett
Cyrus N. Brown
A.E. Burr
William P. Bush
Darius M. Caughell
William B. Chambers
John W. Cobb
Isaac Griffin Collins
Richard S. Connelly
William B. Crandall
Charles W. Crary
Henry M. Crinkhite
Willis H. Cross
Abram DeGraff
George W. Draper
J.B. Drummond
E.F. Ellsworth
W.N. Fleetwood
John W. Follette
Addison W. Goodale
John R. Gregory
John D. Hall
Horace Hamilton
Lemuel H. Hammond
Jonathan K. Haynes
Peter Emmet Hubon
Charles Hutchinson
Elon Joseph Lawton
George W. Little
Lewis Maine
George R. Mann
Gordon C. McClelland
John H. Merrill
Joseph Milliken, Jr.
William W. Newton

Eliphalet Nott, Jr.
James E. Pomfret
G.B. Reid
Darius Scofield
Charles E. Smith
George Sprague
William A. VanRensselaer
Benjamin F. Vosburgh
Thomas W. Wall
H. Colbert Wardlaw
Cornelius A. Winship
Oscar H. Young

Class of 1859:

Newton H. Adams
Charles H. Allen
Harvey Napoleon Austin
John Birdsall
Jeptha R. Boulware
Charles H. Burbeck
Henry H. Carpenter
Lester R. Carrier
Norris M. Carter
David Curry
John Lowman Everitt
Nelson Fanning, Jr.
Mahlon Felter
George H. Fossard
S.H. French
Addison S. Harlow
James M. Harper
William A. Herrick
Henry L. Horton
William M. Hughes
Nathaniel Jennings
Stephen P. Johnson
E. William Johnson
William A. Madill
Martin L. Mead
Cornelius Duel Mosher
John T. Myers
Reuben F. Parkhill
John Shiriff
Daniel Small
Eli Small, Jr.
Charles H. Smith
Ira P. Smith
George C. Spafford
James Sweeney
William W. Thomson
William B. Toole
Lyman Moore Tuttle
S. Howard Udell
John J. VanRensselaer
Isaac L. Welsh
Theodore C. White

Class of 1860:

Robert A. Babbitt
James G. Bacon

A.G. Barney
J.P. Bidwell
A.J. Brooks
Nathaniel Sandford Cheeseman
Asbury M. Day
Charles S. Dickinson
John M. Dwan
Charles A. Gibson
R.H. Gray
Washington Kilmer
John Dudley Lovering
Francis J. Mattimore
Cornelius B. O'Leary
John N. Oliver
Henry Tyler Phillips
William H. Robertson
J. Phelps Shumway
Frank H. Tuttle
David F. VanAken
J.H. Vickery
DeWitt Clinton Wade
Franklin A. Young

Class of 1861:

Thomas Beckett
N.G. Brooks
Abram Giles Brower
Asahel Burt, Jr.
Charles A. Catlin
William S. Cooper
John Rea Creighton
Myron J. David
John Savage Delevan
J.M. Doty
Henry Duane
Charles B. Fry
Horace Tracy Hanks
Henry Reed Haskins
Jeremiah D. Havens
William L. Hollister
Willard Otis Hurd
Charles Hogeboom Porter
Porter L. Reynolds
Milton A. Sanford
Norman B. Sherman
William Henry Stuart
Nelson P. Tuttle

Class of 1862:

J. Newton Arnold
Herman Bendell
Charles G. Bristol
Caleb Clark
Henry K. Clarke
Lyndhurst C. Dodge
Owen J. Evans
Hiram H. Field
Walter M. Fleming
Charles M. Frisbie
Louis C.B. Graveline
Howard J. Horton

Albert P. Jackson
Theodore Young Kinne
Edmund K. Ladue
Ivory Lowe
William G. Millar
J. Frank Patterson
John L. Perry, Jr.
Griffin Reno
John N. Rippey
Edwin C. Tappan
William D. Townes
John L. VanAlstyne
Albert VanderVeer, Sr.
Sherman W. Ward
Edward Cooke Webb
Silas P. Wright
Alfred M. Young

Class of 1863:

William L. Baldwin
George Frederick Barker
DeWitt C. Beebe
Otis H. Blanden
William N. Bonesteel
Robert W. Brady
John E. Burdick
William Alonzo Carson
Erastus D. Chipman
J. Cash Coleman
Henry C. Cotton
Henry T. Dana
Chester B. Darrall
Warren E. Day
John H. DeWitt
Byron S. Flower
Porteus C. Gilbert
Edward M. Goodwin
Justus E. Gregory
Daniel S. Hardenberg
William M. Hendrickson
John Hotaling
Jackson A. Hubbard
Alfred B. Huested
Randall E. Ingersoll
Samuel B. Irwin
Abram V. Ketchum
Joel H. Mead
Richard T. Mead
Jacob Simmons Mosher
Peter M. Murphy
Daniel Peabody
Pierson Rector
Phineas S. Rose
Charles E. Seger
Abraham E. Skillman
Enoch V. Stoddard, Jr.
A. Dean Tubbs
Francis L. Turner
Robert C. Tuttle
Edward Ely VanDeWarker
Henry VanGuysling

Andrew T. Veeder
William N. Whiteside

Class of 1864:

Gideon Hawley Armsby
Hiram Becker
George H. Bosley
Horace L. Bower
N. Roe Bradner
Harvey J. Christman
James B. Cochrane
John E. Comfort
George Hardin Dorn
D.D. Drake
Edward F. Edgerly
Henry A. France
James W. Freeman
Cornelius A. Groot
Benjamin Rush Holcomb
James Patterson Kimball
J. Leavitt Lambert
Henry Laning
Dwight Morgan Lee
Jehiel Lefler
Gustavus McFadden
William H. McLean
Leslie Martin
Robert H. Melius
W.H.H. Morris
John O'Flaherty
Benjamin Franklin Pope
Cyrenius C. Powell
Christopher C. Reid
John Russell
Charles Safford
Frank A. Shurtleff
Charles E. Spring
J.T. St. John
John Sweeney
Charles B. Tefft
Charles H. Terry
George H. Thoma
Edward Thomson
Myndert VanPatten
Robert H. Van Patten
Henry P. Vosburgh
Timothy E. Wilcox
Harrison R. Winter

Class of 1865:

Duncan Stuart Allen
Douglas Ayres
Charles J. Bacon
James T. Barnard
Edwin Barnes
Reuben Barney
David Albert Barnum
Williams Anson Bliss
Benjamin F. Brown
Ira DeWitte Brown
John W. Cooper

Thomas D. Crothers
Cornelius J. Dumond
Emmett Flagler
Dwight Flower
Robert M. Fuller
James S. Gillett
Alexander C. Goff
Thomas Phillips Graham
Alexander Hamill
William B. Hostetler
Daniel B. Howard
Delos L. Humphrey
William L. Johnson
Samuel Norton Laird
Orrel McFadden
Friend James Otto
Lewis Warrington Pendleton
James A. Phillips
William H. Robb
George Rowe
Conand Sawyer
Hugh Sloan
Alonzo R. Stephens
Gustavus Treskatis
Jason B. Van Hoosen
Henry Clay Van Zandt
William L. Warren
George G. Whitaker
Edward I. Wood
Levi Wood
William Zeh

Class of 1866:

James L. Allaben
Russell G. Andrew
Charles Benjamin Barber
Harvey W. Bell
William Anson Bliss
Henry W. Boorn
Henry W. Boynton
David S. Bradford
William H. Brown
Albert B. Burger
William G. Burnham
Ovid L. Butts
Henry A. Clarke
Albert V.D. Collier
D. Henry Cooke
Henry A. Crary
William H. DeLong
Edward J. Dickinson
Isaac Fowler
Ezekiel Gallup
Benjamin D. Gifford
Charles S. Grant
Allen C. Grover
Charles S. Hazeltine
Guy Holbrook
William H. Hull
Peter H. Hulst
James L. Humphrey

Enoch Eaton Johnson
John W. Johnston
Otho S. Knox
Sylvester D. Lewis
James F. McKown
Edward S. May
Daniel Merville
Isaac T. Monroe
James F. Murray
Philip C. Neher
Albert S. Newcomb
Daniel V. O'Leary
Darius S. Orton
George H. Overholt
Clair S. Parkhill
Truman E. Parkman
Henderson A. Phillips
Isaac E. Randall
Thomas O. Reynolds
George W. Rossman
George A. Stockwell
Uriah J. Swain
Anthony P. Ten Eyck
John C. White
George O. Williams
Charles E. Witbeck

Class of 1867:

Xyris Turner Bates
James D. Bragg
James R. Colby
David Henry Cook
Nathan Garnsey Daggett
Edward J. Davis
Isaac G. Edson
Grenville A. Emory
Jacob F. Getman
Horatio Gilbert
Edwin Haines
Charles S. Hard
Giles S. Hulett
George P. Johnson
George A. Jones
Herbert Judd
William M. Lawlor
Charles Long
Stephen McLallin
Jacob L. Miller
William H. Nichols
David Norwood
Benjamin Wait Noxon
James H. Reed
James B. Rouse
James F. Shurtleff
Charles J. Simons
Charles W. Stratton
William D. Swain
George Tilden
Adolphus L. Tremblay
James L. Wentworth
Alvin D. Wheelock

412

John Van Etten Winne
Charles Meredith Woodward

Class of 1868:

Edward R. Aiken
Henry W. Allen
Fordyce H. Benedict
Jas. Augustus Blake
Asa B. Bowen
Joseph R. Brown
Orson Frank Cobb
George A. Cox
Edwin Crocker
John F. Crounse
David S. Fairchild
Merritt B. Fairchild
Joseph E. Ferry
Edwin L. Ford
John Allen Frisbee
Andrew J. Guffin
Lorenzo Hale
Francis M. Hamlyn
Romeo E. Hyde
James Kelly
Julius J. Kempe
Henry Dennis Losee
Schuyler Lott
Adam Mackie, Jr.
William H. Mead
Nelson H. Mesick
Jacob B. Norwood
Edward F. Quinlan
Charles F. Scattergood
John Milton Shields
Lewis A. Van Wagner
John Atkins Wilber
William A. Wilson
John N. Wright

Class of 1869:

George G. Bosworth
Jacob Myers Briggs
Solon Briggs
Edward A. Carpenter
James Reid Davidson
George A. DeYoe
Isaac De Zouche
Adrian J. Ebell
Patrick E. Fennelly
James M. Griffin
Adelbert Hewitt
Robert M. Hunt
David A. Lawton
Revillo T. Longendyke
Carl G. Metcalf
William Morgan
William H. Murray
George E. Paul
Henry G. Reid
Irving C. Schureman
Herbert Shurtleff

John Smithwick
James H. Struble
Frank Sturdevant
Andrew W. Van Slyke
Alfred L. Wands
John J. Ward
Philip J. Zeh

Class of 1870:

Elmore S. Albee
William W. Appley
John M. Bigelow
Richard H. Cameron
Daniel C. Case
C.H. Chamberlain
Harris J. Cornish
Philip I. Cromwell
William H. Curtis
Jacob C. De Freest
Egbert W. Dutcher
William Hailes, Jr.
Frank E. Johnson
Levi LeRoy King
William H. Kinnier
DeWitt M. LaMoree
Killian V.R. Lansingh
Charles M. Lefler
Frank McRae
Thomas H. Mann
Robert H. Neefus
Maurice Perkins
Luther J. Purdy
Byron U. Steenberg
Willis G. Tucker
Lucien E. Wells
Alexander B. Willis
Ross Wilson

Class of 1871:

Jas. K. Abbott
James J. Alexander
William T. Baynes
Frank G. Buckbee
George D. Cochran
George Conkling
H.L. Cookingham
C.W. Ensign
E. Jay Fisk
Jacob F. Force
James H. Gallup
A.A. Getman
William C. Gifford
O.E. Herrick
John S.V.R. Hoff
Stephen A. Ingham
John H. LaGrange
James H. Lasher
William H. Lingenfelter
Inmon S. Lowell
Caleb Lyon
James R. Mathews

J.J. Miller
A.S. Mygatt
R.S. O'Connell
James H. Reddy
R. Herbert Starkweather
John Benjamin Stonehouse
John C. Strader
Robert Thomson
John K. Thorne
Gebhard L. Ullman
Eugene Van Slyke

Class of 1872:

Almon S. Allen
J. Emerson Allen
George H. Benjamin
Joseph H. Blatner
Joseph Bonter
S. Townsend Bowne
Frank M. Boyce
H.H. Clapsaddle
Frank M. Garbutt
Edward A. Green
John Udolphus Haynes
James Stewart Hill
Charles Edmond Jones
J. Wiltsie Knapp
George S. La Moree
William E. Milbank
John H. Moon
Alexander Nellis, Jr.
Philip T. O'Brien
Jesse T. Owen
George A. Pierce
George Rice
Austin Arndt Snell
Jeremiah R. Sturtevant
Nathan F. Sweatman

Class of 1873:

Marvin Babcock
William C. Bailey
Charles E. Buffington
John H. Carmichael
Daniel H. Cook
Charles E. Crandall
Eugene M. Draper
George Emerson
Herman Crocker Evarts
Charles K. Frasier
William Geoghan
Cornelius J. Hasbrouck
Hiram T. Herrington
Alonzo E. Hull
Brayton A. Johnson
Isaac H. Lent
William W. McGregor
George L. Merritt
Horace C. Miller
Linzie T. Morrill
George B. Murray

S. Oscar Myers
Oscar Quental
Cyrus M. Rulison
Winfield S. Shields
Henry H. Smith
Melvin H. Turner
George L. Van Allen
Adam T. Van Vranken
Christian C. Vedder
John C. Wall
Henry B. Whitehorne
Horace C. Wiggins
Jacob C. Wood

Class of 1874:

Edward B. Atkins
Charles Giles Bacon
Caleb C. Bedell
Solon F. Bliss
J. Lyman Bulkley
Alonzo Churchill
Daniel W. Colcord
Daniel T. Condict
Valentine Cornell
George F. Dickinson
Cyrus Ecker
Alexander W. Fairbank
James Duane
    Featherstonhaugh, Jr.
Harris J. Fellows
Henry W. Giles
Henry T. Hammond
Robert Grant Havens
Edwin S. Hoyt
David Hughes
Henry V. Hull
Dwight R. Kenyon
Matthew McClellan
Samuel McClellan
William A. Maltby
Andrew Mathews
Jasper Mead, Jr.
Henry E. Mereness
John E. Metcalf
Horace C. Miller
Charles T. Montgomery
Luther Bartlett Newton
Alden March Oliver
Miles J. O'Reilly
John S. Peaslee
Frank S. Peters
James M. Porter
R.H. Platt Sawyer
James I. Scollard
John B. Todd
Edgar V. Trull
John D. Warren
Isaac Gerard Wheeler
Robert M. Whyte
William J. Wilcox
Thomas Wilson

Wyllis F. Wood
Hiram K. Worden
James K. Young

Class of 1875:

Franklin P. Beard
John N. Bradley
Warren M. Brand
Herman Chase
Berthold M.J. Conlin
George F. Cox
James O. Davis
John D. Day
George E. Elmendorf
Benjamin F. Evans
Lewis Fernalld
Robert Fuller
Francis Edwin Hale
William Asbury Hall
William N. Hays
Henry P. Holmes
John W. Houser
James B. Kershaw
Joseph McCarrell Lansing
David S. Neer
Nathaniel Emmons Paine
William F. Patterson
Henry C. Peck
T. Kirkland Perry
Milford L. Pine
William L. Purple
Elbert T. Rulison
Julius R. Schmidt
Clarkson Crosby Schuyler
Seth G. Shanks
Arthur V.H. Smyth
Peter Snyder
John W. Sterricker
William Stevens
Daniel P. Van Court
William H. Van Derzee
George M. Viall
George W. Wentworth
Eben A. Wood

Class of 1876:

No class graduated in 1876

Class of 1877:

Dorman Baldwin
Jas. F. Barker
Frank P. Blair
John E. Colburn
Jesse Crounse
John A. Crowley
Robert J. Cullen
Ezekiel H. Davis
Horace Burbank De La Mater
William E. Dolan
William J. Donald

Alois Donhauser
William H. Edsall
Henry Sheldon Edson
Thomas R. Featherstonhaugh
John E. Hall
James T. Hard
Luther E. Hawkins
James C. Healey
J. Ashbel Johnson
Arthur G. Kenney
Rushmore Lape
Maurice J. Lewi
David H. Lown
Mark M. Lown
Fred DeL. Mandeville
Charles McCulloch
John Spertzell O'Hara
Gilbert S. Olin
Alexander J. Peets
Clarence J. Peets
Sanford C. Roe
Selwyn Russell
George A. Sloan
Horace T. Sprague
Edward V. Stryker
Henry A. Waldron
James Warwick

Class of 1878:

Frederick H. Brewer
Edward W. Carhart
Charles I. Conover
John H. Cotter
Horatio Craig
Earl D. Fuller
George F. Gardner
Stephen A. Gates
Pierre C. Hoag
George L. Hopkins
Charles A. Ingraham
Austin D. Johnston
Henry LaHann
Uriah B. LaMoure
Henry Lilienthal
Almer A. Lyker
George W. McLaughlin
Adelbert H. Mambert
DeWitt J. Matteson
George F. Morris
William L. Pearson
George P.K. Pomeroy
John P. Prendergast
Theodore St.John
John C. Shiland
George F. Smith
William O. Stillman
Frank B. Sutliff
George W. Van Tassel
William D. Waldradt
Edward E. Whitehorne

Class of 1879:

George Mann Abbott
Menzo Barkman
Ezra Albert Bartlett
Edward Everett Brown
Charles Spencer Burnett
Kenyon Arnold Bushnell
Walter Clark Crombie
Gilbert J. Dickson
Sanford J. Engle
Edmund Frost Fish
William Bassett Fish
Charles G. Fisher
Allen Fitch
Hezekiah D. Fuller
George Washington Gregory
Orlando J. Hallenbeck
Albert Drury Hill
Charles Franklin Huddleston
John Thomas Keay
Osman F. Kinloch
Henry Webster Lawrence
Henry Lewis, Jr.
Robert Addison Linendoll
William E. Lothridge
John J.D. McAllister
Andrew L. McMillan
Edson W. Masten
William J. Nellis
Otto Ritzman
John L. Schoolcraft
Daniel Sickler
Frank E. Simons
James Alexander Smeallie
Fred B. Streeter
Peter L. Suits
Martin Tygert
Thomas B. Van Alstyne
Clinton D.W. Van Dyke
Sheldon Voorhees
Adam Walrath
George Henry Watson
John Joseph White
Alfred W. Wilmarth

Class of 1880:

William Foster Bell
Frederick P. Bellinger
Stephen C. Burton
Alonzo P. Casler
Edgar C. Collins
Francis Oliver Cornell
Stephen S. De La Mater
Daniel F. Donoghue
Alvin H. Eccleston
Oscar Arthur Ellithorp
John W. Gould
Albert C. Griffin
William Henry Hagadorn
Clinton B. Herrick

Lehman B. Hoit
Michael Henry Hughes
William Edward Keegan
Horace Samuel Knowles
William Allen Lester
Cornelius Jacob Letcher
William B. Madison
Frank J. Merrington, Jr.
Alexander Combie
  Montgomery
John A. Moore
Willard Henry Morse
George S. Munson
Warren B. Palmer
Charles E. Parish
Carroll Hamilton Phillips
Gorton Herbert Race
Meyer L. Rhein
Dennis Patrick Shevlin
Myron H. Simmons
Morris H. Strope
Leander Swartwout
Erastus A. Taylor
William Henry Anderson
  Turner
Sabbati E. Ullman
Robert W. Warner
Charles E. Weidman
Hamilton A. White
J. Seward White
Charles F. Wicker
Edward S. Willard
William C. Wood
Thomas Davis Worden
Henry Worth Wright

Class of 1881:

Alva E. Abrams
William L. Allen
Fayette E. Ashley
Frank Beebe
Louis E. Blair
George A.R. Blake
Elvin D. Bradley
Nathan A. Caldwell
Clarence A. Chaloner
Frederic L. Classen
Warren C. Cooper
Edward L. Crandall
Charles H. Crawford
Charles M. Culver
C.C. Duryee
Nelson R. Everest
David S. Fleischman
Frank B. Foote
William E. Fortune
Leonard A. Frasier
Henry L. Furbeck
John Hammond
Ira Harris
Thomas Hays

D.E. Higgins
Frank Potter Johnson
Henry N. Johnson
Nelson W. Kelso
Edward C. Kennedy
Lawrence E. Kinney
George A. Krug
Edward S. Lawrence
John Fraser Lockwood
William Pitt Mason
Menzo B. Mattice
Howard Miller
William T. Miller
James H. Mitchell
Frederick Dana Morrill
John W. Morris
S. Hall Morris
William J. Murphy
Daniel D. Murray
Marshall E. Nellis
Theodore W. Nellis
Jeremiah O'Connor
Howard S. Paine
Lauren F. Rose
Eleazor Rulison
Fayette Schley
Frank G. Seaman
Warren C. Spalding
George F.A. Spencer
Edward J. Stephens
Rufus W. Terwilliger
Everet P. Van Epps
Henry R. Van Rensselaer
George H. Van Wagner
Lansing T. Vedder
William Butler Webster

Class of 1882:

Hiram C. Abrams
William M. Armstrong
Henry Delos Blanchard
Richard J. Brown
Frank V. Brownell
Harry M. Burtch
Frank Burton
Cassius P. Byington
Calvin E. Carpenter
Edward S. Coyle
William S. DeGolia
Wallace E. Deitz
James S. Dornet
Bernard Eagan
Henry C. Finch
Reynaldo Juan Fitzgerald
William E. Fox
Willard Gillett
Frank L. Harter
Daniel Clinton Hazen
Adelbert D. Head
Willard R. Hillegas

415

Fred Holcomb
George J. Holmes
George H. Houghton
Levi Clark Hubbard
George Hudson
Edward Frank Johnson
William B. Kamp
Frank B. Locke
George E. Lyon
John W. Mann
Edward Frank Marsh
Edgar Erastus Marvott
Walter B. Miller
Adam Y. Myers
James R. Newton
Frank A. Palmer
Milton Parsons
William J. Peddie
William B. Platner
Horace R. Powell
Frederick H. Ray
Joseph W. Riley
Addison O. Roberts
Sydney F. Rogers
William B. Sabin
Ernest Seward Sampson
Walter W. Scofield
Lemon Thomson, Jr.
Josiah H. Vroman
Thomas Ç. Walsh
Isaac C. Washburn
John B. Washburn

Class of 1883:

Charles F. Aldrich
Will Burrette Ambler
Ramon Arnao
Lourie Ashton
Charles S. Barney
William Winthrop Betts
Charles Bolz
George A. Bradbury
Peter F. Curley
William Davis
Frank T. DeLano
Russell J. Dimon
William S. Donnelly
Martin J. Dwyer
Joseph Emerson
James Entwistle
Frank H. Fisk
William F. Gardiner
Wilson St.Clair Gibbs
Charles A. Gillette
Walter D. Hasbrouck
Franklin R. Hays
Newton E. Heath
Henri A. Jendrault
George L. Johnson
Edwin B. Karner

Frank T. Kunker
J. Charles LaDow
Fred L. LaDue
Louis N. Lanehart
Alfred M. Leonard
Irving D. LeRoy
Charles P. McCabe
Herbert L. Odell
J. Wilson Poucher
John F. Reilly
William L. Schutter
John H. Skillicorn
Israel M. Slingerland
Frank L. Smith
Joseph Lesley Smith
Theobald Smith
John H. Stephens
Joseph M. Stone
David H. Strahan
Maurice Ten Brink
Allen R. Thompson
Theodore F.C. Van Allen
John N. Van Patten
Jay D. Van Wirt
Charles F. Wharton
George E. Whipple

Class of 1884:

Robert Babcock
Fred S. Bloss
J. Edwin Bowen
Edmund F. Bronk
Charles M. Coe
Clinton G. Cooley
Joseph D. Craig
William A.E. Cummings
Pierson C. Curtis
Franklin M. Devoll
Jacob M. Falk
David J. Fitzgerald
Joseph A. Flynn
Fred R. Greene
Louis A. Harris
John V. Hennessy
Clinton G. Hickey
George W. Holding
Hamilton Hollidey
Winfield G. Hubbard
Hiram Leonard Ives
Arthur A. Jones
W. Clinton Kellogg
James W. King
Elmer E. Lansing
James A. McCaughin
George McTammany
Willard C. Marselius
William B. Mesick, II
Edgar W. Morehouse
Jacob A. Rich
Walter Foot Robinson

Luman B. Rulison
James Selkirk
Patrick E. Stafford
Michael D. Stevenson
George E. Swift
Charles F. Timmerman
Robert A. Walker
Bela J. Ward
M. Arthur Wheeler
Eliphalet N. Wright
Edgar Zeh

Class of 1885:

Isaac N. Albright
Ernest L. Angus
Samuel E. Armstrong
Edgar F. Brown
Terence Carroll
Andrew C. Crounse
Sylvanus C. Curran
Irving S. Edsall
William C. Fawdrey
Charles C. Flint
Charles W. Geel
David Gilliland
Robert George Goudie
Alfred N. Guffin
Josiah Hasbrouck, Jr.
Alexander Johnson
Charles R. Knapp
Elmer E. Larkin
Ralph A. McDougall
Martin MacHarg
Albert Marsh
James P. Marsh
Edwin A. Miller
Adelbert E. Moody
Douglas C. Moriarta
Hermann Palmer
Silas H. Parks
E. Hudson Rider
Thomas P. Scully
George M. Stillman
Fred J. Tompkins
John H. Van Rensselaer
Howard J. Wood

Class of 1886:

George H. Baker
Joseph E. Baynes
Adam J. Blessing
William P. Brierley
Alfred L. Browne
William B. Campbell
Arthur S. Capron
James Carr
James A. Clyne
Eugene H. Coons
John A. Cutter
William H. DeLaMater

416

Noah L. Eastman
Elmer E. Finch
John F. Fitzgerald
Alfred K. Freiot
Herman C. Gordinier
Alfred H. Hoadley
James A. Holley
Dayton L. Kathan
Arie V. Klock
William H. Lemrow
Harrie M. Lincoln
Richard H. McCarty
Francis Thomas McIntosh
William McNaughton
Charles B. Mallery
Joseph S. Parent
Ransom J. Perry
James H. Reilly
John A. Robson
John Wesley Sheffield
Wellington G. Steele
Arthur D. Stowitts
Edward H. Taft
Adrian P. Van Deinse
Charles T. Walton
Stephen Henry Webster
William Maxwell White
Richard A. Woodruff

Class of 1887:

Eugene Morton Austin
James H. Bissell
Charles M. Bradley
William W. Broga
Henry T. Brooks
Peter G. Cotter
Cornelius W. DeBaun
M. Francis Drury
Robert E. Fivey
Elmer L. Fletcher
Marquis D. French
Wilmer I. Gordon
John A. Heally
Garrett L. Hogan
Richard J. Hogan
Arthur W. Johnson
Eugene Merrill Jones
Owen F. McAvenue
Willis G. MacDonald
Andrew McFarlane
George Hamilton McMurray
Webster Miller
Charles H. Moore
Henry F.C. Muller
Herman V. Mynderse
Clarence M. Paine
George Freeman Palmer
Robert J. Palmer
John Spencer Phillips
Henry J. Potter, Jr.
Henry Z. Pratt

James E. Sadlier
Francis W. St.John
George K. Smith
Charles VanWert
Thomas H. Willard
Henry C. Young

Class of 1888:

Robert Matthews Andrews
John Archibold
Fred M. Barney
David J. Barry
Rudolph Bestle
Fred Carr
Charles F. Clowe
James Cronin
Charles B. Cunningham
Zopher F. Dunning
John Joseph Evans
Willard H. Fox
Alfred F. Hodgman
William Hutchinson
Michael Keenan, Jr.
Frank H. Lee
George C. Lempe
Ellis Lengfeld
Emerson A. Ludden
John M. McClellan
Robert F. McFarlane
John S. Newcomb
William Thomas Peet
Evertt E. Potter
John S.B. Pratt
John W. Quinlan
George Palmer Rider
Charles Darius Rogers
Edward F. Sheehan
Dennis M. Smith
Frank T. Stannard
Myron E. Stephens
John J. Timlin
A.L. Tuttle
Edwin B. Wells
Frank A. Winship
Adelbert Warner Witter

Class of 1889:

Andrew Herbert Bayard
Frank Augustus Bell
Howard Francis Bonesteel
Burton Sylvander Booth
James Edward Brennan
Charles Gilchrist Briggs
Henry Wilson Brown
Charles Smith Bumstead
A. Marshall Burt
Charles Harlow Callender
William Melanethon Campbell
Samuel Chesebrough
Fred S. Deyoe

Alphonzo Cajetan Dorval
Richard Francis Duncan
Robert Furman, Jr.
Frederic Croswell Gorham
Charles Edgar Greenman
Hurand Harootune Hekimian
Elmer Ellsworth Johnston
James Benedict Kennah
Wilbur Fisk Lamont
George Emory Lochner
Archibald G.W. Losee
Clive Charles McCullough
Jesse Montgomery Mosher
Charles William Nichols
Emmett Niver
Alonzo Thomas Powell
Jesse Wood Roscoe
Alanson Decatur Rose
William Rufus Seeber
James Ezra Smith
Marion Robert Smith
Frank Simeon Snow
Charles Wight Snyder
Leonard John Somers
James Read Strang
William Van Doren
Thomas Catlin Washburn
Merlin Jay Zeh

Class of 1890:

William Augustine Alexander
Horatio Seymour Ansley
Robert Brittain
Alfred Royce Burndage
Frank Melville Clement
Willis Sylvester Cobb
Edward Bernard Coburn
Edward Vincent Colbert
Clement Salts Crosby
Frederic Crounse, Jr.
Charles De La Montayne
John Emmans De Mund
Melville Day Dickinson
James Francis Earley
Thomas Henry Flynn
John Philip Gilligan
John Adelbert Hagar
Frank Morgan Hall
William Henry Happel
Thomas Helme
John Houghton
John Warner Kniskern
Michael Jay Lawler
George Griffin Lewis
Robert Samuel Lindsay
Frederic William Loughran
James Henry Lyons
John Joseph Lyons
Seth Adelbert Mereness
George Tomlinson Moston
Walter Graham Murphy

Arthur Guernsey Root
Edgar Seymour Simpkins
Minot Alpheus Steele
John Jay Sullivan
Ichabod Thomas Sutton
James Henry Tobin

Class of 1891:

William Samuel Ackert
John Molyneaux Bowman
Merton Wheelock Brown
John Hunting Cobb
Walter Henry Conley
Charles Edmond Davis
Frank Edward Dean
Franklin Edward Deuerlein
Joseph William Droogan
William John Fleming
Joseph Freedman
Nathan David Garnsey
Edward Alton Hoffman
Edward Lee Johnson
Henry Warner Johnson
Edward Joslin
John Whitman Joslin
Sherman S. Kathan
Joseph Eugene Kelly
William James Kernan
William Newell Knowlton
Robert Brockway Lamb
Louis LeBrun
Sherwood LeFevre
Warner Abbott Miles
Lewis Ryan Oatman
John Clement O'Haire
William James Pennington
Michael Francis Phelan
George Henry Reynolds
Frank Kelly Roarke
Ward Beecher Saltsman
Will Orvis Scott
Abram Baker Simmons
Harmon Arthur Staley
James Henry Timmers
Evert Evertsen Tracy
Harvey Ward Van Allen
Arthur Burton Van Loon
George John Van Vechten
George Austain Williams
James Wesley Wiltse

Class of 1892:

Leo Frank Adt
Patrick Joseph Barrett
LeRoy Becker
Robert Woodworth Bell, Jr.
Henry Hobert Bradley
John Charles Brown
Donald Gillies Buchanan
Henry Beaman Burton

Fred Bellinger Casey
Albert Crocker Cobb
Frederic Joseph Cox
Peter John Dervin
Bennett White De War
Peter James Fagan
George Michael Fisher
Eugene James Gallager
Washington Irving Goewey
Bert Louis Goldthwait
Homer J. Grant
John Butler Grover
Arthur Clesson Hagedorn
George Sherman Haswell
Robert Aloysius Heenan
Stanton Hendrick
John Byron Hull
Frank A. Husted
William P. Kelly
William Grant Lewi
William Alexander Liddle
Howard Eaton Lomax
Charles Harrison Loveland
Elmer Ellsworth Martin
Duncan McNab, Jr.
Frederick Ammi Mead
Charles Benjamin Mosher
Leo Handel Neuman
Charles LaMont Parker
Chauncey Adams Patterson
Harry Seymour Pearse
LaRose Rancour
Elmer Ellsworth Reichard
Smith Malon Roods
Walter Buskirk Rossman
Charles Robert Seymour
Ira Ernest Shaffer
Willard Hamilton Sweet
David Lewis Taylor
Franklin Stuart Temple
Clement Frank Theisen
Lansing VanAuken
Clarence David Vrooman
Franklin George Warner
Alfred George Wilding
Frederic Allen Williams

Class of 1893:

Edward Joseph Bedell
John Belcher Beebe
Edward Moses Bell
Lewis Nye Bump
Edward Gilbert Cox
Orville Curtis
Herbert Edward De Freest
Robert Edwin Doran
Aden Clarence Gates
Robert Alexander Grant
John Sebastian Guinan
Augustus Albert Guy
Charles Webster Hamm

Amos Wieting Hedden
Charles Henry Herrick
LeRoy Frank Hollis
Anselme Ephrem Houle
Ward Evans Hunt
George Herbert Janes
Thomas Williams Jenkins
John Jones
Fisher M. Joslin
William Henry Laughlin
Edward Morton Leach
John Bell Ledlie
Patrick Thomas Markey
Charles Edwin Marshall
Theodule Morrisseau
Flavius Packer
San Crombie Po
Joseph William Racette
Martin Silas Reid
George Lyman Richardson
Collie John Robinson
George Francis Rogan
John William Russell
Thomas Addis Ryan
Walter Brind Sabey
Frank Burton Sanford
William Campbell Sebring
Melvin Sheldon
Joseph Benjamin Swett, Jr.
Robert Hill Tedford, Jr.
Lucas Grove Tuttle
George Henry Van Gaasbeek
Louis Van Hoesen
Fred Dan Vickers
John Stewart Wade
Percy Gardiner Waller
William Warner Wentworth

Class of 1894:

Charles Francis Archambeault
George Hatch Beebe
Charles Bernstein
Joseph Barton Betts
Henry Ward Briggs
George Brookins
James Burton
Arthur John Capron
William Wesley Clark
Robert Nelson Clemons
Charles Higgins Cole
John Henry Cotter
Erwin James Cusack
Otis H. Deck
Williiam Henry George
Walter C. Gilday
Walter Wesley Goddard
George W.E. Goodell
Eugene Howard Goodfellow
Wilfred Silvester Hale
Owen Elon Jones
Charles Ten Eyck LaMoure

Stephen Madatian Long
Harry Warner Luchsinger
John Rankin McElroy
John Francis McGarrahan
George B. McGraw
John Roddy Mahan
James Manning Moore
Bernard Edward Mulligan
William James McKown
Ellwood Oliver
James Timothy Park
Andrew Jackson Rogan
Arthur Sautter
Thomas Conant Sawyer
Ralph Sheldon
Fred Byron Stellwagen
Charles Howard Travell
Fred Phillips Van Denbergh
Milan Theron Ward
Earl Wadsworth Wilcox
William Jessup Woodruff

Class of 1895:

John Marble Allen
Edwin Van Gaasbeck Baldwin
William Samuel Bristol
Archibald Buchanan, Jr.
Charles Sylvester Butler
Thomas Michael Clarke
Federick William Cordes
Francis Joseph Crummey
Alfred Desrochers
Daniel Damian Donovan
Charles Gartner
Archibald McClure Gilbert
Harry DuBois Goetchius
Sherwood Ackler Haggerty
Dorr William Hardy
Frank Hazelett Hurst
Frank Gale Hyde
Arthur Many Johnson
Thomas Bassett Keyes
Durand Reed Kinloch
Everett Starke Kinloch
Joseph Adelard Laurion
Louis Oscar Le Sieur
James Peter McGrath
Edward Norris Kirk Mears
Howard William Murphy
Charles Leonard Myers
Samuel Pashley
Edward Ferguson Pickford
Lee Pultz
Walter Kendrick Quackenbush
William Monroe Rapp
Fred John Resseguie
Arthur Thayer Robinson
Fred Sauerbrie
Reed Alonzo Sauter
Daniel Joseph Shay
Leonard Gove Stanley

Richard Llewellyn Stoddard
Harold Bishop Stowell
Herbert Nichols Tanner
Charles Rodman Townsend
Charles Haverly Turner
Richard Fletcher Van Heusen
William James Wansboro
Charles Edward Weidman
Charles E. Weidman
John Archibold Wilder

Class of 1896:

Sanford Bassler
Albert Carlton Baxter
Julius Warren Blakely
William Irving Brandow
John Preston Carver
Frederick Timothy Clark
Walter Milton Clark
Edward James Collier
John James Dever
Frederick Burr Dezell
Rudolph Francis Diedling
Harry Ogden Fairweather
Arthur Ezra Falkenbury
Henry Field
Leland LeGrand Fillmore
John C. Fusmer
Edward Gillespie
George Bernard Grady
Ira Daniel Hasbrouck
Frank Augustine Hennessy
Erving Holley
John Wesley Jennings
Garrett Vander Veer Johnson
Henry Ward Keator
Frank Arthur Keller
James Thomas McKenna
Frank McLean
Frank Baldwin Maynard
Parker Herbert Murphy
Francis Patrick O'Brien
Elbert Alonzo Palmer
Edward Jenkins Parish
Amasa Parker Muir
Francis Xavier Pidgeon
Albert Husted Rodgers
Thomas Avery Rogers
Waldo Henry Sanford
Will Henry Schwartz
Jesse Melville White Scott
James Charles Sharkey
Henry L. K. Shaw
Edward Goodsell Stout
Roscoe John Taylor
Burton Van Zandt
John David Vedder
Joseph Edward Vigeant
Edward John Wieneke
Thomas Goldsmith Wright

Jerome Edward Young
Philip Samuel Young

Class of 1897:

Ira Applebee
Thomas Joseph Arundel
Eugene William Baltes
Daniel J. Barry
Harry Edwin Battin
John Jacob Beard
Edward Waterbury Becker
Charles Heald Bennett
Edward Nicholson Bibby
Herbert Oscar Brust
Charles Gray Cole
Joseph Gilbert Coleman
Sanders Peter Cornell
William Clapp Cuthbert
Robert Calhoun Davies
John Wyman Dean
Robert Lincoln Ellithorp
Calvin Emerick
John Henry Fallon
William Lewis Fodder
Edward Leo Gaus
John Giffin
Walter Scott Graham
Frederick Howell Greene
Lewis Theophilus Griffith
William Church Griswold
Fred Newman Guyer
Eugene Joseph Hanratta
Reuben Leo Howland
Reuben Hayes Irish
Herman Wilcomir Katz
Peter Herman Keeler
Buel Latcher
Marshall Latcher
Fred C. Leonard
William George Lewis
Harry Judson Lipes
Leonard McClintock
Edward Francis McCormack
William C. McCulloch
Francis James McKown
Fred Markle
Harry Alvin Merchant
George Coe Merriman
James Joseph Noonan
Joseph Allan O'Neill
Allen Monroe Ottman
Payn Bigelow Parsons
George Burton Pearson
Charles Harper Richardson
Andrew Joseph Ronan
George Eugene Schoolcraft
William John Sheehan
William Ethelbert Silcocks
Clarence Jonathan Slocum
John Archibold Stevenson

Garrett Warren Timmers
John Willard Travell
Richard Van Beusekom, Jr.
Charles Nicholas
  Van Denberge
Delbert Wilbur

Class of 1898:

Robert Wesley Andrews
John Albert Barnes
Henry Rogers Bentley
Otis Zalmon Bouton
Meleatus Bruce
Hiram Arthur Bryant
Frederick Fillmore Burtis
William Nesbitt Campaigne
Willard Oscar Carpenter
Thomas Dundon Collins
James Monroe Cronk
Raymond Goulden Edmans
Julian Allen Gaul
George Miller Gilchrist
William James Green
Menas Sarkis
  Boulgourjoo Gregory
William Edward Hendry
Frank Hinkley
Lyle Breslau Honeyford
Emmett Howd
Burton Kenyon Hoxsie, Jr.
Frederick Israel Jansen
David John Jenkins
Frank Merriam Johnson
Clayton Taylor King
Rollin Alexander Kirkpatrick
Charles Franklin Kivlin
Earl Parsons Lasher
Roy Lathen Leak
William John McGrath
Charles Goul McMullen
William Radley Miller
John Joseph Mulcahy
Aaron Lewis Newton
William Rushmore Nichols
Joseph Patrick O'Brien
Pierce James O'Brien
John Jacob Osterhout
Edward Charles Podvin
Frank Luther Possen
Charles Samuel Prest
Edward Augustine Quinlan
James Francis Rooney
Lebbeus Burton Schneider
Charles Abram Shultes
Creighton Walter Skelton
George Birch Stanwix
Edmund Stevens
William James Swart
Gilbert VanValkenburgh
  Thomas
Alvah Harry Traver

Benno George Troidle
Edgar Albert Vander Veer
Douw Lansing Van Derzee
Fred Bain Weaver
William Luther Wilson
Walter Harold Wood

Class of 1899:

John Milton Adey
Clifford Henry Allen
George Everett Beilby
Austin Westley Bender, Jr.
Lester Betts
Frederick Douglas Branch
William John Cavanaugh
Charles Rodgers Conklin
Augustus Ernest Cordes
Gilbert Worden Crissey
Fred Augustus Deal
Nicholas James Delehanty
Joseph Orrin Desobe
James Edgar Doig
Warren Harkness Everett
Adolph Richard
  Vandermoor Fenwick
George Haughton Fish
James Henry Flynn
Edward Paul Foley
Rupert William Ford
Albert Ellsworth Garland
Christian Gottlieb Hacker
Julius Eugene Haight
Henry Powers Hammond
Edward L. Hanes
Dean Samuel Harrison
William Gregory Healey
Eugene Eunson Hinman
William Thomas Hudson
Walter Leslie Huggins
Harry Fisk Hull
Howard Frost King
Robert Ernest Kinloch
William Kirk, Jr.
William Thomas Knowlton
Thomas John Lally
Joseph Aloysius Lanahan
Walter Adnah Leonard
Whittlesey Dubois Lester
Bernard Livingston
Daniel Albert McCarthy
James Edward McDonald
Berthier Whitford Mather
Peter Harris Moak
Ransom Sanford Moscrip
Leon Gray Ogden
Karl Albert Parshall
George Sanford Post
William Hugh Rankin
George Washington Ross
Thomas William Salmon
Walter Howard Sanford

Isaac Beers Schauber
Clayton Earl Shaw
Fred Adams Smart
Edward Shepard Smith
Lee Somerville
Edgar Roscoe Stillman
Byron Luther Sweet
George Scott Towne
Merritt Elmer Van Aernem
Francis Edwin Vander Veer
Michael Francis Wansbury
William A. Wardner
Harry J. White
Howard Lattin Wood
William Hamilton Young

Class of 1900:

Frank Duestin Bigarel
Kleber Alexander Campbell
George Peter Coopernail
John Livingston Crofts
Thomas Hart Cunningham
William Edward Cunningham
Lawrence Kilpatrick Dugan
Luther Emerick
John Jackson Gallup
Reid Gilmore
Harry Hemming Gormly
Lester Hayden Humphrey
Howard Alexander LaMoure
George Lenz
Hemayak Houhannes
  Loussararian
Charles Guy Lyon
Peter McPartlon
William Gansevoort Mack
Louis David Masson
Samuel David Miller
Louis Francis O'Neill
William Petrie
William Wells Sanford
Waldren Allen Stearns
Ernest Albert Sweet
Arthur Anderson Will

Class of 1901:

Charles James Baum
Arthur Joseph Bedell
George Samuel Burns
John Wilson Burns
Robert Beatty Castree
Joseph Ambrose Cox
Thomas Edward Deveny
John Henry Dingman
Edward Gerald Griffin
John Michael Griffin
Edward Joseph Hannan
Clayton Kendall Haskell
John Francis Heffernan
Arthur Fenwick Holding
Thomas Francis Judge

420

James Everett Kelly
Joseph Waldron Moore
John Bertman Neary
Daniel Duane Parrish
Nishan Pashayan
William Brink Rosecrans
Clarence L. Sicard
George Alphens Smith
Michael Joseph Thornton
Jacob Wachsman
Max Wachsman
Leland Orlo White
Charles Witbeck

Class of 1902:

LaSalle Archambault
Thomas Carney
Elwin Champlin
Kent Stanley Clark
John Bowman Congdon
Hugh Michael Cox
Edward Arthur Dawson
August John Freutel
John Henry Gutmann
Stillman Smith Ham
Earl Holcomb Jackson
Robert Johnstone Kahn
Frederick Hubert Ladd
Fred E. Lettice
Moses Joseph Mandelbaum
Joseph Mark
Edwin Alonzo Mason
Henry Erie Mereness, Jr.
Willis Edgar Merriman
Frederick Cornwall Reed
Frank Malcolm Sulzman
Clifford Walter Sumner
Junius Parker Talmadge
Elbert Goodman Van Orsdell
Charles P. Wagner
George VanVoris Warner

Class of 1903:

Samuel Halcomb
  Behrend Basch
Frederick Ernest Bolt
Donald Boyd
J. Howard Branan
John Edward Canfield
Henry Milligan Chandler
Sylvester Cornell Clemans
Russell Clute
Herbert Thomas Crough
Archie Irving Cullen
Archibald John Douglas
Louis LeBell Dulberger
Edwin Maurice Griffith
Conrad Rowland Hoffman
R. Burdett Hoyt
Frank Keator
Frederick John MacDonald

Charles Richard Marsh
Frank Clay Maxon, Sr.
Miles Ambrose McGrane
John Crapo Merchant
Addison Robert Miller
William Leo Mulcahy
Thomas Stephen
  Augustine O'Connor
Mark M. O'Meara
Virgil Dural Selleck
Millard Francis Shafer
Edwin Forrest Sibley
Frank Templeton Smith
George Henry
  Humphrey Smith
James Newell Vander Veer
Isaac Ernest Van Hoesen
Philip Wolfman

Class of 1904:

Palmer Romaine Bowdish
George Lay Branch
Charles William Chapin
Guy Forsythe Cleghorn
Chester Thompson Cobb
Thomas Folwell Cole
John Isaac Cotter
Marcus Albert Curry
Arthur Thomas Davis
William Sebastian
  De La Hoyde
Bransen Keemper De Voe
Malcolm Douglas
Thomas Joseph Dowd
Silas Lorenzo Filkins
Leland Delos Fosbury
Joseph Nicholas
  Bennett Garlick
William Entwistle Garlick
Everal Caleb Haviland
Harold Eliphalet Hoyt
George John Jennings
William George Keens
Arthur Kline
George Spencer Lape
Harry Lovejoy Loop
Dennis Alphonsus Murphy
Robert Joseph O'Brien, Jr.
Daniel Vincent O'Leary, Jr.
Joseph Day Olin
John Hendry Reid
Burt Luverne Shaw
Benjamin John Singleton
Edward Augustine Stapleton
Arthur Wesley Thomas
Chester Erastus Hudley Tracy
Richard Henry Van Denburg
Frank Barton Wheeler
Frank Edward White
George David Wilde

Guy Vail Wilson
Maurice Wolkowitz Wolff
Trevor Crandall Yates

Class of 1905:

Kenneth Daniel Blackfan
James Marmaduke Boddy
Homer Andrew Bushnell
George Morris Casey
Archie Bert Chappell
Arthur Preston Clark
Kenn Romeo Coffin
Miles Jacob Cornthwaite
John Henry Famian Coughlin
Walter Allen Cowell
John Dixon Crane
Orrell Charles Curtis
Theodore David Dockstader
Patrick John Donahoe
William Mulvihill Dwyer
John Peter Faber
Thomas Joseph Flynn
Perlia Elijah Garlock
William Joseph Garvey
Charles Erastus Green
Fred Flanagan Gremore
Charles William
  Loomis Hacker
Walter Ennis Hays
Chester Arthur
  Alan Hemstreet
Thurman Alson Hull
Lemuel Rankin Hurlbut
Frank James Hurley
Matthew Joseph Keough
Oscar Franklin Larson
Edward Miltimore
Francis Joseph Noonan
George Washington Papan, Jr.
Herbert Bowen Reece
William Garfield Rommel
Henry Stanton Rowe, Jr.
Harry Rulison
Frank George Schaible
John Ralph Schermerhorn
Frederick Foster Schirck
Arthur Hamilton Schuyler
Francis Joseph Scott
Benjamin Franklin Seaman
Hamilton Munn Southworth
Charles William Stratton
Charles Clark Sweet
James Harvey Van Buren
Edward Hellis Vines
George Walrath
Alfred LeRoy Warner
Roscoe Conkling Waterbury
James Watson White
Edwin Barnes Wilson

421

Class of 1906:

Henry Francis Albrecht
Fred Nicholas Bibby
John Breen
Roy Munro Collie
Morey Charles Collier
Charles Elisha Collins
Frederic Charles Conway
Edward Adt Dean
Adelbert Stephen Dederick
Theobald Frederick Doescher
Lee Roy Dunbar
Willis Woodford Dutcher
Vernon R. Ehle
Hermon Ernest Gak
George Reinbold Goering
Stowell Burroughs Grant
Percival William Harrig
Joseph Friend Harris
Clinton Benjamin Hawn
Samuel Orestes Kemp, Jr.
Winfield Snell Kilts
William Andrew Krieger
Price Lewis
Floyd Dempster Michael
David Cushing Nolan
Charles Albert Prescott
Walter Ancel Reynolds
John Fletcher Robinson
Willis Nelson Simons
Eugene Gillis Steele
Lemon Dwight Washburn
Edward Gove Whipple

Class of 1907:

Charles Sanford Allen
Floyd Jerome Atwell
George Warren Beebe
Joseph Lewi Bendell
Edward George Benson
Howard Philip Carpenter
William David Collins
Erastus Corning
Marcus Denis Cronin
Walter Thomas Diver
Joseph Lewi Donhauser
Edward Herman
   Frederick Frisch
Alfred Thomas Gabriels
Louis Herbert Gaus
Norman Charles Goodwin
Alfred Woodward Grover
Alejandro Buitrago Guilloid
Augustus Joseph Hambrook
Edward William Jackson
Dean Wardell Jennings
Clarence Robert Kay
Roy Charles Keigher
David Kidd
Richard Andrew Lawrence

Tiffany Lawyer
Jacob Henry Linden
Robert Sutterfield Lipes
John Sears McCormack
James Edward Maloney
Jerome Meyers
Zenas Van Duzen Orton
William Clare Porter
Stephen John Henry Reed
Fred James Rice
James Terrance Riley
Frederick Seilheimer
William Francis Shanley
James Joseph Shea
William Care Treder
Herbert John Wright

Class of 1908:

Earl Erret Babcock
Fred J. Barnet
William Edward Barth
John Adkins Battin
Hartley Edward Boorom
Samuel Pierson Brush
Eugene Howard Burnes
William Henry Conger
Joseph Davis
James William Fleming
Nelson Kaufman Fromm
Earl William Fuller
Frank Garten
John Rouse Gillett
Edwin Francis Hagedorn
Rosslyn Philip Harris
Stanton Perry Hull
Jacob Travers Krause
Alexander Mitchell
   Loewenstein
John Joseph Aloysius Lyons
Charles Gibson McGaffin
Robert Daniel Manning
George Bolton McMurray
Robert Copeland Mooney
William Leslie Munson
John Paul O'Keeffe
Charles Bates Phillips
George Philo Pitkin
Milton Wooley Platt
John Joseph Rainey
Edward John Riley
Bert William Roy
George S. Silliman
Ray Ernest Smith
Aaron Sobel
Herbert Edgar Sperry
William James Thompson
Joseph Edward Windbiel
John T. Wingate
Paul Virgil Winslow

Class of 1909:

Edward Johnson Abbott
Morris Bellin
William Arthur Bing
Lewis Webster Burdick
Craig Thomas Burns
William Francis Conway
William Henderson Davidson
Edward Daniel Donohue
Harry Houghton Drake
Orla Andrew Druce
Wakeman Clark Egerton
Gilbert Charles Fisk
Henry Blacklidge Gillen
William Breese Gillespie
Eddy Stearns Haswell
Harley Heath
Thomas Milton Homes
James Richard Hunter
Ellis Kellert
Charles James Kelley
Robert Schofield Long
Eugene Francis McGillian
James Gibbons McGillicuddy
Thomas Andrew McGrath
Burlin George McKillip
Frederick William McSorley
Edward Raymond Messer
Alexander Francis Mosher
Neil Bertram Palen
Arthur Emerson Pitts
William Rufus Rathbun
Clarence Leonard Russell
Charles Emerson Slater
Frederick Eugene Vaughan
Walter Harry Waterbury
Calvin Bassler Witter
James Joseph York

Class of 1910:

William David Aldrich
William Dewey Allen
Wallace Joseph Charles Aubry
Wardner Daniel Ayer
John Frederick Beiermeister
George Bibby
Claude Bledsoe
Cornelius Joseph Buckley
John Bennett Burke
James Whitefield Byrne
Frank Gibson Calder
Eugene Francis Connally
Arthur George Cooke
John Richard Devine
George Watson Dufty
John Arthur Farrell, Jr.
Richard Berchmans Gray
Henry Martin Grogan
Philip Conrad Hacker
Elwin Wallace Hannock
James Charles Hassall

422

Patrick Joseph Hirst
William Knowlton Johnson
Walter Scott Lilienthal
Walter Edward Lundblad
Harold MacDonald
Edward Barthlomew Manion
John James McCall
John James McShane
Roy Jay Marshall
Howard Casper Murray
Charles Frederick Myers
George Bradford Randall
Willard Tipple Rivenburgh
Leander George Rymph
Saul Joseph Selkin
John Forrest Southwell
John Albert Sullivan
Harold Augustus Traynor
Harry Franklin Van Loon
John Edmund White

Class of 1911:

Martin Joseph A'Hearn
Antonio Martinez Alvarez
LaVerne Adelbert Boulon
Milton Gardner Burch
Michael Ercole De Luca
Roy Manier Eaton
Percy Henry Finch
Walter Clayton Fox
Frederick Joseph Garlick
Bertram Wesley Gifford
Clayton Longueville Gifford
George Mills Glenn
James Joseph Hart
Irwin Johnston
Frederick Louis Kreicker
Arthur Krida
Harold Arthur Lucas
William Edward McCormick
John Ashby McElwain
Maurice James McGrath
Walter Daniel McKenna
Thomas William Maloney
William Henry Mason
Charles Edward Maxwell
Horace Clifford Montgomery
Frank Mathias Neuendorf
Henry Joseph Noerling
Edmund Joseph O'Donnell
Abraham Lewis Olshansky
Chauncey Butler Packard
Augustus Charles Post
Ralph Baker Post
Peter Francis Purcell
Francis Bernard Quinlan
William Francis Rafferty
Hiram Burdette Riggs
Scott Booth Schleiermacher
Emil John Senn
William Thomas Shields, Jr.

William James Sweeney
Abraham Phineas Terk
Arthur Eddy Wells
Melvin Thomas Woodhead

Class of 1912:

Max Alonzo Almy
Horace Edward Auringer
Bertram Truman Baker
Clifton Bogardus
John Lawrence Both
Joseph Henry Bowers
John Joseph Cahill
Alton Brooks Daley
Sol Charles Davidson
John Lounsbery Edwards
George Augustus Green
Paul P. Gregory
Walter Robert Grunewald
John Duncan Gulick
Vasileos Michael
  Koundourianes
Royal Estabrook La Grange
Albert Lenz
Norman Howe Liberty
Charles Immanuel Loeble
William Edgar Low, Jr.
Donald Angus MacDuffie
Joseph Ambrose McPhillips
Domenico Carlantonio Mauro
Ward Winthrop Millias
James Henry Mitchell
Floyd Hazard Moore
Clarence Edmond Mullens
Homer Hollett Oaksford
Daniel Francis O'Keeffe
Daniel Tobias Read
Fred Lester Ritter
Michael Augustine Rogers
William Henry Seward
George Aaron Sharp
Arthur Henry Stein
Charles Edward Stott
S. Wallace Todd
William W. Trotter
Floyd Alberti Weed
Jeremiah W. West
Arthur Hastings Wheeler
Ira Condict Whitehead, Jr.

Class of 1913:

William Alfred Ackroyd
Wesley Mason Adams
Morris Bryan Beecroft
Orvis Adoniram Brenenstuhl
David Truman Brewster, Jr.
Darwin Alfred Bruce
John Leonard Byrnes
Garret M. Clowe
Walter Roy Liddel Coakley

Rufus Baker Crain
Nathaniel Crost
Burke Diefendorf
Jacob Aloysius Drooz
Dwight Guilford Dudley
Paul Charles Fleri
Hugh Vincent Foley
George Victor Genzmer
Elmer Ray Gladstone
Hugh Sewell Gregory
Raymond Hensel
Harry Smith Howard
Alson Jay Hull
Eugene Fellner Hull
Ray Holly Humphrey
William James Jones
Whitney Hotaling Joyce
Arthur Saul Kay
William Herman LaDue
Roy Ludlum Lippincott
John Wellington Mambert
Raymond Francis McAloon
Schuyler McColloch Martin
Gaetano Guiseppe Nicosia
Michael Edward Nolan
Elmer Harrison Ormsby
John Swart Parker
Robert Edward Plunkett
William Carl Rausch, Jr.
Conrad Aloysius Rissberger
Jacob J. Schneider
Ernest Charles Schultz
Woodard Shaw
Walter Joseph Smith
Axel Fridolf Swanson
John Daniel Tadaback
Harold Dwyer Tobin
Guy Brownell Van Alstyne
Frank John Williams
Charles Wesley Woodall

Class of 1914:

John Daming Arnett
Abraham B. Ball
David Wiltsie Beard
Edward Joseph Buxbaum
John Peter Byrnes
Edward James Callahan
George Clay Carter
Edward Cochrane John
  Costellow
John Kenneth Crandall
George Jacob Culver
Daniel Sylvester Cunning
Frank Edgerton Deeds
Nicholas Antonio Falvello
Samuel Sanders Fischoff
Albion James Fitzgerald
Frank Carmine Furlong
John Warren Gard

Clarence Gardinier
Parker Arthur Groff
Robert Wilhelm Helm
John Thomas Hopkins Hogan
William Patrick Howard
Edwin Horton Huntington
Lawrence Jacobius
George Rudolf Jordy
Charles Aubrey Joy
Harry Vincent Judge
Joseph Thomas Loughlin
John Stoddard McCormick
Thomas Hugh McGrail
Floyd Guy Nellis
Wilber Sylvester Newell
William O'Connor
Harry Okun
Julius Joseph Padula
Harry Day Parkhurst
Charles Adelbert Perry
Robert Reid, Jr.
Charles Queveda Rendell
Harry Stephen Reynolds
Edward Louis Robbins
James Israel Schoonmaker
Frank Arthur Searle
Lewis Jeriah Smith
Theron Smith
William I. Walsh
John Waluk
Willard Elmer Wheelock
Cecil Charles Whittemore
Fred DeGrande Wilson
Leon Wolff
Lawrence Randolph Worell
Harry Theodore Wygant

Class of 1915:

Percy Huntly Austin
Walter Schneider Bennett
John Edward Burke
Arthur Hiram Congdon
Albert Nelson Crouch
Stephen Horace Curtis
Hugh Smith Chidester
Gerald Edward Dailey
Frank Edward Dean, Jr.
Irwin Van Olinda Decker
Arthur Maultby Dickinson
Francis Thomas Duffy
James Manning Dunn
Lawrence Joseph Early
Frederick George Eaton
Guy Fish
Leon Willis Green
William Lester Grogan
Ralph Marsh Hall
Raoul Albert Hebert
John Edward Heslin
Stanley Morton King
James Sarsfield Lyons

Wilbur F. MacDonald
William Bernard McKeon
Joseph William Miller
Martin Alvin Murphy
William Francis Nealon
Charles Luman Nichols
John Joseph O'Connor
Jonathan Pearson
George Stiles Reitter
Homer Isaac Rexford
Arthur Grant Rodgers
William Joseph Ryan
Ernest Raymond Schilling
Benjamin Herman Shapiro
Byron Gray Shults
Robert Cunningham
   Simpson, Jr.
William Patrick Sweeney
Charles William Tomlinson
William Bernice Davidson
   Van Auken
Leonard Kip Van Dyck
Herbert Austin Vogel
Fred Vosburgh
Archibald Albert Walker
Bernath Weiss
Joseph Wrana

Class of 1916:

James MacFeeters Archibold
Harold Arthur Bancroft
Morgan Otto Barrett
Jacob Blumberg
Edward Oscar Boller
William Charles Brons
John Dennis Carroll
William James Carroll
Richard Patrick Doody
Loyal Lindsey Dunlop
James Walter Fitzgerald
Emanuel M. Freund
Glenn Daniel Frost
Karl Gebhard
William Goldhush
John Luverne Hemstead
Hyman Hershberg
Frederic William Holcomb
Howard Conkling Johnston
John Christian Knapp
Charles Augustus Krauss
Francis James Lawler
Francis Buckley Maguire
Royal Harrison Mayhew
Edward Leo McDermott
John Williams McKeever
Walter Hugh McShane
Edward Bernard O'Keeffe
Matthew Francis Olstein
Robert Morris Palmer
Orla J. Park
Harold Artemus Peck

Ray Eugene Persons
George William Pullen, Jr.
Abraham Max Rabiner
George Mark Richards
Clarence F. Rinkle
Lester Edwin Sanford
Frank Phillip Schneider
Leslie Boyd Seaport
Howard Barton Swan
Harry Knibb Tebbutt, Jr.
Leo Ross Tighe
Howard C. Van Keuren
Earl Charles Waterbury
Theordore Stephen West
Raeburn James Wharton

Class of 1917:

Stanley Earl Alderson
Milton Aronowitz
James Michael Bernhard
Sidney William Bisgrove
Anathol Michael Breault
LeRoy Joseph Butler
Byron Edwin Chapman
Norman Scott Cooper
Leon Charles Cote
Lawrence Henry Cotter
Howard Wilcox Davis
Edward Thomas Delehanty
Louis Joseph De Russo
Albert Stuart Ferguson
William Edwin Gazeley
Samuel William Green
Daniel Francis Hannon
Harold Colvin Haviland
Kent Wood Jarvis
Howard Marion Kenyon
Raymond Francis Kircher
Maximilian Kohlenberg, Jr.
Robert Atherton Mac Taggart
John Francis McGovern, Jr.
Charles Mester
William Panitch
George Trecise Polk, Jr.
John Joseph Randall
Jacob Resnik
John H. Robbins
John Hourne Robertson
Ivan Michael Schneible
Norman Leo Sheehe
George Milo Thomas
Ralph Waldo Turner
Chester Bruce Van Gaasbeek
Irving Van Woert
George Clark Vogt
Frank William Wehle
Aaron Weinberg
Earle Wayne Wilkins
Burchard Alfred Henry Winne

Class of 1918:

Charles Pahl Archambeault
Clarence Walter Barth
Edward Buckley Campbell
Hubert Francis Carroll
Albert Henry Faber, Jr.
Charles Willard Green
Charles James Higley
Patrick Henry Huntington
Gerald Reid Jameison
Donald Dean Prentice
George Edward Smith

Class of 1919:

Romeyn Treadwell Allen
Jacob Epstein
Carl Charles Giannotti
Joseph O'Connor Kiernan
George Nelson Leonard
Alfred Lawrence Madden
Alexander Mason
William Francis McDermott
Webster Merchant Moriarta
John Joseph Phelan
A.W. Pietra
Edson Hun Steele

Class of 1920:

Douglas Anderson Calhoun
Bernard Roger Coleman
Joseph Cornell
Lawrence James Dailey
P. Lawrence De Noyelles
Alfred Herman Duerschner
William Lawrence Gould
Lawrence Daniel Greene
Albert Leonard Hayes
Leland Earl Hinsie
John Albert Kelk
Frederick Burton MacNaughton
Harold Edwin Marden
Thomas Sylvester Mooney
Thomas William Phelan
Walter Fred Preusser
William George Richtmyer
Anton Schwartz Schneider
Homer L. Stephens
Reginald Van Woert
Asher Yaguda

Class of 1921:

Charles Ethan Allen
L. Prescott Brown
Arthur Francis Cody
Edward Joseph Fitzgerald
Donald Briggs Glezen
Harold Jerome Harris
Lynden Andrew Hulbert
William John Jameson
Edwin Charles Johnson

Joseph Paul Lasko
Maver Miller Lee
John Joseph Quinlan
Lyle Adin Sutton
Arthur Charles Swartz
William McCheyne Thomson
Charles Edward Wiedenman, Jr.
Arthur Raymond Wilsey

Class of 1922:

Raphael A. Bendove
Harold Roberts Browne
Harold William Kinghorn
  Dargeon
Alvah Robert Davignon
Ames L. Filippone
Jere John McEvilly
William Mitchell Mallia
Charles Fayette Rourke
Harold Daniel Sehl
George Oliver Tremble
Beverly Leland Vosburgh
John Charles Younie

Class of 1923:

Clarence F. Ackerknecht
Lucy Elizabeth Bourn
John Quinn Donahue
Samuel W. Ebenfeld
David Henry Faulknor
Ruth Gilbert
Raymond I. Gosselin
Edwin Gordon MacKenzie
Nitya Pauvedya
Ferdinando L. Perrone
Louis Simon Poskanzer
Jasper Lewis Robertson
Li Sribyatta
Henry Lewis Turkel

Class of 1924:

Philip Daly Allen
Jean Mason Archibold
  (Thomson)
George J. Bookstein
Katherine G. Brockman
James William Bucci
John Francis Connor
Kenneth Eugene Crounse
Elton Robert Dickson
Earl John Dorwaldt
Grant Frederick Glassbrook
Charles Edward Martin
Douw Schuyler Meyers
Francis Mulcare
Frederick John Pratt
Isaac Shapiro
Francis Leslie Sullivan
Harold Field Teed
David Henry Vrooman

Class of 1925:

Francis William Dodge
Philip Louis Forster
Eugene Frederick Galvin
Herbert Carle Hageman
Charles Howard Harbinson
Joseph Leo Holohan
Henry Dunham Hunt
Daniel E. Kavanaugh
Emerson Crosby Kelly
Franklyn L. Kessler
Stuart Forbes MacMillan
Walter Charles Mott
Leal Luther Perry
Harry E. Reynolds
Arthur J. Townley
Kenneth Chamberlain Waddell

Class of 1926:

Harold Bellin
George Andrew Burgin
John Joseph Curley
Martin Francis Geruso
Francis (James) Sloan Hyland
Francis Anthony Mastrianni
George Francis Reed
Kalmon Rosenblatt
Dominick Edward Rowan
James Edison Smith
Martin Frederic Stein
Willard Hamilton Sweet, Jr.
Benno James Troidle
Walter Kent Van Alstyne
Philip Stanley Van Orden
George Claus Von Borstel

Class of 1927:

John Kenneth Deegan
George Albert Gilbert
Walter Kingsley Grigg
James Anthony Hogan
Anne Horoschak (Nahrgang)
William Alfred Horwitz
Stanley Pritchard Jones
Frank Paul Marra
Harold Patrick McGan
John Fayette Mosher
Max Emanuel Panitch
Emma Chapin Patterson
John Henry Ring
Nelson Hopson Rust
Lawrence Richard Smith
Arthur Joseph Wallingford
Maurice Sanford Wessell

Class of 1928:

Hobart McVicker Agnew
Kenneth MacLean Archibold
Leslie Homer Backus
Kenneth Francis Bott

425

Franklin Wesley Farnam
Caird
James Goodman Carleton
Ada Hazel Curry
Francis James Fagan
Robert Roy Faust
Donald Clarkson Guyer
William Joseph Hoffman
Ralph James Hotchkiss
Frank Edward Hunter
Louis Judelsohn
Gustin Thomas Kiffney
Robert Church Knott
Charles Ranney Lewis
George Ross Mills
Ranald Edwards Mussey
Ward L. Oliver
Samuel Jones Pashley
Clarence Albert Shepard
Emanuel Simon
George Ernest Stevens
F. Constance Stewart
Willard Burrows Warring

Class of 1929:

Joseph B. Boland
Gilbert Arden Clark
Raymond Lester Disch
Walter Elmer Eells
John A. Enzien
Alexander Harry Fishkoff
Lawrence Anthony Gerlach
Clement Joseph Handron
Robert Emmet Harrington
Robert William Harris
John Evan Holt-Harris
George Robert Lavine
David Howard Russell Lester
Michael Joseph Lorenzo
Gilbert C. MacKenzie
Lindus Cody Marsh
Thomas Earl McQuade
Robert Raymond Nesbit
Frank Stanley Randles
Joseph John Russo
Donald Kendig Schwartz
Michael Slovak
Benjamin Maurice Volk
Elmer Wesley Wessell

Class of 1930:

Duncan Leonard Best
Harold Frederick Buckbee
John Edmund Cunningham
Julia Adelaide Delehanty
Quentin E. Dinardo
Maurice Anthony Donovan
Charles Francis Fasce
William Feltman
John Edward Gainor

Hilton Wakefield Gillett
Philip J. Giuffre
Norman Dudley Kathan
Fayette Durant MacDonald
John Lawrence Hogeboom
Mason
William Bernard McDonald
George Elmer Martin, Jr.
David Wendell Morgan
Dwight Hull Porter
Raymond Holmes Warner
Marshall Hayden Wood

Class of 1931:

Hyman Lewis Berson
Charles Emory Betts
John Dardess
Ben Lee Dodge
Ernest Enzien
Jacob Frumkin
Fred Joseph Fumia
Louis David Goldberg
Clarence Dunbar Hart
Rene Hardy Juchli
Chauncey Warren Kenney
Joseph Lawrence Kiley
Kenneth Hutton LeFever
Walter Brandon Macomber
Robert Hardy Marks
William Henry Meyer
Solomon Mosher
Walter Chadwick Nelson
Everett Norman Perkins
John Joseph Pohl
John Paul Rinaldi
Christopher Stahler, Jr.
Ralph Peter Stevens
Louis Tremonte
Roman Robert Violyn
Thomas Sherman White
Raymond Edward Wytrwal
Alexander James Young
Jacob Charles Zillhardt

Class of 1932:

Orville Taylor Bailey
James Charles Boland
Nicholas Frank Brignola
John S. Clemans
Ralph Talmadge Collins
Katharine Stewart Cook
(Gordinier)
Marcus Bernard Einhorn
Victor Jacob Fingar
Albert Fillis Goodwin
Simon Joseph Gormley
Charles Henry Greene
Ferdinand Stephen Haverly
Arnold Francis Judge
Clifford Aaron Kingsbury

August Korkosz
John Harold Larrabee
Hugh Francis Leahy, Jr.
Raymond Gregory Leddy
G. Creighton Lusk
Thomas L. Piazza
Gomer Richards
Carl Ferdinand Runge
Paul Schultze, Jr.
Rosewell Daniel Shaw
Arthur Joseph Sullivan
Garrett William Vink

Class of 1933:

James Vincent Barrett
Dominic Battaglia
Clarence Rheinhard Becker
Edward Reo Bennett
Howard William Berg
Francis Dickson Brown
Roger Conant
William Johnston Cranston, Jr.
Edwin Lorenzo Crosby, Jr.
Robert Earl DeFriest
Daniel H. Deyo
Lester Cole Huested
Bryant Charles Hurlbutt
Jacob Hyman
Eric Frances Joslin
Edward John Keegan
Gerard Laviano
Grace Vaughn Maguire
(Swanner)
James Edward McDonald, Jr.
Joseph Harmon Naumoff
Charles Dennis Rancourt
Robert Elias Rockwell
Elmer George St. John
Kenneth Julius Sartoris
George Heindel Smith
Louis Primus Tischler
Frederick Carl Waldbillig
James Michael Walsh
Walter Wilkinson Williams
Elias Walrath Young

Class of 1934:

Morris Alpert
William L. Bennett
Sheldon Church
William Hays deRouville
Angelo DiDonna
Jay Thomas Dunigan
Edward Frederick Engel
John Francis Filippone
James Edward Glavin
Ralph Edward Isabella
John Joseph Keenan
Henry Franklyn Kreckman
Benjamin Frank Markowitz

William Peter McKenna
William Henry Raymond
Peter Benedict Riley
John Frederic Sarno
John Trolan Sill
Joseph Slovak
Alden Jelliffe Townsend

Class of 1935:

Henry Francis Albrechet, Jr.
Thomas Morris Aldrich
Charles Edward Bessey
Peter Austin Cassella
Joseph William Conrad
Edward Prince Danforth
Joseph Collins Driscoll
Harry Day Eastman
Philip James English
Carl Morris Hillenbrand
Morrison John Hosley
Seymour Milton Katz
Edgar Norman Kemp
Leonard Charles Lang
Harold Joseph Livingston
Francis Michael Noonan
John Joseph Noonan
Philip Parillo
William Joseph Phelan
John Judge Powers
Cornelius Andrew Francis
  Ryan, Jr.
Leonard Joseph Schiff
Paul Martin Schneider
Alonzo Paige Strong
Francis Aloysius Stephens
Charles Renne Sullivan, Jr.
Howard Swire
Joseph Samuel Weltman

Class of 1936:

Fred Frank Albright
Thomas Henry Andrews
Samuel Baer
Joseph Michael Capritta
Abraham Falk
Robert John Floody
Warren Butler Grover
Maurice Kenneth Grupe
Walter Andrew Gunther
Edward Patrick Hanley
Timothy Joseph Howard
Edwin Brannon Kelly
John Michael Kerrigan
Albert Lloyd Larson
Robert Kinkle Lenz
Jay Ralph Lockwood
John Gerald McKeon
Maurey Parkes
Frances E. Persons (Huntley)
John R. Purcell

Morris Shapiro
Alton John Spencer
John Arthur Sumner
Joseph Vincent Tabacco
Leo Arverne Zuckerman

Class of 1937:

Mary Louise Blackmer
Mario Bonaquist
James John Britt
Joseph Francis Colfer
James Harvey Donnelly, Jr.
Henry Charles Engster
John J. Gamble
Charles Russell Hyde
John Joseph Aloysius Lyons
Edward Booth Mates
Alfred Jacob Nadler
David Schwartz Parker
Marshall William Quandt
Samuel Richard Rosen
Charles Martin Single
R. Leith Skinner
Thomas Watson Smith
Donald Edward Stack
John Edward Thompson, Jr.
Donald Charles Walker
Thomas Stephen Walsh, Jr.

Class of 1938:

Donald Langworthy Burdick
William Joseph Burns
Raymond Joseph Byron
Ethel Gladys Cermak
Elisha Yale Clarke
Austin Joseph Corbett
Joseph Bruno Cortesi
Reynold Marvin Crane
Samuel Stanley Dorrance
Roland Lawrence Faulkner
Allen George Gifford
Robert Bruce Gottschalk
Richard Francis Grant
Mary Patten Hunter
William Crane Karl
Emily Louise Koeniger
David John Locke
Donald Rich Lyon
Perry Ligon Munday
Norbert Pierce Ringelman
Samuel Simon
Clement Art Smith
Victor Norman Tompkins
Anthony Joseph Vinci
George Joseph Zippin

Class of 1939:

Palmer Leiter Auker
George Spencer Barrett
Hamilton Boyd, Jr.

Edward William Colby
John Nicol Daly
John Wilkin Deever
Rudolph Frederick Deutl
Ella Elizabeth Foster
Orel Friedman
William Goodrich
Clarence Louis Pierce Hebert
Mary Elizabeth Hincks (Kent)
Seymour Arnold Horwitz
Norman Mason Jackson
Samuel Kantor
Alexander Aurelio Kosinski
William John Lord
Dual Alastair Mac Intyre
Frank Clay Maxon, Jr.
Arnold Waite Pohl
Dale Bryant Pritchard
Henry Herbert Shultz
Maus Wellington Stearns, Jr.

Class of 1940:

Henry Leonard Bejian
Roger Paul Brassard
Dorothy Blake Chamberlin
Bruce Cominole
Carl Rodney Comstock, Jr.
Edward Dana
David Joseph Dickerman
Anne Mary Drislane
William Booth Garlick
Robert Andrew Johnson
Roy Canedy Knowles
Karl Vincent Larson
Walter Edward Lawrence, Jr.
William Charles Maguire
Benjamin Gershwin Oren
James Linden Palmer
Thomas Lewis Rider
Bertram Jacob Lyons
  Sauerbrunn
Edward Bayard Smith Shires
Charles Aloysius Smith
Karl Leavitt Smith
Charles Davis Stinard
Samuel David Strauss
Peter Stephen Sykowski
Michael John Tytko
Edward John Vandercar
George Joseph Ward
William Jack Weaver, Jr.
Robert Eddy Wells

Class of 1941:

William Gillespie Armstrong
Donald Henry Baxter
Melvin Thomas Boright
John Clarke Burke
Wilbur Hinds Caney, Jr.
Jerome Louis Cohen
Irving Cramer

427

Fred Ennis Dexter, Jr.
William Frederick Doney
Bernard Anthony Duffy
Rush Barney Faville
John Ellis Glen, Jr.
William August Griesau
Henry Sherman Hirst
Miriam Lenz Holmes
Robert Nelson Lord
Jay David Mann
Dominick Mele
Oscar John Muller
Richard Elting Passenger
Robert William Raymond
George Joseph Riley
Michael Joseph Scricco
Stanley Simkin
Reade Sanford Sisson
Edward Henry Southwick
Elmer Francis Toth
Henry Albert Weitz
Wilfred Hartley Zwahlen

Class of 1942:

Robert Michael Albrecht
Russell George Allenza
Richard George Berry
John Putnam Blanchard
Michael Angelo Blase
Carl Blackstone Booth
Archibald DeWitt Brown
Charles Harris Brown
Benjamin Cohen
Emanuel Dejnozska
George Rehmi Denton
Thomas Pius Engster
Fred Feldman
Theodore William Fox
Ian Casimir Funk
Tracy James Gillette
John Maurice Johnson
William Laurace Ladue
Tiffany Lawyer, Jr.
William Arthur Little, Jr.
Edgar Sherburne Lovell
James Henry Mitchell, III
Esther Louise Moeller
Arthur Harold Mulligan
Lucien Pastore
Arnold Orson Riley
Thomas Rae Shannon, Jr.
Edward James Sharkey
Stanley Edward Smith
Edward Vicars Stevenson, Jr.
Austin John Tidaback
Elwood George Weisenburn
James Edward Zullo

Class of 1943 (March):

Victor Harold Boogdanian
Dominick DeLisa

Irving Spier Dribben
Roger George Dudis
Edward Cecil Eagan
Richard Rice Evans
David Falk
Arthur Julius Hacker
Albert Haddad
John Wesley Haine
Charles Honig
Joseph Judd, Jr.
Frank Diodore Kalchuk
Melvin Saul Kaplan
Robert Edmund Lamberson
David John McMurray
Anthony William Nardacci
Charles Henry O'Neil, Jr.
John Thomas O'Neil
Joseph Edward Pahl
Dominick Anthony Papandrea
Maximilian Edwin Pesnel, Jr.
Samuel Loomis Pettit
Feori Frederick Pipito
Marvin Posner
Matthew John Gulick Powell
Edward Robert Richardson
Lillian Smith (Eagan)
Samuel Susselman
Howard Cameron Van Keuren
Robert Charles Warner
Clarence Arthur Wyatt
John Archibold Young

Class of 1943 (December):

Jane Andrews (Mack)
Elizabeth Kreisinger Beach
Carolyn Veronica Brignola
Carl Philip Carlson
Paul Michael DeLuca
Virginia Downing (Chase)
Richard Bertrand Drooz
John Eylers Eckel
Harvey Paul Einhorn
James Augustin Galvin
Theodore Edward Gillen
Robert Frederick Goldie
Zygmunt Peter Grabicki
Raymond Harris
Alexander Maximilian
  Hofstetter
Andrew Johnston
Richard Daniel Kearns
John Neil Kennedy
Alfred Walter Lucas
Arthur Gerard Mack
Raymond Alphonse Maslyn
Wilma Anita McVey (Evans)
William Edward Morris
George Wellington Putman
James Elwin Quimby
Joseph Michael Rupsis

William Henry Schwab
John Kennedy Shearer
Robert Jones Shelmandine
John Dodge Sponnoble
Lenore May Sportsman-Miller
Joseph Carleton Stickney
Charles William Stratton, Jr.
Henry Stimson Tripp
Ransom Varley
Tompkins Gerard Watson
George Tomer Carr Way
Abraham Zheutlin

Class of 1944 (September):

Ruth Glueck Addison
Franklin Earl Atwater
Warrington Austerman
Harry Francis Benjamin
Thomas Brandon Carey
Ernest Anthony Cerasano
Jack Julius Coheen
Leo Robert Collins
Robert Pierce Coolidge
Kathleen Virginia Cuddihy
Thomas Frederick D'Aurio
John Edward Davis
Joseph Francis Fazekas
John Vincent Fernandez
Gerald Phillips Gable
Manuel Green
Janet Greenburg
Frederic William Holcomb, Jr.
Theodore Joseph Kantor
Jean Keiser Stevenson
Leonard David Kurtz
Salvatore Paul LaCerva
Matthew Ambrose Larkin
Edward Levitsky
Robert James Moore
George Dudley Nelson
Richard Boyle O'Brien
Frank Granger Osbourne, Jr.
Walter Adam Osinski
Michael Alphonse Pierce
Margaret Schilling
Henry Aloysius Schlang
William Hyacinth Seery
Louis Semenoff
Mary Stevenson
Salvatore Tabacco
Robert DeWitt Vosburgh
John Michael Watson, Jr.
Frederick Hugh Wood

Class of 1945:

Ernest Theodore Anderson
Alexander John Arony
Edward Minckler Auringer
Bert Paul Austin

428

Samuel Newton Bacon, Jr.
Robert Charles Barbieri
William John Barnett
Robert Osborne Barstow
Ethel Burack
Marie Leonore Cote
William Macnicol Daly
Donald Dunlop Dingman
William Richard Dorrance
William Richard Fain
Gilbert Dudley Fish, Jr.
Aaron David Freedman
Peter Roy Gregware
Robert Arnold Hyman (Hall)
David William Hayeslip
John William Howard
Robert Wayne Howard
Robert Stanislaus
   Johnson, Jr.
Sarah Mary Liberson
Edward Roe Loftus
Robert Lewis Maresca
Robert Lee Meineker
Theodore J. Michelfelder
Daniel Francis O'Keeffe
Charles Leo Poskanzer
Thomas Francis Riedy, Jr.
Kenneth Frederick Schoenrock
George Anthony Seleski
Joseph Ayoub Shahen
Roy Theodore Shults
John Graul Sigsby
Arthur Anthony Smith
Edward Frederick Steele
Herman Steinberg
Anthony Joseph Tabacco
John Robert Tietjen

Class of 1946 (March):

William Lloyd Adams
Jonathan Merrell Allen
Alfred Bedford
William John Betinis
Anita Adele Chase
John Lee Clowe
Julius George Colantuono
Robert Walker Cranston, Jr.
Beverly Jean Loesch Dick
Paul Fernando Formel
Herbert Edward Gade
David Gelbard
Coleman Aloysius Glenn
Sherwood Wellington Greiner
Rufus Rosendale Hessberg, Jr.
Philip Harry Hover
Sterling Hicks Huntington
Frank Wilfred Jones
Emil Daniel Karlovsky
Lawrence Frederick Kienle
Robert Merton Kohn

Giles Charles LaBelle
Nathaniel Saul Lehrman
Leon Levine
Roger Edward Marks
Saverio Benedict Mastrianni
Matilda Martha Stewart
   (McIntire)
Lawrence Roy Minard
Glenn Montrose Morris
Paul Walter Myers
Erich Alfred Quer
Richard Winston Repert
Robert Nelson Reynolds
John William Roy
William Nicholas St.John
William Bruse Scharfman
Charles Louis Settembrini
Kenneth Earl Snyder
Richard Earl Spencer
John Philip Timpane
Elizabeth Veeder
Stewart Anthony Wilber
Robert Leon Williams
Henry Edward Zellman

Class of 1947:

Levon Bedrosian
Robert Anathol Breault
Earle Olmstead Brown, Jr.
Louise Tecla Hogle Chase
Glen Ernest Cooley
Sidney John Curran
Christopher Nicholas
   H. Demos
James Bernarde Dinneen
John Douglas
Richard Knowles Douglas
Shirley Louise Ferris
John Albert Fischer
Andrew Carl Fleck
Shirley Elliott Gage Cronin
Julian Bennett Hyman
Harry Mills Judge
Robert Clarence Kessler
John Kline Leach
Philip Lewis Lewis
Charles Wallace Linart
Elbert Hall Loughran
Elbert Franklin
   MacFadden, Jr.
Clifford Henry Marsh
Verne Monroe Marshall
Michael Morse Martin
   Martuscello
Benedict Francis Mastrianni
John Edward McEnroe
Walter Henry Obenauf
William Henry Oldendorf
Thomas Donald Pemrick
Nicholas Preston

George Russell Prout
Norman Righthand
William Thomas St.John
Winfield Stryker
William Charles Taylor
Seymour Thickman
Charles Van Buskirk
Glenn Derrah VanGaasbeek
Harry VanVelsor
Harold Brecker Williams
Henry Ernest Wolfe, Jr.
Benham Robert Wrigley
George Eayres York

Class of 1948:

John Richard Anderson
John Beeble
Edward Carpenter
   Brandow, Jr.
Richard Fabian Catalano
George Alexander Chalfant
Francis Chanatry
Barbara D. Weed Christine
John Edward Coe
Thomas Murray Drislane
Leonard J. Duhl
Lawrence Joseph Early
Joan Livingston Egbert
William Thomas Ellis
Marie Katherine Ernst Cuadra
Gerald Joseph Farrell, Jr.
M. Leonard Genova
Cleston Wayne Gilpatrick
William Vincent Golkowski, Jr.
Mary Nettleton Hall
Howard Theodore Hermann
John Henry Patrick Holden
Barbara Y. Young Hulse
Jane H. Witmer Kienle
Lois Caddick Menzies
Alan Miller Moodie
Robert William Morrissey
William Henry Murray
Virginia Loucks Oliver
Stewart Robert Panzer
Nicholas N. Petrochko
Robert Francis Reid
James Edward Ryan
David Lawrence Sparling
Lawrence Stark
David Smithson Stewart
Irving VanWoert, Jr.
Lee Frederick Vosburgh
Joe Martin Webber
Robert Norman Wilbur
Norman Zheutlin

Class of 1949:

John Willmott Abbuhl
Elbis Allalemdjian Shoales

Gardiner Cabell Bennett
Janis Lea Best
Paul Melvin Bindelglas
Martin Brandfonbrener
Francis Shattuck Carr
Albert Stephen Close
Harold Lewis Colburn, Jr.
Bernard Stevens Duval
Frances Elliott Ehrlich (Price)
Rodney Byron Fruth
James Patrick Furlong
John Henry Gabler
Alexander George Gabriels, Jr.
Angelo Garofolo
Robert Arthur Gerber
Robert Leonard Goodman
Frederick Harrison Grabo
Walter Otto Halden
Archie Handler
Robert Joseph Hochstim
Byron Chester Hollenback
Margaret Ann Krikker
Raymond Abram LaRue
Sol Levinson
Allan MacCollam
Laurence Charles McGonagle
William Mark McKinley
Walter Joseph Meekins
James Elmer Meyer
George Morris Northrup
Barbara Chilton Noyes Doran
Boris Jerome Paul
Matthew Presti
James Francis Purcell
Thomas Robert Reid, Jr.
James Alexander Robertson
Morrill Shapiro
Martin Cummings Wilber
William Armstrong Wright

Class of 1950:

Ambrose Anthony Alfonsi
Elizabeth Quarrier Banker
John Barry Bobear
Elizabeth Johanna Bottcher
Richard Charles Bozian
Arthur Keith Brelia
William Anthony Busino
James Edson Carter
George Percy Child
Rudolph Rocco Del Giacco
Patricia Reid (Denton) Pearce
Theodore Granger Denton
Albert Francis Dingley
Weyland Weiyu Djong
Richard Earl Dohner
Earle William Epps
Marlin Berle Ewing
Hugh Vincent Foley
Grace Ellis Forster

Anthony Thomas Graniero
Rodrique Alvin Gravelle
Walter Kingsley Grigg
David Daniel Hershey
Leo Kovar
John Joseph Kovaric
Paul Ann Kross (Olivier)
Worth Boyd Lintz
Philip Martin Luther
Jack Dillon MacDonald
Albert Charles Maess
George Leslie Marthy
Corinne Josephine
 McLaughlin Snow
Edward Augustine Meyers
Marilynn Lucile Miles
George Francis Nolan
Benjamin Francis Norris
Mary Elizabeth Oakley Garrett
Clarence John Oerter
Donald Theodore Olson
Lloyd Aaron Owens
Harry Joseph Pedlow
John Joseph Phelan, Jr.
John Sloan Raymond, Jr.
Seymour Resnick
Doris Spector Rome
Walter Joseph Segda
Daniel Judas Shapiro
Noel Gray Smith
Leo Alfred Stapleton
Robert Davis Terry
George Douglas Trustan
Judson Bruce VanGaasbeek

Class of 1951:

Gerald Bentley Austin
Stanley Martin Ball
Joseph Thomas Barrett
Anthony Duke Bower
Frank Cesare
James Horace Cleary
Sanford Cobb
Malcolm Lowell Crump
Sherwood Davidson
Alfred Emanuel Dooley
James Dougherty
Robert Emmett Fisher
Arden Albert Flint, Jr.
John Nolan Forrest
Robert James Gilston
Evelyn Jane Grobow (Redlich)
Raymond Clovis Haas
William Joseph Hickey, Jr.
Melvin Horwith
Erwin Frank Keller
William Amede Kramm
Ralph Henry Levin-Epstein
Jennie Mauceri
Kenneth Alexander Nesbitt

Howard Kenneth Peacock, Jr.
Consuelo Perez-Perez
Donald Oswald Price
John Henry Reid
Jose Reposo
Joseph Francis Rowley
John Lawrence Shields
William Francis Skaife
Karl Robert Sohlberg
John Newhall Stark
David Alfred Tilly
Rocco Anthony Verilli
George Mackey Warner
Robert Peter Whalen
Owen "W" Young

Class of 1952:

Leroy Donald Aaronson
Edward George Allen, Jr.
Arnold Murray Baskin
Bernard Beatman
Joseph Irwin Bernstein
Bernard Forbes Brophey
Wendell Langwith Bryce
Donald Lee Carter
John Henry Carter
Lawrence Anthony Cioffi
John Edgar Connelly
Henry Edward Damm
Sidney Dunowsky (Harvey)
Ray Andrew Elliott, Jr.
Truman Gerald Esau
Ivan Lester Gailey
Harold Goldberg
Vernon Leo Hartley, Jr.
William Hyman
John Joseph Ippolito
Melvin Dean Jones
Alexander Nicholas Letko
Alfhild Lien
John Louis Lyon
John Calvin Macaulay
David Wade Marsters
Arthur Vennall McDowell
John Richard Meharg
Harvey Morton Moral
James Wendell Orr
Lewis Everett Patrie
Edward John Purdey
David Charles Rees
Harold Charles Sadin
John Clifford Sherman
Albert Spritzer
William Errol Louis Stewart
Charles Hayden Tracy
Ann Ruth Turkel (Lefer)
John Baptist Voskian
Josef Herbert Weissberg
Jeffery Wiersum
Daniel Whang
Robert Dean Wickham

430

Jacob Jechiel Wiener
Almon Chapman Wilson
Leslie Milton Zatz

Class of 1953:

Gerald Walter Arthur
George Peter
  Nicholas Boolukos
John Robert Boyle
Herbert Rollinson Brown
Robert John Cassidy
Chao Jen Chen
Matie Elizabeth (Faris)
  Cunningham
John James Dapolito, Jr.
Alan Philip De Mayo
Elizabeth Ann
  Ehrhardt Hamke
Nina Claire Ellenbogen
Arthur Slee Faris
Donald Ralph Feeley
Francis Foresta
Linn Humphrey Forster
Alvin Eugene French
Harold Francisco Game, Jr.
Edward Stanley Goldstein
Robert Michael Griffin
Aubrey Lovell Griffith
Thomas Lawrence
  Hawkins, Jr.
William Henry Hoffman
Alfred Walter Ikefugi
Sherman Joel Kimelblot
Roger Pierre LaRue
Charles George Leonhardt
Robert Webb McDonald
Mary Patricia Millett
Stephen Edward Monaghan
Alberto Luis Montes
Charles Laurence Palmer
William Henry Phelan
Edward Harold Poskanzer
Joan Mary
  Possenriede (Treuer)
Robert Laverne Raleigh
Conrad Joseph Rissberger
Robert Rosenthal
Frederick Chapman Sabin
Samuel Bradley Scrafford, Jr.
Richard Alan Selzer
Jay Irwin Silverman
Robert George Steele
Richard Meredith Steidl
Byron Harvey Terk
Ernest Allen Turpin, Jr.
Peter William Vanace
Hugh Solomon Wisoff

Class of 1954:

Herbert Patrick Adams
Gerald Altschuler

Frank Archetti
Franklyn Henry Ashby, Jr.
Norman Ryder Bates
Silas Robert Beatty
David Beck
Robert Jack Birnkrant
William James Boland
Rudolph Frank Bono
Victor Harold Burdick
William Henry Conklin, III
Anthony Beresford Correoso
Jay Vickers Dewell
Melvin Saul Ehrenhalt
Mary Jane Fina Kinosian
Edward Gillie
Gerard Rudolph Gnade
Stanley Goldberg
Jerome George Green
Peter Matthew Guida
Kenneth Lee Hamilton
Walter Compton Hanewald
Thomas Vanvalzah Hunter
Harri Hans Janssen
Clarence William Jordahl, Jr.
Jesse J. Kaye
Jerry Julius Lasser
John Creamer Leaman
Robert Paul Leather
John Paul Leonard
Kenneth Albert Linstruth
Walter Paul Luikart
Paul Moriconi
Richard Gibson O'Leary
Mark Florain Ortelee
James Joseph Otto
Charles Emanuel Pavlik
John Robert Payne
Ronald Charles Peets
Kathaleen Claire Perkins
William McCammon Pugliese
Theodore Basil Puschak
Dewey Robbiano, Jr.
Paul John Rosch
Gerald Ross
Stephen Burdick Saunders
Bernard Morton Schuman
William Eaton Sill, Jr.
John Victor Skiff, Jr.
Frederick Preston Snyder
William Carlisle Van Ost
John Thomas Wilson

Class of 1955:

Edward Attarian
Philip Andrew Becker
George Leonard Beharry
John Gordon Bell, Jr.
Joseph Lewis Belsky
Richard Wayne Blide
John Anthony Britting, Jr.
Lewis Ned Cahill

Clifford Horace Casey
Thomas Vincent Casey
James Joseph Cassidy, Jr.
Robert Patrick Conlen
William Shelley Cooley
Robert Charles Dyson
James Francis Early
Robert David Ellerson
Bernard Abraham Eskin
Leon Labish Feltman
Joseph Ross Gabriels
Charles Amos Galyon, Jr.
Stafford William Gedge
Alfred Maximins Gomez
William Halstead Jameison
Richard Lester Johnson
Paul Kendrick Jones
Herbert Kaplan
Arnold Lewis Karsch
Gustin Thomas Kiffney, Jr.
Henry Kinosian
John Martin Lanigan
John Champlin Lathrop
Victor Joseph LoCicero
Michael George Mclas
William Henry Meyer, Jr.
Frank Miller
Bruce Richard Mills
Peter Paul Morgan
Calvin Percy Nylander
Luther Wetherby Pearce
Fred Merton Pierce
John Henry Ring, Jr.
Seymour David Rockoff
Gail Allen Rogers
James Campbell Rumbold
Edward Eggleston Seelye
Page Sharp, Jr.
George Armen Stepanian
John Stetson Tanner
Wilson Curtis Tooker
John Arthur Vinett
Richard Adam Wagner

Class of 1956:

Boris Morton Astrachan
Arnold Asher Bank
John Hall Bowker, Jr.
Frederick Rodney Brandlin
Harry Herbert Brown, Jr.
Paul Peter Carbone
Robert Gardiner Chaloner, Jr.
David Corn
Paul Davidson
Kenneth Allen Deitcher
Theodore Donald Eisenstein
Charles Albert Ellis, Jr.
Dennis Royal Filippone
Anthony George Gristina
Jean Alphonse Guay

431

William Herbert Harvey, Jr.
Bernhardt William Hausheer
Henry Franklin Hosley
Thomas Joseph Kiernan
William Vaden Kinnard, Jr.
Frederick Wayne Knapp
Gerald Marvin Kotzin
Peter Castle Linton
James Thomas Maher
William Edward McMahon
Robert Peter Newhouse
John Joseph O'Brien, Jr.
Catherine Josephine Peffer
William Augustus Petersen
Fred Atkins Phillips, Jr.
Robert Harvey Randles
George Emmett Reardon
Lawrence Howard Rockland
David Myron Rosenthal
Richard Otto Schultz
John Hamlin Seaman
Elias Ralph Shemin
William Clarence Sleight
Vincent Edward Slomin
Judson Delap Speer
Robert Alexander Stoller
James Francis Strazzeri
Andrew Howard Potter Swift
Lawrence Bertram Tilis
Arthur Joseph Wendth, Jr.
H. Peter Wintrich
Robert Frederic Yates
Orazio Robert Zumbo

Class of 1957:

William A. Africano
Herbert Almon
  Bartholomew, III
Eric Wilson Best
James Joseph Bingham
Marvin Barry Blitz
Arthur John Boyko
Lennart Albin Carlson
John Albert Carriere
Saebert Lionel Chamikles
John Condemi
Robert Daniel Corwin
George Anthony Cuttita
Richard Morse Darling
Walter Edwin Farin
Donald Leo Farrell
Barry Jay Fenton
Myrtie Carolyn Fisk Kennedy
Oakley Melrose Frost
Rollin Mattoon Galster
Arthur Thomas Gorman, Jr.
Hans Fred Holzapfel
Joseph Cecil Honet
Ralph Jay Kaplan
Joan Viola Kelsch Zangara

James Rogers Kennedy
Howard Harris Kloth
Robert James Lamb
John Irving Larkin
Leonard Herbert Levitan
Leonard Stuart Lustgarten
John Carl Maisel
Emanuel Mirel
Jonathan Cardie Mosse
Robert David Nani
Richard Roan O'Neil
David Pankin
John Andrew Poggi
Kenneth Lee Pratt
Robert Carl Rosan
Wilbur Clarence Rust
Martin Lewis Schulman
Joseph Ghelli Schultz
Margaret Helen Riley Scimeca
David Lawrence Siegal
Paul Skok
Ernest Edward Sponzilli
Terry Anthony Terzakis
Thomas J. Weyl, II
Robert Corey Yates

Class of 1958:

William John Adler
Adrian Robert Beck
Richard George Bertini
Russell Chamberlin Briggs
Cenie Clelia Cafarelli
Henry Camperlengo
Edward Joseph Connor
Arthur Samuel Cummins
John Edmund
  Cunningham, Jr.
Charles Michael DeGennaro
James Arthur Durfee
Joseph George Fink, Jr.
Edward Everett Freeman
Michael Ira Freilich
Pasquale Joseph Fugazzotto
Michael George Fusillo
James Michael Gavin
John Eugene Glennon
Terry Holroyd Goff
Allan Goldblatt
Edwin Arthur Goldstein
Howard Gooen
John Patrick Grogan
Charles Heilbrunn
Barry Joseph Herman
Daniel Norman Hertz
James Francis Hoffman, Jr.
James Anthony Hogan
Glenn David Kinns
Edward Klibanoff
Milton Owen Kling
Arthur Lehrman

Neil Lempert
Walter Levitsky, Jr.
Jerome Levy
Marshall Jay Lobell
Joseph Carmine Loffredo
Mario Benedict LoMonaco
Arthur Maron
James Walter Meade
Samuel Milham, Jr.
Thomas Raymond Nadeau
Pasquale John Palumbo
Carl August Paulsen
Robert Mark Richter
Felix E. Schletter
Henry Anthony Scimeca
Thomas John Scully
Dean John Seibert
Bernice J. Gunsberg Shoobe
Marcus Leonard Shoobe
Nathaniel Silon
Arnold Irwin Slowe
Thomas Francis Spath
Samuel Richard Spitzer
Stephen Gardner Sullivan
Carmine Walter Terraciano
Cornelius Andrew Toner
John Henry Way
Amnon Wein

Class of 1959:

Leonard Antiles
Edward Philip Baker, Jr.
Gary Berry
Robert Murray Blumenberg
William Sheldon Bronk
Martin Edward Bruskin
Kent Houck Butler
Samuel Abraham Cassell
Thomas Joseph Clifford
Milton Harold Dunsky
Howard Jerry Dworkin
Donald Wayne Edwards
Harvey Robert Forester
Ellis Mark Fribush
Richard Louis Gold
Howard Bernard Goldstein
Robert Lee Gossweiler
Donald Grillo
Orlando Taylor Hines
Eugene Marvin Hoenig
George Marshall Howard
Allen Irwin Hyman
Gerardus Smith Jameson
Ludwig Klein
Robert Edward Knack
Durnham Eugene Lamkins
Peter Charles Lombardo
Kenneth Eugene MacArthur
William John McEntee, III
Donald Paul McKibbin

432

Dale Cumming Metheny
Leonard Robert Miller
Robert Edmund George O'Mara
Wellington John Pindar
Irving Marvin Polayes
Robert Norman Rabkin
John Lawrence Rigatti
Amon Rosenthal
George Rubino
Clarke Russ
Ralph George Schilling
Stanley Alvin Schwartz
Roy David Shaffer
Russell Franklin Shaw
George Lewis Siegel
Ian James Spence
Seymour Robert Stall
Michael Joseph Subtelny
Claude Dominique
  Toran-Allerand
Jan Barentse Wemple
Roger Alan Yerry

Class of 1960:

Anthony Joseph Arena
Robert Lee Barenberg
Joel Benjamin Bettigole
Robert Gardiner Bump
Donald Eugene Butkus
Francis Caprio
Robert Lawrence Chesanow
George Thomas Craig
Elynore Clark Cucinell
Samuel Anthony Cucinell
Manuel Francisco
Richard Birdsong Getman
John Lawrence Gleeson
Marvin Jordan Godner
John Francis Greaney
Stephen Mark Greenwald
Patrick Fumio Hagihara
Antione C. Harovas
Peter Hathaway
David Coleman Heyman
John Terry Hornblow
Keith Allyn Horton
William Browning Jones
Donald Eugene Kamm
James Dillon Kessler
Robert Kiesel
Marion Matouk Landon
Richard Admiral Larson
Laurence Conkling Lee
Jerome Ivan Levine
Albert Loffredo
Laszlo Makk
Robert Hugh Maliner
Frank George Marsh, Jr.
Robert Belser McGan
William Whitney Miller, Jr.
Stuart Tobias Nevins

Donald George Paish, Jr.
Donald Michael Posner
Richard Paul Propp
Michael Daniel Rosco
George Sardina
Herman Chaim Schoen
Robert Martin Schwartz
Stephen Sell
John Martin Sherwin
Mark Jay Sicherman
Arthur Elliott Smith
Merritt Fuller Spear
Jack Tatirosian
James Irvine Thompson
Edward Joseph Tisdell, Jr.
Leon Ralph Wanerman
Mary Anne Webber Zimbran

Class of 1961:

Jay Lewis Abbott
Maxwell Abramson
Vija Aisters-Bauer
Richard William Antemann
Frederick Marion Appleton
Harvey Wilfred Austin
Anthony Joseph Bardinelli
Kenneth Ralph Barney
David John Barry, Jr.
Kenneth Better
John Robert Bosco
Neil Charles Brown
Harvey William Buchsbaum
John Paul Carroll
Robert Earl Carroll
James Lesley Claghorn
Edmund Robert Clement
Ethan Theodore Colton, III
Errikos Pipis Constant
Anthony John DeTommasi
Robert Marshall Easley, Jr.
John Henry Eisele, Jr.
George Gary Fuller
Jack Edward Giddings
Dante Louis Gismondi
Morton Harold Goldberg
John Joseph Gregory
Philip Maurice Grimley
Timothy Mather Harris
Richard Leslie Henderson
Maurice Edward Keenan, Jr.
Leonard Joel Kirschner
Ambrose Michael Krupczak
Anthony James Leone, Jr.
Alfred Charles Lucier
Philip Arnold Manaker
James Jay Manion
Edmund Otto Matzal
Bernard Francis McEvoy
Dorothy May McMurphy Stage
Robert David Meyers
Michael Millikan

Gerald Moss
Charles William Needham
Albert Fowler Peters
Norman Bronson Pike
Donald Lowell Price
James Harry Puleo
Prescott Christian Rasmussen
John Bullard Schoonmaker
George Ernest Sims
Ralph Wesley Stephens
Bruno Paul Tolge
Clyde Winston Turner
Paul Otto Vogelsberg
Gerald Andrew Wagner
Richard Nash Wilcox

Class of 1962:

Lewis James Alrutz
Samuel Antiles
Bennett Richard Baskin
Frederick William Bauer, Jr.
William Lang Bayer
Edwin Stanton Beatrice
Gordon Townley Bourns
John Edward Boyd
Carl Henry Braren
Richard William Brenner
Donald Chapman Buckbee
LeGrand Cannon Burns
Robert Cannon Burns
Raymond Edward Carr
John William Colton
James Montgomery
  Dalrymple, Jr.
Elliot Danforth, Jr.
Chester Anthony DiLallo
Robert Everett Fay
John Robert Furman
Michael Garofalo, Jr.
Robert Cole Granger
Cynthia Berberian Hale
Thomas Hale, Jr.
Roger Frederick Harding
David Beattie Hickox
Donald Eugene Humphrey
Arthur Newton Isenberg
Chris James Kachulis
Roger Stanley Kimball
Jan Garrett Kloek
Richard John Klugo
Eugene Louis Mascoli
George Dwight Maud
Kent Devore Miller
Roger LeRoy Miller
Ralph Patrick Morone
Stephen Mulville Murphy
Paul Everard Phillips
Donald James Proferes
Marc Allen Ralston
Frederick Charles Robinson

433

Richard Walter Robinson
Robert M. Rosenblatt
Nicholas Joseph Rotondo
Joseph George Ralph Russo
James Lee Schaepe
Charles Joh Adolph
    Schulte, III
Myron Gilbert Schultz
Morton Jay Seligman
Robert Paul Sengelmann
Edwin Charles
    Shuttleworth, Jr.
Stephen Joel Sills
John Randolph Soeter
Stewart Earl Springstead
Martin Frederic Stein, Jr.
Edward Owen Anthony Terino
Allan Richard Warren
Nicholas Dewey Wing
Jerry Carl Worsham
Francis Kaoru Yamamoto

Class of 1963:

Ronald James Anderson
Irving Nathan Bachner
Martin Barandes
Stanley Arthur Barnett
Donald Alexander Barrett
Henry Otto Paul Binner
Philip Carl Bonnanno
Donald Franklin Borden
David LaVerne Burkebile
John Samuel Clarke
John Marshall Cohen
Thomas Joseph Cunningham
Nicholas Danforth
Richard Stanley Fields
Ralston Rainey Fillmore
Walter Anthony Flanagan, Jr.
Charles Thomas Fruehan
John William Gainor
Patricia Elizabeth
    Gehrt London
Robert Theodore Giombetti
Edward Goldberg
Paul James Hannaway
Carl Peter Held
William Bond Henry
Alfred Emanuel Horowitz
Peter George Kansas
Matthew Adam Kayson
Edward John Khantzian
John Andrew Klamar
Melvin Thein Kyaw
Robert Edward LaHage
John Adam Lang, II
Robert Kline Leet
Lawrence Francis McDonald
Dean Nelson Martin
Karl Robert Meyers

Richard Lewis Nail
Willard Burdette Olmstead
James Orr
Valmore Alexis Pelletier, Jr.
Arnold Sayer Rapoport
Nathan Parker Reed
Michael Spencer Rifkin
Roger Frank Robison
Jon E. Rosenblatt
David William Roycroft
Elizabeth Roycroft Weick
Geoffrey Cass Ryder
Henry James Tipper Sears
James Wright Shorey, Jr.
Sheldon Vischer Smith
Clara L.E. Staunton
Orrin School Stern
John Harold Streit
James Michael Sullivan
Allen Tulgan
Charles Umansky
Arthur Joseph Wallingford, Jr.
Frederick Allen Wilson
Nancy Green Worsham

Class of 1964:

Anita Louise Troja Anderson
Robert David Ansel
Richard Fredric Balsam
Brian Edward Bednarz
Ralph Gerald Bennett
Stephen Sheung-tsit Chan
David Lee Chittenden
Robert Edward Davidson
Christopher Starson Demtrak
H. Thomas Dodds
Philip Joseph Donovan
John Allen Duers
Ernest MacLaren Enzien
Thomas Louis Feher
James Raymond Ford
Alfred Robert Frankel
Lawrence Milton Gifford
Victor Wilbur Gilbert, Jr.
Ralph Joseph Grasso
Thaddeus John Gutkowski
Harold Reynolds Hahn
Ruth Janet Hall
Kenneth Clovis Hopper
Myron Robert Hurwitz
Robert Charles Judson
Norman Dudley Kathan, Jr.
Donald Robert Kelly
Peter Taylor Kirsch
Betty C.M.L. Kuo
Victor Latunde Lawoyin
Robert Glendon Long
Robert James MacDonald
Perry Hopkins Marshall
Lloyd Herbert Maurer

Charles Thomas McHugh
Alan David Megibow
Michael Raymond Milano
Gary Edward Mombello
James Patrick O'Brien
Henry Donald Parry
Arthur Robert Pearson
Donald David Pollock
C. Peter Rasmussen
Robert Hamilton Rexrode, Jr.
John Albert Savoy
Lewis Isaac Schainuck
Laurence Alan Sherman
Charles Padley Shoemaker, Jr.
Philip Arden Snell
Edward Allen Sorenson
Sheldon Burroughs Staunton
Robert Michael Stote
Norman Sudikoff
Martin Robert Symansky
Robert Russell Taylor, Jr.
Fred Harold Vohr, Jr.
George Francis Walsh, Jr.
Cornelius Wendell
    Wickersham, III
David Alan Woodward

Class of 1965:

Albert Anthony Apicelli
Alan B. Ashare
Eric Roy Biedermann
Charles William Bollinger
John Booss
Warren Webster Bovie
James Thomas Casey
Robert Karl Chruscicki
Isaiah Clark
Jerry Lee Clausen
John Christian Crowther
Robert Allan Duff
Donald Carl Durbeck
David Alfred Eppard
Louis Maier Fink
Firmin Forrest Gabriels
Mary Ertlschweiger Geiger
Martin Louis Gerstenzang
Ralph Aroune Giannella
Stephen Robert Goewey
Donald Thomas Gouger
Margaret Loretta Hayes
James Henry Hepp
Lawrence Andrew Holfelder
Edward Anthony Iannuccilli
Cloyd Cleveland Kerchner
Robert George Kercull
Kaarina Maire Kettunen
Emil John Kleinholz
John Joel Kohut
Joel Peter Lawler
John R. Lion

Frank Anthony Lizzi
Anthony Ronald London
Doris Ruth Markowitz
  Greenberg
John Leahy Marshall
Frank Murray Midgley
Gary Donald Miller
Daniel Charles Minton
David Robert Nalin
James Jacob Nigriny
Anthony Salvatore Pagliara
Joseph Adrien Parent, Jr.
Malcolm Wallace Pettit, Jr.
Robert Leonard Phyliky
David Samuel Pointon
Douglas Wayne Rainforth
Sanford Martin Reich
George John Roff
Melvin Jerome Silverstein
Dennis Bernard Smith
Alexander Benjamin Snyder
Fred Charles Storm
Gerald Delano Verdi
Barbara Ruth Curran Wagner
Carl Elliott Walter
George Weingarten
Warren Frederick Woodworth
George Banker Zeiner

Class of 1966:

Richard Christopher Adams
Harold Michael Bass
Richard Elliot Belsey
Charles Joseph Bertuch, Jr.
Paul Anthony Branca
Edward Michael Braun
James Stanley Breivis
Dennis Alan Brown
John Adam Capsavage, Jr.
Gerald Allen Casid
David Herbert Chepovsky
Richard Lawrence Cooley
Michael George Coppa
Arthur Earl Crago
George Peter Delyanis
William Henry Donovan
James Hugo Drews
Steven Leslie Eisen
Robert Roy Faust
Gerard Eusebius Fegan
Leonard Robert Geiger
David M. Gottesman
Roland James Graydon II
Jon Bruce Hagadorn
George Sanford Hambly
David Gerard Handron
Kathryn Thomas Handron
Robert Sander Hipp
Neil Hollander
Peter Jansons

Jacob David Kalmanson
Arthur Howard Knowlton
J. Brett Lazar
Eugene William Leibowitz
David Douglas Long, Jr.
Robert John Lull
Albert Carl Maier
James Elliott McClung
Ronald Carroll Meyer
Donald Jerome Murdoch
Robert Bennett Nathanson
John Curtis Prindle
Russell Wright Robertson
Jeffrey Paul Rudnich
Maureen Sze Savadove
Paul Charles Schreiber
Walter Ronald Skowsky
Jerry Mundall Slayback
Steven Knox Spencer
Susann Joyce Steinberg
John Martin Supple
Edwin Griffin Taft
Robert Eugene Tank
Thomas Michael Techman
Philip Albert Thurston
Guy Edward Torstenson
Joseph David Valentine
Thomas Alfred Vest
Betty Rohloff Vohr
Alan Harvey Weinstein
Carl Rudolph Wirth
Richard David Zallen

Class of 1967:

Peter Frederick Andrus
Van Order Austin
James Louis Berene, Jr.
Robert David Clemons
Willard John Davies
Robert Maurice Dewell
George Jerome DiDonna
Robert William Dodt
Walter Moody Doolittle
L. Stephen Endsley
Matthew Anthony Farina
Dennis John Farnham
Gault Macalister Farrell
Patrick Fazzari
Gerald Felsenthal
Joseph Coleman Gibbons, Jr.
Mark David Groban
Stephen Flack Gunther
William Charles Hallstein
Samuel Charles Hannah
Alfred Aloysius Hartmann
Michael Thomas Hogan
Robert George Holley
William J. Hunt
Peter Morgan Johngren
James Scott Johnston

Francis Robert Jordan, Jr.
James Everett Joy
Francis Paul Kalibat
David Armour Keeler
Barry Michael Kutzen
Wayne Condon Laverty
Richard Eugene Lavigne
Thomas Henry Lesnik
John O. Lusins
George Bas Maroulis
David Wilson Marsland
Richard Gustave Masson
Joel Michael Miller
Robert Figuers Moseley, III
Angelo John Pappanikou
John Hartman Persing
Robert Firth Pickels
Albert John Popp
George Platt Potter
Richard William Price
Lucy A.W. Sandler (Winters)
Robert Franklin Savadove
Laurence Shandler
Thomas Peter Smith
Buel Alexander Staggers
Lorin Marc Swagel
Donald Billings Wheeler
Donald Robert Wright
Christine Flora Wurstlin

Class of 1968:

Joseph Agris
Samuel Alan Aronson
James Charles Arseneau
John Scripture Arthur
William Francis Benedict
Caroline Vogel Blonde
Lawrence Blonde
Richard Jay Buchbinder
Peter Thomas Burkart
Donald Joseph Capuano
Charlotte Cummings Carnes
A. Andrew Casano
William Edward Cioffiro
Edward Holton Clarke
James Robert Kilmartin
  Condon
Philip Francis Corbett
Edward Allan Curran
Steven Richard Dennis
Vincent Robert DiGregorio
Herbert Joseph DiMeola, Jr.
Robert Thomas Eagan, Jr.
Lawrence Benjamin Eisenberg
Albert Marvin Ellman
Everett Roy Forman
Stephen Gerard Gelfand
James John Glynn
Carl Martin Goldblum
Allen Leslie Goldstein

435

Ronald Alan Goodsite
Suzanne A. Crewe Graham
Neil Edward Green
Stanley Nicol Gutelius
Roger Harvey Heilman
Arthur Stewart Hengerer
Jeffrey Douglas Hubbard
Paul Kechijian
Barry Griffith King, Jr.
George Francis Lee
Denis Norman Lusignan
Guy Charles McCoy
Jack John Messina
John Michael Myers
Lawrence Richard Newton
William Steven Oberheim
William Joseph Paladine, Jr.
Joseph John Palombi
Anthony Andrew Pelosi
James Thomas Pizza
Iraj James Sarfeh
A. Harry Sharbaugh, Jr.
Robert Mitchell Sheridan
Harvey Jack Shwed
Lawrence Kenneth Siegel
Wendy Ruth Tinklepaugh
　Soloway
Jane Van Delft
Peter Dugliss Walzer
Donald Edward Ware
Stephen Alan Weil
Martin Howard Wennar
Stephen David Wolfe
L. Thomas Wolff
Alfred Herman Woodworth
Joseph Anthony Zito

Class of 1969:

Richard Bruce Altemus
William Swanson Barry
William Pritchard Batsford
Robert Henry Brakemeier
Kenneth Alexander Bruce
Ronald Thomas Burkman
John Richard Buscher
Price Martin Chenault, Jr.
John Crosby Clapp
Robert Valine Dallas
Thomas John Decker
Charles Bailey Deichman
William Felt Dickes
Gerald Joseph Doyle
Peter Wright Engster
Christopher Chukwuemeka
　Enu
Peter Clifton Ewing
Barbara Faulkner Mufti
Roy Mack Fazendeiro
Paul Kenneth Frederick
Louis Charles Hacker

David Jeremy Haidak
Douglas Glendenning Hamilton
Michael Lester Herman
Leo Nelson Hopkins, III
Jonathan Mark Insel
G. Timothy Johnson
William Gordon Johnston, Jr.
Neil Jay Kellman
Daniel Joel Koretz
Robert Lang
David Bruce Lawrence
Gerald Martin Lazar
James Mitchell Livingston
Chalmers James Lyons
Richard Knoll Mannal
Michael Martin McConnell
William Bernard McDonald
William Henry Montano
Ellen Cecile Moore
Thomas Michael Mulcahy, Jr.
Rebecca Faith Nachamie
William Raphael Nemzek
Dennis Powers Norfleet
John Dennis Norton, III
John James Olichney
Nicholas David Procino
Joseph Stuart Randall
Carol Susan Ribner
William John Richards, Jr.
Robert Jay Riggen
William Clayton Rosen
Seymour Joseph Rosenbloom
Richard Leonard Scharf
Harvey Daniel Scherer
Fred Sheldon Schwartz
Christopher John Seekings
Franklin Thurman Seidlich
William Melvin Singer
Thomas Lynn Snyder
David Hugh Sprague
Emilio Tirado, Jr.
Anthony Collins Van Dyck
Harvey Philip Wald
Russell Weed Underwood
　Walker
John Charles Wheeler
Ausma Lapin Wright
Scott Cady Yeaw
John K.H. Yen
Harvey Zalaznick
Donald Francis Zinn

Class of 1970:

Mark Abel
Edward Robert Alexson
Ann Vincenia Als
Gregg Thomas Aspnes
Anita Balodis Allemant
Gary Edward Barnett
James Philip Barrett

Bonnie Buchner Baswell
David Lee Porter Baswell
Paul Andre Bilder
Ann Climo Birk
Guy Elie Blaudeau
William Meneely Boehme
Edward Leo Boyle, Jr.
Melvin Lewis Bram
Peter Barnard Brand
Steven James Burakoff
Christine Fry Burns
James Stewart Campbell
Charles Richard Carozza
Edward Bowersox Clark
Michael Theodore Cooperman
Maria Theresa Cotch
Donald Edward Craven
Myles Ralph Desner
Eric Colburn Disbrow
Steven Henry Dorfman
Charles Wesley Dumper
Jeffrey Marc Dunn
John Jay Elms
Anthony Falbo
Michael Russel Fischetti, Jr.
Paul David Garson
Frank Joseph Gaudiano
John Joseph Geren
Anita Gewurz Tartell
Walter Lawrence Groff
William Neil Grosch
Diane Joyce Henderson
Robert Philip Hoffman
Martin Oliver Kosich
Albert Yen Chak Lam
John Joseph Len
Charles J. Lenetz
Edith Alva Levine
Steven Malcolm Litinsky
Richard Bishop Lyman
Ted Emmanuel Manos
Alan Harvey Markowitz
Alan Michael Miller
R. Curtis Mills
Helen Marr Mitchell
John Francis O'Brien
Sharon Janice Pelton
Mary Anne Rathbun
Brian Ribak
Frederick Burton Rose
Allan Jay Sandel
Brian Lee Sayer
Daniel Louis Scharf
Edward Chapin Schmidt
Howard David Shapiro
Mark Howard Shelofsky
Spencer Raymond Silverbach
Peter Charles Stickney
John Howard Strimas
William Moore Vanneman, Jr.

436

Richard Murray Weinberg
Sol Zeil Weinzweig
George Randolph Westby
Kirby Franklin Winfield
Arthur Peter Zeitlin

Class of 1971:

Robert Albert Appert
Alan L. Auerbach
Robert Barton Babcock
Thomas Albert Bailey
Joseph Alan Baldanza
Harvey Lloyd Baron
Bruce Beinenstock
Bryan Steven Bilfield
John Henry Blewett, Jr.
Duane Robina Bonds
Michael Alan Boxer
James Bruce Burnett
Ralph Joseph Carotenuto
Victor Leonard Carpiniello
David Henry Coene
Francis Tenison Deane
Richard Clarence Dennis
Mark Peter Dentinger
Richard Michael Dickerman
John Edward Dooley, II
Ernst Rudolf Dorsch
Alexander Filipp
Joseph Forestiere
Martin Harry Fried
Madeline Elizabeth Gerken
Robert Philip Goldman
Thasia L. Goodwin Woodworth
Dennis Stuart Gordan
Ronald Jonathan Graf
Paul Michael Haidak
James Russell Hengerer
Richard Gordon Honig
Leighton Young Huey
Vincent Joseph Jaeger
Charles Yoichi Kawada
David A. Kessler
Sanford Lewis Klein
Thomas Klepetar
Daniel A. Kramer
Michael Harvey Lager
Gary Carl Lang
Charles William Lasky, Jr.
Laurence Arvin Levine
Frederick Elliot Lewis
James Charles Leyhane
Albina Matlega
Sue May Liu Mincey Melcher
Peter David McGan
Jerry Meislik
Michael Philip Melcher
Michael Francis Moore
Joseph John Mormino
William Nisbet, Jr.

William Dale Overfield
Nils Wallin Peterson
Judith Jackson Petry
Matthew Paul Rogan
Neal Lawrence Rogers
Robert Rosenfeld
John Charles Ruckdeschel
Marc David Rudich
Joseph Y. Rudnick
Philip Anthony Saccoccia, Jr.
Larry Neil Scherzer
William Aaron Shachtman
Peter Dresdner Shapiro
Alan Phillip Sitron
Michael Robert Sorrell
Jay White Sprong
Patricia Marie Sutton
John Stephen Van Orden
John George Wassil, Jr.
Robert Werblin
Neil Turner Wolfman
Stephen Alan Youngwirth

Class of 1972:

Morton Barry Albert
Leonard Eggleston Averill
Richard Ball
Robert Allen Berkman
Wilfred Normand Beaucher
Howard Laurence Berman
Jerome Dennis Berney
Allan Richard Bernstein
Gordon Terrant Bird
Edward Louis Bove
Robert Burakoff
David Edmund Burns
George Edward Burns
Bruce Raymond Cassidy
Eric David Cohen
Charles Joseph Cote
John Paul Cranston
Margaret McClave Craven
  (Kieserman)
Robert Kenneth Crone
Parker Nelson Davies
J. Kenneth Davison
Thomas Stanford Eagan
Robert Gary Ellison
Mark Lester Fruiterman
Barry James Gainor
William Jarrard Goodwin
David Frederick Graf
Thomas Allen Graf
David Creighton Grenoble
Vincent Francis Guida
Kenneth Fred Haas
Lawrence Allan Horn
Robert Geer Insley
C. Gregory Jellinek
Richard Owen Johnson
Robert Jay Kantor

John Robert Kearns
Robert Michael Kelleher
Randall Sheldon Krakauer
Richard Kroll
John James LaFerla
Andrew Michael Lapica
Gary Joseph LaTourette
Laurel Sprung Lipshutz
Kevin George Looser
Jeffrey Lozman
Richard Taylor MacDowell
James Campbell MacIntyre, II
E. Scott Macomber
Gregory John Maksymowicz
James McClung Mathers
Michael Herman Metzler, III
George Congdon Miller, II
Jeffrey Steven Mogelof
Charles Brendan Montano
William Allen Nathan
Carmine Albert Olivieri
Arthur Edward Orlick
Thomas Lawrence Parsley
Barbara Anne Perina (Merkt)
Salvatore Lawrence Pipito
Dale M. Roberts
Earl Paul Robinson, Jr.
Norman Reid Romanoff
David L. Rothman
Barry Frederic Rudnick
William Palmer Schecter
Herbert Hodder Scherzer
Jonathan R. Schwartz
Peter Bruce Sherer
Alan Jay Silverstein
Stephen Thomas Sinatra
Mark Sheldon Singer
Richard Alan Smith
Edward Michael Staub
Richard Allan Stevens
Guy Collin Stong
Barry Stuart Yoss
Lawrence Charles Zweibel

Class of 1973:

Kenneth Robert Adler
Frederick Peter Ambrose
Edward Paul Amento
Paul Ludwig Armerding
John Francis Assini
Bruce Allan Bagley
Michael Joseph Bartek
Barbara Ann Boccia
Scott Howard Breen
Jonathan Clyde Britell
Carmelita Viola Britton
Allan Lee Bucknell
Spencer Lamont Butterfield
Richard Edwin Carroll
Thomas Frederic Celello
James Charles Chingos

437

Stephen Douglas Codish
Stephen Mark Cohen
David Reyburn Coursin
Kenneth Louis Director
Richard Lenox Farrell, Jr.
Louis Patrick Gagliardi
Garry Bruce Gewirtzman
Eric Albert Goe
Ronald Bruce Goodspeed
Richard Ian Gracer
Eric Joseph Gross
William Paul Guthinger
Harry Louis Haroutunian
William Charles Hartnagel
William Joseph Hennessey
Earl Lynn Horton
Donald Raymond Howard
Douglas Joseph Ivan
David Stevens Jackson
Michael Allan Kieserman
John Wilkinson Kirkland, Jr.
Deborah S. Krohn Rogers
Pablo Manuel Lawner
Helyn Marie Lefgren
Yolanda A. Pepka Leparulo
Steven Allan Leveston
Paul Albert Levine
James Gross Lichter
Bruce Roberts Line
Donald Keith Lundgren
James Alexander Menke
Edward Gage Merzig
Alfred Monteilh
Alan Moskowitz
Frank Michael Mroz
John Bryan Murphy
Frank John Ninivaggi
Harry Charles Odabashian
Joseph George Olivieri
Albert Peter Pepka
Frederick Joseph Pope
Winford Andrew Quick
Robert Biddle Rockwell
William James Rockwell
Jeffrey Mark Rosenbaum
Bruce David SanFilippo
Derace Ian Schaffer
Robert Neil Schannon
Mary Kathryn Senterman
Edwin Albert Spath
Charles Edward Staunton
Harry Emile Steiner
Peter Morris Stevens
Suzan J. Smith Stong
James Walter Stratton
James Edward Striker
Ishmael Jose Torres
Steven Michael Turbiner
John Bernard Waldman
Donald Ben Wasem
William Joseph Wetzel
Craig Jay Youner

Brian Richard Young
Kenneth Howard Zaslow

Class of 1974:

Stephen Joel Abrams
Eloise Aguirregoitia
Morris Antzelevitch
Robert Dennis Bacsik
Sterling Sheldon Baker
Michael Robert Barnett
William Robert Bell
Francis Anthony Bellino
Edward Salvatore Berretta
Alan Jay Berrick
Stanley Edward Blyskal
John Joseph Botti
Edwarda Maria Buda
Charles Anthony Buscema
Kathleen Mary Connell Raviele
Michael Crade
Ralph John DeVito
William Ryan Dooley
Philip Trafton Drew
Rosemarie Ensat
John Thomas Fallon, III
John Anthony Ferraro
Jacqueline Mary Fogarty
James Patrick Furlong, II
Karen Maria Gaudio
Robert Jay Gay
Mark Nathan Goldberg
Michael Barry Grieco
Charles Grody
Jay Gross
William Carl Hall
Michael John Hardies
Judson Clark Harrington
Charles Milton Hensgen
Sherman Webster Horn, II
Gerard Jay Hunter
Richard Thomas Jackson
Robert Edward Johnson
Mark Elliot Kahn
Zvi Simcha Klopott
Murray Korc
James Andrew Kowles
Gregory Brian Krohel
Lawrence Melvyn Lanes
Charles Warren Lapp
Jill Annette Largent
Janice Louise Lee
Steven Lelyveld
Alan Richard LeRoy
Kenneth Brian Levites
Cornel Jose Lupu
Henry Humbert Macler, Jr.
Michael Peter Madaio
John William Malo
Clifford Chen Marr
William Stanton Martens II

Eugene Charles Maso
Geoffrey William McCarthy
Susan Any McIntosh Ostrowski
Elisabeth Anne McKeen
Neal Warren Nadelson
Larry Ira Novak
John Henry Noyes
Mark Ian Oestreicher
Kenneth Stuart O'Neil
Michael Barry O'Neill
Gary Pagano
Kenneth Marc Pariser
Patricia Theresa Pisciotto
    Rosien
Anthony Alfred Raviele
Jeffrey Clark Rider
Jerry Rosenbaum
Robert Rosenthal
Ronald Roth
Robert Felix Ruggiero
David Michael Salerno
John George Sarris
Craig John Schaefer
Ronald Steven Scheinzeit
Paul Robert Sherban
Steven Morris Silver
Jeffrey Stuart Sneider
Andrew James Solan
Henry Leo Sonneborn
Thomas Francis Spethmann
Jay Davis Sprenger
Jeffrey Robert Stall
Donald Alan Stangler
Andrew Joseph Sullivan
John Raymond Warkentin
Robert Emmett Wehmann
Charles Henry Weissman
T. Michael White
Bruce James Yee
Kenneth M. Zoller

Class of 1975:

Denise Finck Barasz
Mark Barasz
Ruby Gain Bendersky
Garry Michael Bombardier
Andrew Ian Bressler
Andrew Roland Burgess
Brian Tourney Burke
William Davies Burman
John Floyd Burton
William Anthony Busino, Jr.
James Douglas Buttorff
Daniel Alexander Capen
James Joseph Ciarcia
George Michael Cibik
Jonathan Collin
John Stewart Colocousis
Mary Ellen Coulter
James Cameron Cruickshank

John DiOrio, Jr.
John Edward Drake
Richard Allan Feit
Nicholas DiPietro Filippone
Albert Anthony Fiorini
John Patrick Fogarty
Paul A. Forman
David Scott Frederick
Erik Jay Funk
Mark Philip Gold
Martin Alan Goldsmith
Steven Jeffrey Goodman
Alan H. Greenberg
  (Lin-Greenberg)
Antoine M. Hakim
Terry Diane Heiman
Michael Steven Heller
Jessica Lisa Hurwitz
Richard Louis Hurwitz
Edward Julius Jacobs
Charles Steven Kalman
William Russell Kimball
Alan Robert Klibanoff
Peter John Koltai
Harold Vincent Lamberson, Jr.
Jeffrey Harris Lane
Christian Harris LeFevre
Bruce Allan Lenes
Robert Joseph Levai
Bruce Farrell Levy
Stanley Mark Lewis
Luke K. LiCalzi
Neil Michael Lindenman
Lynn Clark Lowe
Edd Gilbert Lyon
Arthur Charles Marsh
Paul Sigmund Mayer
James Grosvenor McAnulty
John Cornelius McPhillips
Austin I. Mehrhof, Jr.
Paul Miller
Mark Jay Mittenthal
Monika K. Mommsen
John Joseph Moore, Jr.
John B. Mueller
Charles Joseph Neilson
Robert Keith Nielsen
William Collins Nugent, Jr.
James Campbell Peters
Arthur G. Pettygrove
Donna Marie Pietrocola
  Pinheiro
Steven Pinheiro
Paul Howard Ratner
Alan Ira Richman
Samuel Edward Rogers
Michael Wayne Rosenberg
David M. Ryon
Henry S. Sacks
Alfred Saleh
Martin Edward Schick

Anthony R. Scialli
Scott Z. Seminer
Joel Abraham Sender
Glenn Stephen Shear
Frederic P. Skinner
Merrill J. Solan
Jack Sylman
Celeste C. Szewczyk Mueller
Allan L. Tompkins
John Alan Walsh
Christopher C. Way
Lawrence David Weber
Linda E. Weber
Gary Frank Willen
Thomas Craig Williams
Theodore Harold Zeltner
Allen W. Zieker

Class of 1976:
Arthur Mark Altbuch
Robert James Anderson, Jr.
Stephen John Andreski
Mitchell Seth Barden
Catherine Elizabeth Bartlett
Debra Ann Bell
Margaret Block
Lawrence Howard Bloom
Judith Diane Bodnar
Kenneth Phillip Brooks
Paul Gerard Burns
Donna Anne Caniano
John Raymond Cetner
Susan Dale Charlamb
Linda L. Civerchia-Perez
Diane Irene Cohen
Arthur Richard Copeland
Austin Joseph Corbett
Douglas Baird Coursin
John Joseph Cronan
Desmond Rudolph Del Giacco
Alan Matthew Denner
James Vincent DiLorenzo, Jr.
Dean Arthur Dobkin
Ronald Bresler Durning, Jr.
David Eugene Eberly
Craig Alan Emblidge
Charles Raymond Fikar
Thomas James Flotte
Carl Seth Freeman
Ivan Alan Friedrich
Philip Joseph Gara, Jr.
Jared Haft Goldstein
Stephen Michael Gollomp
James Stephen Gracer
Robert Charles Greenbaum
Joan Elizabeth Greulick Byron
Neil Kingsly Groff
Gregory Randall Harper
Stephen Keith Heier
Kevin John Herlihy
Donald Vern Holbert

Chris James Holmblad
Dorothea Melva Hoover
Linda Jane Howard Rogers
Robert Gary Josephberg
Kirk Randy Kanter
Douglas Neil Karrel
Paul Emmett Kaufman
John Russell Kittredge
Ralph Lewis Kramer
Patrick Ki-Cheong Lam
Lawrence Stephen Lansing
George Bernard Leber
Anthony Paul Levatino
Richard Louis Levine
Ronald Anthony Loffredo
Kenneth Charles Low
Daniel Francis Lukowicz
Scott Ellis Maizel
Nelson Lawrence Miller
Catherine Marie Mills
James Joseph Montagano
George Benjamin Neal
Gary Steven Needell
Abraham Nussbaum
Jeffrey Lewis Oberman
Daniel James O'Connell
Mark Walter Oldendorf
Steven Michael Opal
Richard Rocco Pesce
Douglas Michael Petroski
Leonard Karl Pickard
Mary Elizabeth Rappazzo Hall
Howard Ratech
Bruce Eric Robbins
Lee Robbins
Gary Robert Rombough
Joel Jay Roslyn
Rob J. Roy
Vincent Joseph Russo
Terrence James Sacchi
Robert Edward Schatz
Jeffrey Steven Schottland
John Vincent Scialli
Stephen Salvatore
  Sgambati, Jr.
Christopher Alderson Shaut
George Thomas Shelton
Neal Jonathan Sherman
Edward Alan Sherwin
Genadij Sienkiewicz
Glenn Marshall Silverman
Lawrence Wynn Silvers
Susan Singer
Beverly Jill Smith
Robert Joseph Sterling
Gary Lee Sutter
Stephen Anthony Switlyk
Linda Joy Taggart
Gary Bruce Tebor
Hal David Teitelbaum
Robert Charles Tillack

439

Richard Bruce Toll
Richard Hall Truex
Peter Lawrence Van Brunt
Gary Russel Wakeman
Howard Norman
   Walsh-Weinberg
Carl George Macomber Weigle
Edward Bruce Weiser
Michael Curtis Welch
Eric Henry Westin
George Joseph Zambetti, Jr.

Class of 1977:

Robert Byron Athanasiou
Donald Anthony Aviano
Donald Norman Bardole
Marino Baselice
Teresa Styk Briggs
Robert Victor Buehl
Daniel Mark Downs
Stuart Bruce Cherney
Alfred Kwan-Hon Cheung
Wayne Roger Christie
Richard Carl Cimma
Michael Bruce Clark
Joseph Graham Coroso
John Czajka
Joseph Paul D'Addesio
Isabella Anna Danel
Allan Michael Delman
William Francis DeLuca, Jr.
Peter Harrison Spencer Dillard
Steven Philip Dunn
George Kellogg Dreher, Jr.
Linda Ann Dubins
Theresa Ann Eretto (Switlyk)
Ira Esformes
Dezso Dennis Faludi
Michael John Franklin
Jeffrey Michael Friedman
Carolyn Ann Frymoyer
Paul Allen Frymoyer
James David Fuchs
Cecilia Ann Gmuer
Harold Robert Goldberg
Murray Bruce Gordon
Wayne Michael Grabowski
Michael L. Graver
Wlliam Evans Greiner
Mary Terese Greulick
Virginia Nicholson Harvey
Jonathan Edward Hasson
Douglas Lloyd Hatch
Oswald Lawrence Haye
Frederick Sterling Hesser
Marc Allan Hirsh
Glen Alan Hiss
Richard Karl Howard
John Hanley Huntington
Thomas Salvatore Ingarra

Brian James Izzo
David Ethan Kaplan
David Michael Karp
Kevin John Karpowicz
Steven Matthew Keller
Peter Hamilton Kelly
Richard Storrs King
Alan Jan Kivitz
Paul E. Kross
Marc Eric Lanser
Daniel Craig Larson
Leonard Stuart Lilly
Barry Scott Lindenberg
Madelyn B. Paltzik Lipman
Mary Jane Major Knowles
Jay Barnard Mandelkorn
Glen Eric Mathisen
Paul Michael Mauriello
Woods McCahill, Jr.
Michael Edward McGrath
John Joseph Meharg
David Scott Mendelson
Fred E. Mensch
Barry Lee Myones
John J. Nanfro
Florence Anne Nolan
John Anthony Nolan
Gunta Iris Obrams (Patterson)
William Hemphil Olson
Marvin Stanley Packer
Bradley Holmes Paddock
Arlene Mary Palazzolo
Robert Jeffrey Panzer
Mark Edgar Parker
Frederick Alvin Peachman
Jonathan Paige Pendleton
Edward Francis Phillips
Jonathan A. Polikoff
Evan Paul Provisor
Jeffrey Orson Riley
Kevin Wilson Roberts
Russell Reed Rothenberg
Stephen Michael Scappa
John Frederic Schenck
Martin Alan Schiff
Barbara Phyllis Schneider
Donald Richard Schoch
Jay Allan Shechter
Kenneth Anthony Sherban
Elizabeth Horan Skovron
James Arthur Slavin
Vicki Marlene Sommer (Kivitz)
James Bryant Stephenson
Mark Steven Stern
Charles Michael Sulzman
Theodore Ben Swirat
Charles Stephen Szlatenyi
Charles Pearce Van Duyne
Neil Evan Wahlberg
Gregory Colman Walsh
Toni Beth Walzer

Edward Robert Wassman, Jr.
Timothy Wolfe
Lewis Dana Youngwirth
Mark Steven Zimmerman

Class of 1978:

Deirdre Margaret Achtellik
Marianne Wurth Arseneau
Karole Susan M. Avila
Lawrence Barnowsky
Elizabeth Jane Beautyman
Pamela Renne Benitez
Robert Anthony Bergamini
Robert Ira Bierenbaum
Bruce Robert Blazar
Jeffrey David Blonstein
Glen Peter Bombardier
Ann Beth Breuer
Thomas Michael Bulle
Harry Daniel Burack
William James Butler
John Jacob Byrne
Thomas Edward Canavan
Carol Louise Clericuzio
David Andrew Collins
Richard Edward Constable
Jeffrey Alan Cooper
Lorraine Elizabeth Davis
Richard Blaise Deatsch
Harry John De Pan
Dennis David Dewey
Adrian Sandra Dobs
Iris Elizabeth Dominy
John Patrick Donovan
Amy Ducatman Dunn
Eugene Christopher Durkin
Leigh Glen Durlacher
Edmond Joseph Fitzgibbon
Perry Lee Fleisher
Toinette Helen Fontrier
Bradley Alan Ford
Leonard Edward Forner
Hal Jeffrey Freiman
Monte Richard Friedman
Hal Gerstein
Steven Brian Gilman
Peter Godfrey
Leon Alexander Goldstein
Malcolm Howard Gottesman
Alan Christensen Gulick
Ruth Jessica Hanford
Jonathan Cross Hausheer
William Banks Hinshaw, Jr.
John Vincent Ioia
Daniel Morris Jacobs
Mark Vadim Jarowenko
Risa Kagan
Leslie Ellen Kahl
Catherine Ann Kiley
Charles Havener Kite

Karen Ruth Kriss (Hempel)
Paul Armand Kurth
Mark Stephen Laible
Deborah Sue Leadholm
Jackson Kuo Lee
Ronald Lee Lipkowitz
Janet Phyllis Lord
Duane James Marchyn
Robin Elaine Markle
Lawrence Michael Markman
Amelia Mary Martinko
Arthur Vennell McDowell III
Kevin Xavier McKennan
Todd Alan Meister
Meryl Handelsman Mendelson
Kenneth Todd Meyer
Donald John Mirate
Irving Mizus
Catherine Ruth Mokede
Patrice Ann Moreno
(Scranton)
Jeffrey Frederick Morgan
Bruce David Nash
Barry Martin Nathan
Joseph Maxwell Newmark
William Walter Noyd
Bernard Richard Nunziata
Daniel Joseph O'Hern
Kathryn Teresa O'Keeffe
Marcia Jane Pabo
Jack Paul Parillo
Lorretta Lorraine Patton
Mark Donald Perry
Frederic Rakowitz
Kathryn Marie Reavey
Roger Bruce Rehr
David Michael Renison
T. Robert Rhodin
Aaron Glen Rosenberg
Kenneth Jay Rosenthal
John Walter Russin
Michael Alfred Santoro
I. James Sarfeh
Lowell Franklin Satler
Frederic Scott Schoen
Bruce King Shively
Warren Silverman
Gary Saul Siverstein
Robert Alan Skib
Martin Lewis Snyder
Beverly Ann Stearns
Mark Steven Taylor
Rudolf Christian Ulirsch
Carol Anne Wakeley
Wilbert Williams, Jr.
Judith Carol Wollman
Michael Yeng-Tjien Wong
David Bennett Yanoff

Class of 1979:

John David Abraham

Richard Clay Angrist
Peter Lee Bailey
Laurie Margaret Balagurchik
Lawrence Glen Bassin
Mark Neil Blatt
John Joseph Cambareri
Rolla Bruce D. Campbell
Paul Chris Chalmers
David Ming Cheng
Jan Stephen Close
Terrence Walter Coleman
Mitchell Scott Collman
John Ashby Covington
Paul Robert Danker
John White Decker
Ronald Stefano DeThomas
William Arnold Diedrich
David Bruce DiMarco
Maureen Donnelly
Barbara Steinmentz Ducatman
John Madison Eckel, Cpt.
Patricia Ann Eretto (Schoen)
Irene Beth Faust
Howard Robert Feder
Joanne Louise Floyd
Thomas David Fogel
James Ward Follette
Steven Mark Frisch
Steven Hedden Gardner
Janet Elain Gargiulo, C.S.J.
Joseph Gerardi
Zachary Bruce Gerbarg
David Glabman
David Brian Glasser
Kim Goldenberg
Gary Lloyd Gottlieb
Joel M. Gottlieb
Richard Alan Greene
Dawn Iris Greenwald
Catherine Anne Grellet
John Haines Gridley, Jr.
Margaret Mary Grogan
John Edward Hargrave, Jr.
Kathleen Marie Harper
Margaret Merriam Hawn
James Fletcher Horn
Brandon Zane Horowitz
Deborah Ann Hrustich
Christopher Jon Huyck
Michael Sam Jennis
Michael Howard Jofe
Deborah Mitchell Jonas
Mitchell Kenneth Karten
Mark Alan Kaufman
Christopher David Kearney
John Jay Kelly
Gary John Kolanchick
Sharon Korr
Laurence Sheldon Landow
Charles A. Lattanzi
Fred Laufer

Philip Emanuel LeBoit
Malcolm James Low
Harold Bertram Luke
Jay Stanley Luxenberg
Daniel Rob Mackenzie
Michael Marmulstein
John Duncan Marshall
Anthony Pasquale Mastroianni
Peter John Meier, Jr.
David W. Merens
Ann Victoria Michalek
Steve Z. Mitchell
Ronald Vincent Musto
Steven Paul Nachtigall
Gary David Oberg
James Joseph Otto
Naomi Louise Parry
Richard Lloyd Paulson
Dennis Joseph Peat
Janet Marie Pelerossi
Marc Brian Perlman
James Clark Pert
Stanley J. Pietrak
James Thomas Pozniakas
Laurence Alan Primack
Nancy Ann Ryan
Nanette Frances Santoro
Stuart Jay Schnitt
Gary Arnold Schnur
Richard Schreiber
Steven Scott Schreiber
Roy Eric Schwartz
David Louis Semenoff
George David Shapiro-Weiss
Janet Susan Shapiro-Weiss
Michael Evett Shy
George Carl Siniapkin
Bryan Smead
Harold M. Sokol
Neil Howard Spitalny
Gregory David Stahl
Jeffrey Michael Sumner
Thecla Serena Tamulski
Winston Anthony Tapper
Jay Scott Toder
Charles Allen Trout
Anthony Amaechi Umolu
Arthur Robert Vakiener
Jacques Simon Van Ryn
Donna Marie Venezia
(Walterstein)
Virginia Anne Wade
Steven Jay Walerstein
John Henry Wales
Marilyn Mills Walkey
Robert Charles Warner
Steven Eliot Weinstein
Gary Alan Weinstock
Dennis Van Weiss
Claire M. Weitz (Covington)
Frederick Keyser Wiese

Nina Florence Wimpie
Jacques Leon Winter
Diane Doris Wirz
Michael L. Zarr
Samuel Hyman Zwillich
Robert Matthew Zwolak

Class of 1980:

Jill Marie Abelseth
Suzanne Marie Ackley
Daniel Davis Alterman
Edmond Nazaire Amyot
Robert David Aronoff
Roxana Francisca Barad
Jeffrey Howard Baybick
Sarah Hassell Beaton
Jeremy Robert Becker
Richard Adam Beyer
Alan Bindiger
Robert Arthur Binner, Jr.
James William Biondi
Beatrice F. Bloom
Naomi Terry Herman
  Bloomfield
Richard Boehler
Bruce Gary Bonn
Naomi Stampfer Brand
Frederick William Brandt
Cathy Anne Buch
Patricia Anne Burden
Richard Michael Buschatzke
Margaret Rose Carley
Phyllis Chang
James William Cilecek
Joseph Anthony Corsetti
Nicholas A. Cossa
Jeffrey Samuel Daniels
Robert L. Dannenhoffer
James Michael DeMasi
David Paul Dever
Carl Michael Devore
Cynthia DiLaura Devore
Stanley William Docyk
Nancy Jeanne Leininger Downs
Mary Ellen Drislane
Robert Harold Dropkin
Walter Evans Edge II
William Christopher Ehmann
Alan Jeffrey Fogel
Paul Raymond Forrest
Amy Sue Fox
Edward Paul Franks
Rose Elizabeth Fredericks
Robert Leslie Fried
Daniel Edward Gabriels
Michael Alan Garone
Richard Robert Gilston
Eric David Gordon
Martin Ira Griffel
Charles Vincent Grizzanti
Bruce Harvey Handelman

Edward Joseph Hannan
Mary Margaret Haus
Stephen Alan Hillman
Jeffrey Alan Hirst
Mark Michael Hoffman
Michael Joseph Horgan
Lynette Joy Horowitz
Jing Weng Hsieh
Ann Marie Hughes
Patricia Louise Hughes
George Jang
Lenworth Norris Johnson
Gerald J. Joyce
Donald Jue
William Ralph Kanter
Katherine Jean Karlsrud
Henry Joseph Katz
Theodore N. Keltz
Douglas Jarnigan Kilgus
Thomas Edward Klein
Eileen Kominsky
Robert Jed Korenberg
Stephen Simon Kornbluth
Paul Kevin Kosty
Philip Ronald Kreitzer
Andrew Jay Kurman
John Michael Landsberg
Richard A. Lane
Timothy Albert Lane
Leonard Lefkovic
Stephen Nathan Levy
Robert Enoch Litman
Lorraine Carol Marie Lorch
Marek Michael P. Lorenc
Lee Roy Lumpkin
Konrad Tadeusz Marchaj
Anne Katherine
  Marthy-Noonan
John Joseph Masko III
Thomas Michael Mauri
Jean Marie McMahon
Peter Charles Meade
Mark Anthony Miani
Stuart James Miller, Jr.
Morris Meyer Milman
Pamela Jean Moore
Tracey Judith Moreno
Elliot Michael Morris
Gerald David Morris
Karen Alfreda Muller
Michael Joseph Mulvaney
Kenneth Jay Neuburger
James Matthew Noonan
Lawrence Joseph Parsley, Jr.
Brian Richard Port
William Mark Reiter
Lisa Sharon Rome
Deborah Geraldine Ruiz
Ira Philip Schecker
David Michael Schultz
Sharon Shapiro
Kenton Douglas Sharman

Rosemary Rudolph Shy
Francis Siracusa
Barbara Elaine Staub
Keith Lance Stein
John Robert Stewart, Jr.
Barry Neil Straus
James Christopher Strazzeri
Susan Goldstick Thrasher
John Joseph Wasenko
Steven Howard Weiss
Jeffrey Leonard Wisnicki
Estelle Ikuko Yamaki
Albert Yuen
Barry Jon Zadeh
John Raymond Zech

Class of 1981:

Kayat N. Abuza
Jeffrey L. Ainspan
Mary A. Albrecht
Richard H. Alfred
John A. Arcuri
Jane S. Atkins
David M. Barnert
Richard A. Barnett
Roger A. Barrowman
Allan P. Baustin
David A. Bernstein
Arnold J. Blank
Sheldon Breitbart
Robert A. Briskin
Jordan M. Bromberg
Thomas J. Byer
Robert T. Callear
Howard C. Charles
Ricki-Lahn Biondi Chopyk
Richard A. Ciulla
Timothy P. Cullinan
Elizabeth M. Cyran
Mary P. Dearing
Christopher D. DeCamp
James L. Donahue
Barry S. Donner
Robert F. Dunton
Mark H. Eckman
Michael J. Elinski
Patricia A. Elliott
Sarah L. Elmendorf
Francis J. Fenaughty
Cynthia G. Ferrucci
Brenda E. Field
Arthur B. Fontaine
Michael J. Fortin
Stuart B. Fourman
Lyle S. Goldman
Nanette R. Gordon
Kenneth E. Grant
Andrew C. Gunther
Michael J. Halvonik
Deborah A. Hayek

Richard O. Heck
Kathie L. Hermayer
Peter G. Hickox
Susan L. Hirsch
Ronald E. Hoenzsch
Nanette B. Hoffman
Daleela G. Jarowenko
Robert A. Kaslovsky
Deborah A. Kaufman
Steven C. Kaufman
Wendy S. Kellner
Karen M. Kennette
James E. Kolb
Lynn M. Konchanin
Joan Kotun
David H. Kuehler
J. Todd Kuenstner
Scott H. Kurtzman
Lawrence J. Levitan
David H. Livingston
Zbigniew P. Lorenc
David A. Mack
Leslie E. Magnus
Howard S. Malamood
Victoria T. Mansour
Arthur J. Matzkowitz
William D. Mayer
Daniel P. McCauliffe
Randolph M. McConnie
Harry Minassian
Michael D. Misbin
Ronald L. Moy
David E. Nardacci
Adam R. Nortick
Francisco J. Pablan
Salvatore J. Pelligra
Arthur W. Perry
Jeffrey B. Persons
Scott F. Pickering
George R. Pokorny
David M. Poppel
Danae M. Powers
James P. Ralabate
David L. Reino
Alan J. Ritter
Mark I. Robbins
John P. Robert
Bartholmoe Rodriguez
David P. Romeo
Jeffrey S. Rubenstein
Diana P. Sandberg
Saverio J. Sava
Duncan E. Savage
Jeffrey L. Schlactus
Margery B. Schonfeld
Joseph C. Schuster
Richard J. Seeger
Bruce A. Seideman
Thomas J. Sena
Peter N. Sfakianos
William E. Shay

Lee Wolpin Shukla
Daniel M. Siegel
Paul Z. Siegel
Michael R. Silver
Mitchell S. Singer
Clifford M. Snapper
Michael P. Sonnekalb
Joseph D. Spataro
Douglas A. Tebor
Cindy S. Tobin
Stephen E. Tracy
Herschel Tress
Steven M. Tucci
Andrew S. Washtel
Raymond H. Welch
Andrea Wheeler-Winnick
David M. Widlus
W. Gregory Wierzbowski
Morris Wisniewski
Henry Wodnicki
Ron K. Wolner
Robert A. Zorowitz

Class of 1982:

Kristina M. Amyot
Paul M. Apostolo
Gail H. Auster
Steven T. Baldwin
Mitchell H. Bamberger
Richard K. Barton
Kerry S. Bergman
Lynn D. Bertram
Thomas J. Bombardier
Curtland C. Brown
Carol J. Burgess
Michael L. Burke
Christopher M. Burns
Robert A. Cameron
Dana E. Castro
Benjamin B. Chang
Niles E. Choper
Timothy F. Christian
Mary Ciccarelli
Molly E. Clark
Martin J. Cleary
Jonathan L. Clemens
Sheila L. Cochrane
Michael B. Cohen
Stephen H. Cohen
Patrick J. Coleman
Bruce E. Cooper
Kenneth G. Cornetta
Richard H. Dalcol
David A. Danar
Steven C. Dennis
David J. Dickoff
Paul J. Dowling
Raymond M. Dunn
Robert Dweck
Gregory G. Dworkin

Martin J. Edelman
Kenneth Eisenberg
Frederick K. Emge
Jean Evans
Phoebe L. Everson
Gary E. Falkoff
William Feeney
Janice E. Finkelstein
Vittorio Fiorenza
Armando Fuentes
Christopher L. Garenani
Bradford S. Germain
Anne E. Giglio
Michael M. Goldberg
Richard P. Goldmann
David W. Goodman
Robin I. Gottesman
Lisa J. Gruenberg
Mark N. Hadley
Marianne T. Hardy
Bruce E. Harro
Robert E. Hawkins
Robert J. Hedderman
Steven Hoogasian
Peter M. Horvath
Kathleen M. Kelly
Ronald P. Konchanin
Neal M. Kotin
Wolf-Dieter Krahn
E. Michael Kramer
Zachary B. Kramer
Benita P. Kurtzman
Alan F. Levitt
Christopher J. Luttmann
John F. Madden
Paul A. Malek
Andrew D. Mann
Victor W. Mark
Randolph S. Martin
Thomas D. Matte
Patrick J. McCreesh
Charles S. McEnroe
Brian J. McGrath
Barry R. Meisenberg
Daniel R. Miller
Donald R. Morere
Daniel A. Morgenstern
Patrick G. O'Connor
Thomas H. Openshaw
Inez L. Pagnotta
Jeffrey T. Paul
Douglas R. Pechette
Andrew C. Peterson
Thomas Pittman
John E. Prairie
Nancy R. Reisman
Christopher T. Ritchlin
Arnold M. Rosen
Dennis A. Ruff
Barbara A. Russo
Judy Sandick

443

Michael P. Scherl
Gene Schoonmaker
Scott A. Schwartz
Wayne A. Schweitzer
Doria A. Scortichini
Josephine Scotto di Carlo
Philip E. Shapiro
Robert S. Shapiro
Robert J. Shelley
Clark B. Sherer
Naomi M. Shields
Anne E. Sierk
Richark P. Silton
Edward Skwiersky
William B. Steinkohl
Elizabeth A. Streeten
Marc A. Swerdloff
Lonice M. Thomas
Daniel R. Tobin
Tomas M. Tomanek
Debra A. Tristram
Peter J. Tutuska
Glenn A. Vahjen
Evan Vosburgh
Robert S. Walsh
Robert F. Wayner
Robert Weitzman
Arthur C. Winter
Dean E. Wolanyk
Edward Young

APPENDIX G: ALBANY MEDICAL COLLEGE
GRADUATES 1953-1982
Ph.D. AND M.S. DEGREES

Class of 1953:

M.S.
Larry Coletti (Physiology and Pharmacology)

Class of 1955:

Ph.D.
George P. Child (Physiology and Pharmacology)
Marie Roder Green (Pathology)

M.S.
Alan Peter Rofsky (Biochemistry)
Fred Rapp (Pathology and Bacteriology)
Judy Aranka Gottfried Spitzer (Biochemistry)
Michael Vanko (Biochemistry)

Class of 1959:

Ph.D.
Joseph Raymond Bianchine (Pharmacology)
Michael Vanko (Biochemistry)

Class of 1960:

Ph.D.
James Lawrence Barlow (Microbiology)

M.S.
Joseph George Fink (Pharmacology)

Class of 1961:

Ph.D.
Gerald Moss (Biochemistry)

M.S.
Katherine Elizabeth Fritz (Pathology)
John George Olenick (Biochemistry)

Class of 1962:

Ph.D.
Norman Bloomfield (Microbiology)
Ryk Peter Spoor (Pharmacology)

M.S.
Robert Gangi Familiar (Physiology)
Howard Martin Gruft (Microbiology)
John Francis McGarrahan (Biochemistry)
John Mario Petta (Pharmacology)

Class of 1963:

Ph.D.
Donald Arthur Boon (Biochemistry)
Robert Delaney (Biochemistry)
Harry Stephen Margolius (Pharmacology)
Robert Charles Shuster (Biochemistry)

M.S.
Charles Francis Fasce, Jr. (Biochemistry)
Charles Padley Shoemaker (Physiology)

Class of 1964:

Ph.D.
Arnold Joseph Wohl (Pharmacology)

M.S.
Konrad S. Tischer (Biochemistry)

Class of 1965:

Ph.D.
John F. McGarrahan (Biochemistry)
Donald H. Namm (Pharmacology)
Jeffrey K. Saelens (Pharmacology)
Edith L. Scott (Biochemistry)
Roy W. Stevens (Microbiology)

M.S.
William T. Ryan (Biochemistry)
David Harvey Schlesinger (Physiology)

Class of 1966:

Ph.D.
Charles F. Fasce, Jr. (Biochemistry)
Katherine E. Fritz (Experimental Pathology)
Philip J. Privitera (Pharmacology)

Class of 1967:

Ph.D.
John H. Galivan (Biochemistry)
Dong Nack Kim (Experimental Pathology)
Mary Young Lorenson (Biochemistry)
Seymour J. Rosenbloom (Pharmacology)

M.S.
James J. Glynn (Physiology)

Class of 1968:

Ph.D.
James P. Barret (Pharmacology)
Samuel G. Murphy (Microbiology)
Andrew G. Ulsamer (Biochemistry)

M.S.
Samuel Frumkin (Biochemistry)

Class of 1969:

Ph.D.
Gerald Daly Barry (Physiology)
Sally Sloan Hipp (Biochemistry)
Alfred G.E. Kitchen (Pharmacology)

Robert Leo Marois (Pharmacology)
Frederic L. Siegelman (Biochemistry)
Robert T. Witty (Physiology)

M.S.
Pamela E. Ferdinands (Microbiology)

Class of 1970:
Ph.D.
Thomas F. Gale (Anatomy)
Emil Paul Hornyak (Toxicology)
Norman L. Katz (Pharmacology)

M.S.
William H. Ford (Toxicology)

Class of 1971:
Ph.D.
Arthur C. Marsh
(Molecular Biology and Pathology)
Henry S. Sacks (Microbiology)

M.S.
Nicholas J. Vianna
(Preventive and Community Medicine)

Class of 1972:
Ph.D.
Michael Anthony Gallo
(Experimental Pathology and Toxicology)
Margaret Wiener Kennedy
(Experimental Pathology and Toxicology)
Yun Sik Kwak (Molecular Biology and Pathology)

Class of 1973:
Ph.D.
Robert George Briggs (Biochemistry)
Raymond J. Fabian
(Experimental Pathology and Toxicology)
James Charles Killeen, Jr.
(Experimental Pathology and Toxicology)

Class of 1974:
Ph.D.
John Thomas Fallon, III (Pathology)
Jonathan Clark Newell (Physiology)
David Michael Salerno (Biochemistry)
Frederic Parkhurst Skinner (Pathology)
Robert E. Wehmann (Biochemistry)

Class of 1975:
Ph.D.
Teresa Styk Briggs
(Molecular Biology and Pathology)
Harold Vincent Lamberson, Jr.
(Molecular Biology and Pathology)
Michael G. Levitzky (Physiology)
Thomas Gerard Rosano (Biochemistry)
Mukti Hariharan Sarma (Biochemistry)

M.S.
Nancy Ruth Barhydt
(Preventive and Community Medicine)
Linda Emilie Berlin
(Preventive and Community Medicine)
Kenneth Anthony Sherban (Anatomy)
Richard Allan Smith (Biochemistry)

Class of 1976:
Ph.D.
Arthur Richard Copeland (Pathology)
Gregory Randall Harper (Pathology)
John Ervin Kaplan (Physiology)
Richard Winfield Mast
(Comparative and Human Toxicology)
Robert Henry Rej (Biochemistry)

M.S.
Philip Durgen Bradley (Toxicology)
Jean-Ellen Bowman (Anatomy)

Class of 1977:
Ph.D.
Robert Allen Berkman (Physiology)
Frank Arthur Blumenstock (Biochemistry)
Christopher Paul Cheney
(Molecular Biology and Pathology)
Jon Charles Fulfs (Toxicology)
Job Rentze Li (Molecular Biology and Pathology)
Janice R. Lorenzen (Physiology)
Russell Francis Mankes (Toxicology)
Thomas P. Mawhinney
(Molecular Biology and Pathology)
Robert O. Webster
(Microbiology and Immunology)

M.S.
Naomi T. Bloomfield (Toxicology)
Joel Jay Feintuch (Physiology)
Christopher Jon Huyck (Biochemistry)
James Matthew Noonan (Biochemistry)
Louis I. Sobel (Anatomy)
Thomas Francis Tracy, Jr. (Anatomy)
Timothy C. Truscott (Anatomy)

Class of 1978:
Ph.D.
David Hitchcock Rogers (Pathology)
Randy Neal Roth
(Comparative and Human Toxicology)
Steven Michael Tucci (Anatomy)
Stephen Joseph Ullrich (Biochemistry)
Robert Matthew Zwolak (Pathology)

M.S.
Edward Wallis Doucet (Anatomy)
Ronald Conrad Jones
(Comparative and Human Toxicology)
Judith Jones Ryon (Pharmacology)
Lydia Wingate
(Preventive and Community Medicine)

446

Class of 1979:

Ph.D.

Thomas Albert Barbolt
    (Experimental Pathology and Toxicology)
Gina Aldith Church (Biochemistry)
Paul James Feustel (Physiology)
Elizabeth K. Korniat (Biochemistry)
Philip Wai-Lap Tham
    (Molecular Biology and Pathology)

M.S.

Sandra Alice Patterson (Physiology)

Class of 1980:

Ph.D.

Calvin L. Astry (Pharmacology)
David F. Connelly (Physiology)
Charles T. Gombar (Pharmacology)
Brian Andrew Mayes
    (Comparative and Human Toxicology)
Randolph James Noelle
    (Microbiology and Immunology)
James Michael Plummer, Jr.
    (Microbiology and Immunology)
Paul T. Schumacker (Physiology)
Jay Babcock Silkworth
    (Comparative and Human Toxicology)
Joseph Christopher States
    (Molecular Biology and Pathology)

Class of 1981:

Ph.D.

Mary Rose Czajka (Anatomy)
Albert S.B. Edge (Biochemistry)
Sharon Clare Gross (Biochemistry)
Arnold Johnson (Physiology)
Robert Edward Shangraw (Physiology)

M.S.

Gennaro Daniels (Anatomy)
Diane Dodd (Biochemistry)
Beth A. Gainsburg
    (Microbiology and Immunology)
Jonathan Edward Jensen (Physiology)
Susan Gale Robbins
    (Microbiology and Immunology)
Margaret Urban-Pickering (Pharmacology)
Mary Anne Wyatt (Biochemistry)

Class of 1982:

Ph.D.

William P. Bartlett (Anatomy)
Michael James Brennan (Pathology)
Anthony Paul DeCaprio
    (Experimental Pathology and Toxicology)
Mary Litchfield Ellsworth (Physiology)
Connie R. Faltynek (Biochemistry)
F. Carl Haase (Biochemistry)
Mark Walden Lundy (Pathology)

Louise M. Principe, C.S.J. (Pharmacology)
Michael Arthur Sanzo (Biochemistry)
Marlowe Jed Schneidkraut (Physiology)
Philip W. Snedeker (Physiology)
Paul M. Stein (Physiology)
Philip E. Stieg (Anatomy)

M.S.

Joseph Edward Caezza (Biochemistry)
Jorge Cerda (Physiology)
Eric Stephen Roccario (Physiology)

APPENDIX H: MAP OF ALBANY MEDICAL CENTER

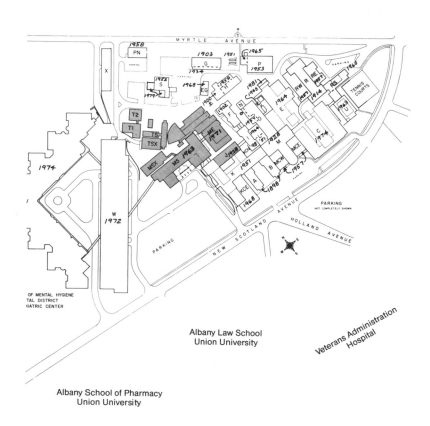

Albany Law School
Union University

Veterans Administration
Hospital

Albany School of Pharmacy
Union University

BUILDING GUIDE

A OFFICES
B OUTPATIENT SERVICES
C PATIENTS-OPERATING ROOMS-LABS
E PATIENTS
EG EMERGENCY GENERATOR PLANT
F ADMINISTRATION-EMPLOYEE LOCKERS
G HUN MEMORIAL-OFFICES
H GARAGE & MAINTENANCE
I OFFICES-LAB-HEALTH SERVICE
J ALBANY MEDICAL COLLEGE
K PATIENTS-CLINICS-EMERGENCY DEPT
KCE CLINICS
KCN POST OFFICE-BARBER & BEAUTY SHOPS
L MEDICAL RECORDS-CENTRAL SUPPLY
M PATIENTS-X-RAY
MCE BUSINESS OFFICE
MCW X-RAY

ME ALBANY MEDICAL COLLEGE-
    MEDICAL EDUCATION BUILDING
    LIBRARY-CLASSROOMS-TEACHING
    FACILITIES-OFFICES
MS ALBANY MEDICAL COLLEGE-
    MEDICAL SCIENCE BUILDING
    RESEARCH LABS-CLASSROOMS-
    TEACHING FACILITIES
MSX MEDICAL SCIENCE ANNEX-
    OFFICES & PATIENT FACILITIES
N MAINTENANCE OFFICE
O BUILDING SERVICES
P LAUNDRY
PN PRACTICAL NURSE SCHOOL
R
RE ALBANY MEDICAL CENTER
RW SCHOOL OF NURSING
RS

S PEDIATRIC DEPT.-OFFICES
TS THEOBOLD SMITH-
    RESEARCH LABS & OFFICES
T1 ALBANY MEDICAL COLLEGE-
T2 RESEARCH LABS & OFFICES
TSX THEOBOLD SMITH ANNEX-
    RESEARCH LABS
U INTERNES RESIDENCE
V CAPITAL DISTRICT
    PSYCHIATRIC CENTER
W PARKING GARAGE
X POWER PLANT
Y HOSPITAL ANNEX
    628 MADISON AVENUE

N.Y.S
DEPT OF
MENTAL
HYGIENE

TITLE	DRAWING NO	REVISION
PLOT PLAN	1277	
ALBANY MEDICAL CENTER		
ALBANY MEDICAL CENTER HOSPITAL OFFICE PLANNING & CONSTRUCTION	AUG 12 - 74	

LEGEND

ALBANY MEDICAL CENTER HOSPITAL
ALBANY MEDICAL CENTER SCHOOL OF NURSING
ALBANY MEDICAL COLLEGE

448

Index

449